BURLESQUES

FROM CORNHILL TO GRAND CAIRO

AND

JUVENILIA

BY

WILLIAM MAKEPEACE THACKERAY

With Illustrations by the Author, George Cruikshank, and Richard Doyle

London

MACMILLAN AND CO., Limited

NEW YORK : THE MACMILLAN COMPANY

1903

CONTENTS

BURLESQUES

A LEGEND OF THE RHINE

CHAPTER VII

CHAPTER VIII

CHAPTER IX

CHAPTER X

CHAPTER XI

CHAPTER XII

CHAPTER XIII

REBECCA AND ROWENA

CHAPTER I

NOVELS BY EMINENT HANDS

FROM CORNHILL TO GRAND CAIRO

BURLESQUES

A LEGEND OF THE RHINE

A LEGEND OF THE RHINE

CHAPTER I

SIR LUDWIG OF HOMBOURG

WAS in the good old days of chivalry, when every mountain that bathes its shadow in the Rhine had its castle: not inhabited, as now, by a few rats and owls, nor covered with moss and wall-flowers, and funguses, and creeping ivy. No, no! where the ivy now clusters there grew strong portcullis and bars of steel; where the wall-flower now quivers on the rampart there were silken banners embroidered with wonderful heraldry; men-at-arms marched where now you shall only see a bank of moss or a hideous black champignon; and in place of the rats and owlets, I warrant me there were ladies and knights to revel in the great halls, and to feast, and to dance, and to make love there. They are passed away:—those old knights and ladies: their golden hair first changed to silver, and then the silver dropped off and disappeared for ever; their elegant legs, so slim and active in the dance, became swollen and gouty, and then, from being swollen and gouty, dwindled down to bare bone-shanks; the roses left their cheeks, and then their cheeks disappeared, and left their skulls, and then their skulls powdered into dust, and all sign of them was gone. And as it was with them, so shall it be with us. Ho, seneschal! fill me a cup of liquor! put sugar in it, good fellow—yea, and a little hot water; a very little, for my soul is sad, as I think of those days and knights of old.

They, too, have revelled and feasted, and where are they?—gone?—nay, not altogether gone; for doth not the eye catch glimpses of them as they walk yonder in the grey limbo of romance, shining faintly in their coats of steel, wandering by the side of long-haired ladies, with long-tailed gowns that little pages carry? Yes! one sees them: the poet sees them still in the far-off Cloudland, and hears the ring of their clarions as they hasten to battle or tourney—and the dim echoes of their lutes chanting of love and fair ladies! Gracious privilege of poesy! It is as the Dervish's collyrium to the eyes, and causes them to see treasures that to the sight of donkeys are invisible. Blessed treasures of fancy! I would not change ye—no, not for many donkey-loads of gold. . . . Fill again, jolly seneschal, thou brave wag; chalk me up the produce on the hostel door—surely the spirits of old are mixed up in the wondrous liquor, and gentle visions of bygone princes and princesses look blandly down on us from the cloudy perfume of the pipe. Do you know in what year the fairies left the Rhine?—long before Murray's 'Guide-Book' was wrote—long before squat steamboats, with snorting funnels, came paddling down the stream. Do you not know that once upon a time the appearance of eleven thousand British virgins was considered at Cologne as a wonder? Now there come twenty thousand such annually, accompanied by their ladies'-maids. But of them we will say no more—let us back to those who went before them.

Many many hundred thousand years ago, and at the exact period when chivalry was in full bloom, there occurred a little history upon the banks of the Rhine, which has been already written in a book, and hence must be positively true. 'Tis a story of knights and ladies—of love and battle, and virtue rewarded; a story of princes and noble lords, moreover: the best of company. Gentles, an ye will, ye shall hear it. Fair dames and damsels, may your loves be as happy as those of the heroine of this romaunt.

On the cold and rainy evening of Thursday, the 26th of October, in the year previously indicated, such travellers as might have chanced to be abroad in that bitter night, might have remarked a fellow-wayfarer journeying on the road from Oberwinter to Godesberg. He was a man not tall in stature, but of the most athletic proportions, and Time, which had browned and furrowed his cheek and sprinkled his locks with grey, declared pretty clearly that He must have been acquainted with the warrior for some fifty good years. He was armed in mail, and rode a powerful and active battle-horse, which (though the way the pair had come that day was long and weary indeed) yet supported the warrior, his armour and luggage, with seeming ease. As it was in a friend's country, the knight did not think fit to wear his heavy *destrier*, or helmet, which hung at his saddle-bow over his portmanteau. Both were marked with the coronet of a count; and from the crown which

surmounted the helmet, rose the crest of his knightly race, an arm proper lifting a naked sword.

At his right hand, and convenient to the warrior's grasp, hung his mangonel or mace—a terrific weapon which had shattered the brains of many a turbaned soldan: while over his broad and ample chest there fell the triangular shield of the period, whereon were emblazoned his arms—argent, a gules wavy, on a saltire reversed of the second: the latter device was awarded for a daring exploit before Ascalon, by the Emperor Maximilian, and a reference to the German Peerage of that day, or a knowledge of high families which every gentleman then possessed, would have sufficed to show at once that the rider we have described was of the noble house of Hombourg. It was, in fact, the gallant knight Sir Ludwig of Hombourg: his rank as a count, and chamberlain

of the Emperor of Austria, was marked by the cap of maintenance
with the peacock's feather which he wore (when not armed for
battle), and his princely blood was denoted by the oiled silk
umbrella which he carried (a very meet protection against the
pitiless storm), and which, as it is known, in the Middle Ages,
none but princes were justified in using. A bag, fastened with a
brazen padlock, and made of the costly produce of the Persian
looms (then extremely rare in Europe), told that he had travelled
in Eastern climes. This, too, was evident from the inscription
writ on card or parchment, and sewed on the bag. It first ran,
' Count Ludwig de Hombourg, Jerusalem '; but the name of the
Holy City had been dashed out with the pen, and that of ' Godesberg ' substituted. So far indeed had the cavalier travelled !—and
it is needless to state that the bag in question contained such
remaining articles of the toilet as the high-born noble deemed
unnecessary to place in his valise.

'By Saint Bugo of Katzenellenbogen !' said the good knight,
shivering, ''tis colder here than at Damascus ! Marry, I am so
hungry I could eat one of Saladin's camels. Shall I be at Godesberg in time for dinner ?' And taking out his horologe (which
hung in a small side-pocket of his embroidered surcoat), the
crusader consoled himself by finding that it was but seven of the
night, and that he would reach Godesberg ere the warder had
sounded the second gong.

His opinion was borne out by the result. His good steed,
which could trot at a pinch fourteen leagues in the hour, brought
him to this famous castle, just as the warder was giving the first
welcome signal which told that the princely family of Count Karl,
Margrave of Godesberg, were about to prepare for their usual
repast at eight o'clock. Crowds of pages and horsekeepers were
in the court, when, the portcullis being raised, and amidst the
respectful salutes of the sentinels, the most ancient friend of the
house of Godesberg entered into its castle-yard. The under-
butler stepped forward to take his bridle-rein. ' Welcome, Sir
Count, from the Holy Land !' exclaimed the faithful old man.
' Welcome, Sir Count, from the Holy Land !' cried the rest of the
servants in the hall. A stable was speedily found for the Count's
horse, Streithengst, and it was not before the gallant soldier had
seen that true animal well cared for, that he entered the castle
itself, and was conducted to his chamber. Wax candles burning
bright on the mantel, flowers in china vases, every variety of soap,
and a flask of the precious essence manufactured at the neighbouring city of Cologne, were displayed on his toilet table ; a cheering
fire ' crackled on the hearth,' and showed that the good knight's

coming had been looked and cared for. The serving-maidens, bringing him hot water for his ablutions, smiling asked, 'Would he have his couch warmed at eve?' One might have been sure from their blushes that the tough old soldier made an arch reply. The family tonsor came to know whether the noble Count had need of his skill. 'By Saint Bugo,' said the knight, as seated in an easy settle by the fire, the tonsor rid his chin of its stubbly growth, and lightly passed the tongs and pomatum through 'the

sable silver' of his hair,—'By Saint Bugo, this is better than my dungeon at Grand Cairo. How is my godson Otto, master barber; and the Lady Countess, his mother; and the noble Count Karl, my dear brother-in-arms?'

'They are well,' said the tonsor, with a sigh.

'By Saint Bugo, I'm glad on't; but why that sigh?'

'Things are not as they have been with my good lord,' answered the hairdresser, 'ever since Count Gottfried's arrival.'

'He here!' roared Sir Ludwig. 'Good never came where Gottfried was!' and the while he donned a pair of silken hose, that showed admirably the proportions of his lower limbs, and exchanged his coat of mail for the spotless vest and black surcoat collared with velvet of Genoa, which was the fitting costume for 'knight in ladye's bower,'—the knight entered into a conversation with the barber, who explained to him, with the usual garrulousness of his tribe, what was the present position of the noble family of Godesberg.

This will be narrated in the next chapter.

CHAPTER II

THE GODESBERGERS

'Tis needless to state that the gallant warrior Ludwig of Hombourg found in the bosom of his friend's family a cordial welcome. The brother-in-arms of the Margrave Karl, he was the esteemed friend of the Margravine, the exalted and beautiful Theodora of Boppum, and (albeit no theologian, and although the first princes of Christendom coveted such an honour) he was selected to stand as sponsor for the Margrave's son Otto, the only child of his house.

It was now seventeen years since the Count and Countess had been united : and although Heaven had not blessed their couch with more than one child, it may be said of that one that it was a prize, and that surely never lighted on the earth a more delightful vision. When Count Ludwig, hastening to the holy wars, had quitted his beloved godchild, he had left him a boy ; he now found him, as the latter rushed into his arms, grown to be one of the finest young men in Germany : tall and excessively graceful in proportion, with the blush of health mantling upon his cheek, that was likewise adorned with the first down of manhood, and with magnificent golden ringlets, such as a Rowland might envy, curling over his brow and his shoulders. His eyes alternately beamed with the fire of daring, or melted with the moist glance of benevolence. Well might a mother be proud of such a boy. Well might the brave Ludwig exclaim, as he clasped the youth to his breast, ' By Saint Bugo of Katzenellenbogen, Otto, thou art fit to be one of Cœur de Lion's grenadiers ! ' and it was the fact : the ' Childe ' of Godesberg measured six feet three.

He was habited for the evening meal in the costly though simple attire of the nobleman of the period—and his costume a good deal resembled that of the old knight whose toilet we have just described ; with the difference of colour, however. The *pourpoint* worn by young Otto of Godesberg was of blue, handsomely decorated with buttons of carved and embossed gold ; his *haut-de-chausses*, or leggings, were of the stuff of Nanquin, then brought

9

by the Lombard argosies at an immense price from China. The neighbouring country of Holland had supplied his wrists and bosom with the most costly laces ; and thus attired, with an opera-hat placed on one side of his head, ornamented with a single flower (that brilliant one, the tulip), the boy rushed into his godfather's dressing-room, and warned him that the banquet was ready.

It was indeed : a frown had gathered on the dark brows of the Lady Theodora, and her bosom heaved with an emotion akin to indignation ; for she feared lest the soups in the refectory and the splendid fish now smoking there were getting cold : she feared not for herself, but for her lord's sake. 'Godesberg,' whispered she to Count Ludwig, as trembling on his arm they descended from the drawing-room, 'Godesberg is sadly changed of late.'

'By Saint Bugo !' said the burly knight, starting, 'these are the very words the barber spake.'

The lady heaved a sigh, and placed herself before the soup-tureen. For some time the good Knight Ludwig of Hombourg was too much occupied in ladling out the forcemeat balls and rich calves' head of which the delicious pottage was formed (in ladling them out, did we say ? ay, marry, and in eating them, too) to look at his brother-in-arms at the bottom of the table, where he sat with his son on his left hand, and the Baron Gottfried on his right.

The Margrave was *indeed* changed. 'By Saint Bugo,' whispered Ludwig to the Countess, 'your husband is as surly as a bear that hath been wounded o' the head.' Tears falling into her soup-plate were her only reply. The soup, the turbot, the haunch of mutton, Count Ludwig remarked that the Margrave sent all away untasted.

'The boteler will serve ye with wine, Hombourg,' said the Margrave gloomily from the end of the table. Not even an invitation to drink : how different was this from the old times !

But when, in compliance with this order, the boteler proceeded to hand round the mantling vintage of the Cape to the assembled party, and to fill young Otto's goblet (which the latter held up with the eagerness of youth), the Margrave's rage knew no bounds. He rushed at his son ; he dashed the wine-cup over his spotless vest ; and giving him three or four heavy blows which would have knocked down a bonasus, but only caused the young Childe to blush : '*You* take wine !' roared out the Margrave ; '*you* dare to help yourself ! Who the d–v–l gave *you* leave to help yourself ?' and the terrible blows were reiterated over the delicate ears of the boy.

'Ludwig ! Ludwig !' shrieked the Margravine.

'Hold your prate, madam,' roared the Prince. 'By Saint Buffo, mayn't a father beat his own child ?'

'HIS OWN CHILD!' repeated the Margrave with a burst, almost a shriek, of indescribable agony. 'Ah, what did I say?'

Sir Ludwig looked about him in amaze; Sir Gottfried (at the Margrave's right hand) smiled ghastlily; the young Otto was too much agitated by the recent conflict to wear any expression but that of extreme discomfiture; but the poor Margravine turned her head aside and blushed, red almost as the lobster which flanked the turbot before her.

In those rude old times, 'tis known such table quarrels were by no means unusual amongst gallant knights; and Ludwig, who had oft seen the Margrave cast a leg of mutton at an offending servitor, or empty a sauce-boat in the direction of the Margravine, thought this was but one of the usual outbreaks of his worthy though irascible friend, and wisely determined to change the converse.

'How is my friend,' said he, 'the good knight, Sir Hildebrandt?'

'By Saint Buffo, this is too much!' screamed the Margrave, and actually rushed from the room.

'By Saint Bugo,' said his friend, 'gallant knights, gentle sirs, what ails my good Lord Margrave?'

'Perhaps his nose bleeds,' said Gottfried with a sneer.

'Ah, my kind friend,' said the Margravine with uncontrollable emotion, 'I fear some of you have passed from the frying-pan into the fire.' And making the signal of departure to the ladies, they rose and retired to coffee in the drawing-room.

The Margrave presently came back again, somewhat more collected than he had been. 'Otto,' he said sternly, 'go join the ladies: it becomes not a young boy to remain in the company of gallant knights after dinner.' The noble Childe with manifest unwillingness quitted the room, and the Margrave, taking his lady's place at the head of the table, whispered to Sir Ludwig, 'Hildebrandt will be here to-night to an evening party, given in honour of your return from Palestine. My good friend—my true friend—my old companion in arms, Sir Gottfried! you had best see that the fiddlers be not drunk, and that the crumpets be gotten ready.' Sir Gottfried, obsequiously taking his patron's hint, bowed and left the room.

'You shall know all soon, dear Ludwig,' said the Margrave with a heartrending look. 'You marked Gottfried, who left the room anon?'

'I did.'

'You look incredulous concerning his worth; but I tell thee, Ludwig, that yonder Gottfried is a good fellow, and my fast friend. Why should he not be? He is my near relation heir to my property : should I ' (here the Margrave's countenance assumed its former expression of excruciating agony),—'*should I have no son.*'

'But I never saw the boy in better health,' replied Sir Ludwig.

'Nevertheless,—ha! ha!—it may chance that I shall soon have no son.'

The Margrave had crushed many a cup of wine during dinner, and Sir Ludwig thought naturally that his gallant friend had drunken rather deeply.   He proceeded in this respect to imitate him ; for the stern soldier of those days neither shrunk before the Paynim nor the punch-bowl : and many a rousing night had our crusader enjoyed in Syria with lion-hearted Richard ; with his coadjutor, Godfrey of Bouillon ; nay, with the dauntless Saladin himself.

'You knew Gottfried in Palestine ?' asked the Marquis.

'I did.'

'Why did ye not greet him then, as ancient comrades should, with the warm grasp of friendship ?   It is not because Sir Gottfried is poor ?   You know well that he is of race as noble as thine own, my early friend ! '

'I care not for his race nor for his poverty,' replied the blunt crusader.   'What says the Minnesinger ? "Marry, the rank is but the stamp of the guinea ; the man is the gold."   And I tell thee, Karl of Godesberg, that yonder Gottfried is base metal.'

'By Saint Buffo, thou beliest him, dear Ludwig.'

'By Saint Bugo, dear Karl, I say sooth.   The fellow was known i' the camp of the crusaders—disreputably known.   Ere he joined us in Palestine, he had sojourned in Constantinople, and learned the arts of the Greek.   He is a cogger of dice, I tell thee— a chanter of horseflesh.   He won five thousand marks from bluff Richard of England the night before the storming of Ascalon, and I caught him with false trumps in his pocket.   He warranted a bay mare to Conrad of Mont Serrat, and the rogue had fired her.'

'Ha! mean ye that Sir Gottfried is a *leg ?*' cried Sir Karl, knitting his brows.   'Now, by my blessed patron, Saint Buffo of Bonn, had any other but Ludwig of Hombourg so said, I would have cloven him from skull to chine.'

'By Saint Bugo of Katzenellenbogen, I will prove my words on Sir Gottfried's body—not on thine, old brother-in-arms.   And to do the knave justice, he is a good lance.   Holy Bugo ! but he did good service at Acre !   But his character was such that, spite of his bravery, he was dismissed the army ; nor even allowed to sell his captain's commission.'

'I have heard of it,' said the Margrave ; 'Gottfried hath told me of it.   'Twas about some silly quarrel over the wine-cup—a

mere silly jape, believe me.   Hugo de Brodenel would have no
black bottle on the board.   Gottfried was wroth, and, to say sooth,
flung the black bottle at the Count's head.   Hence his dismission
and abrupt return.   But you know not,' continued the Margrave,
with a heavy sigh, 'of what use that worthy Gottfried has been
to me.   He has uncloaked a traitor to me.'

'Not *yet*,' answered Hombourg satirically.

'By Saint Buffo! a deep-dyed dastard! a dangerous damnable
traitor!—a nest of traitors.   Hildebrandt is a traitor—Otto is a
traitor—and Theodora (O Heaven!) she—she is *another*.'   The
old Prince burst into tears at the word, and was almost choked
with emotion.

'What means this passion, dear friend?' cried Sir Ludwig,
seriously alarmed.

'Mark, Ludwig! mark Hildebrandt and Theodora together:
mark Hildebrandt and *Otto* together.   Like, like I tell thee as
two peas.   O holy saints, that I should be born to suffer this!—
to have all my affections wrenched out of my bosom, and to be
left alone in my old age!   But, hark! the guests are arriving.
An ye will not empty another flask of claret, let us join the ladyes
i' the withdrawing chamber.   When there, mark *Hildebrandt and
Otto*!'

CHAPTER III

THE FESTIVAL

HE festival was indeed begun. Coming on horseback, or in their caroches, knights and ladies of the highest rank were assembled in the grand saloon of Godesberg, which was splendidly illuminated to receive them. Servitors, in rich liveries (they were attired in doublets of the sky-blue broadcloth of Ypres, and hose of the richest yellow sammit— the colours of the house of Godesberg), bore about various refreshments on trays of silver — cakes, baked in the oven, and swimming in melted butter; munchets of bread, smeared with the same delicious condiment, and carved so thin that you might have expected them to take wing and fly to the ceiling; coffee, introduced by Peter the Hermit, after his excursion into Arabia, and tea such as only Bohemia could produce, circulated amidst the festive throng, and were eagerly devoured by the guests. The Margrave's gloom was unheeded by them—how little indeed is the smiling crowd aware of the pangs that are lurking in the breasts of those who bid them to the feast! The Margravine was pale; but woman knows how to deceive; she was more than ordinarily courteous to her friends, and laughed, though the laugh was hollow; and talked, though the talk was loathsome to her.

'The two are together,' said the Margrave, clutching his friend's shoulder. '*Now look!*'

Sir Ludwig turned towards a quadrille, and there, sure enough, were Sir Hildebrandt and young Otto standing side by side in the dance. Two eggs were not more like! The reason of the Margrave's horrid suspicion at once flashed across his friend's mind

''Tis clear as the staff of a pike,' said the poor Margrave mournfully. 'Come, brother, away from the scene; let us go play a game at cribbage!' and retiring to the Margravine's *boudoir*, the two warriors sat down to the game.

But though 'tis an interesting one, and though the Margrave

won, yet he could not keep his attention on the cards: so agitated was his mind by the dreadful secret which weighed upon it. In the midst of their play, the obsequious Gottfried came to whisper a word in his patron's ear, which threw the latter into such a fury, that apoplexy was apprehended by the two lookers-on. But the Margrave mastered his emotion. '*At what time*, did you say?' said he to Gottfried.

'At daybreak, at the outer gate.'

'I will be there.'

'*And so will I too*,' thought Count Ludwig, the good Knight of Hombourg.

CHAPTER IV

THE FLIGHT

How often does man, proud man, make calculations for the future, and think he can bend stern fate to his will! Alas, we are but creatures in its hands! How many a slip between the lip and the lifted wine-cup! How often, though seemingly with a choice of couches to repose upon, do we find ourselves dashed to earth; and then we are fain to say the grapes are sour, because we cannot attain them; or worse, to yield to anger in consequence of our own fault. Sir Ludwig, the Hombourger, was *not at the outer gate* at daybreak.

He slept until ten of the clock. The previous night's potations had been heavy, the day's journey had been long and rough. The knight slept as a soldier would, to whom a feather bed is a rarity, and who wakes not till he hears the blast of the réveillé.

He looked up as he woke. At his bedside sat the Margrave. He had been there for hours, watching his slumbering comrade. Watching?—no, not watching, but awake by his side, brooding over thoughts unutterably bitter—over feelings inexpressibly wretched.

'What's o'clock?' was the first natural exclamation of the Hombourger.

'I believe it is five o'clock,' said his friend. It was ten. It might have been twelve, two, half-past four, twenty minutes to six, the Margrave would still have said, ' *I believe it is five o'clock.*' The wretched take no count of time: it flies with unequal pinions, indeed, for *them*.

'Is breakfast over?' inquired the crusader.

'Ask the butler,' said the Margrave, nodding his head wildly, rolling his eyes wildly, smiling wildly.

'Gracious Bugo!' said the Knight of Hombourg, 'what has ailed thee, my friend? It is ten o'clock by my horologe. Your regular hour is nine. You are not—no, by heavens! you are not shaved! You wear the tights and silken hose of last evening's banquet. Your collar is all rumpled—'tis that of yesterday. *You have not been to bed!* What has chanced, brother of mine; what has chanced?'

16

'A common chance, Louis of Hombourg,' said the Margrave: 'one that chances every day. A false woman, a false friend, a broken heart. *This* has chanced. I have not been to bed.'

'What mean ye?' cried Count Ludwig, deeply affected. 'A false friend? *I* am not a false friend. A false woman? Surely the lovely Theodora, your wife——'

'I have no wife, Louis, now; I have no wife and no son.'

In accents broken by grief, the Margrave explained what had occurred. Gottfried's information was but too correct. There was *a cause* for the likeness between Otto and Sir Hildebrandt: a fatal cause! Hildebrandt and Theodora had met at dawn at the outer gate. The Margrave had seen them. They walked along together; they embraced. Ah! how the husband's, the father's, feelings were harrowed at that embrace! They parted; and then the Margrave, coming forward, coldly signified to his lady that she was to retire to a convent for life, and gave orders that the boy should be sent too, to take the vows at a monastery.

Both sentences had been executed. Otto, in a boat, and guarded by a company of his father's men-at-arms, was on the river going towards Cologne, to the Monastery of Saint Buffo there. The Lady Theodora, under the guard of Sir Gottfried and an attendant, were on their way to the convent of Nonnenwerth, which many of our readers have seen— the beautiful Green Island Convent, laved by the bright waters of the Rhine!

'What road did Gottfried take?' asked the Knight of Hombourg, grinding his teeth.

'You cannot overtake him,' said the Margrave. 'My good Gottfried, he is my only comfort now: he is my kinsman, and shall be my heir. He will be back anon.'

'Will he so?' thought Sir Ludwig. 'I will ask him a few questions ere he return.' And springing from his couch, he began forthwith to put on his usual morning dress of complete armour; and, after a hasty ablution, donned, not his cap of maintenance, but his helmet of battle. He rang the bell violently.

'A cup of coffee, straight,' said he, to the servitor who answered the summons; 'bid the cook pack me a sausage and bread in paper, and the groom saddle Streithengst: we have far to ride.'

The various orders were obeyed. The horse was brought; the refreshments disposed of; the clattering steps of the departing steed were heard in the courtyard; but the Margrave took no notice of his friend, and sat, plunged in silent grief, quite motionless by the empty bedside.

CHAPTER V

THE TRAITOR'S DOOM

THE Hombourger led his horse down the winding path which conducts from the hill and castle of Godesberg into the beautiful green plain below. Who has not seen that lovely plain, and who that has seen it has not loved it? A thousand sunny vineyards and cornfields stretch around in peaceful luxuriance; the mighty Rhine floats by it in silver magnificence, and on the opposite bank rise the seven mountains robed in majestic purple, the monarchs of the royal scene.

A pleasing poet, Lord Byron, in describing this very scene, has mentioned that 'peasant girls, with dark blue eyes, and hands that offer cake and wine,' are perpetually crowding round the traveller in this delicious district, and proffering to him their rustic presents. This was no doubt the case in former days, when the noble bard wrote his elegant poems—in the happy ancient days! when maidens were as yet generous, and men kindly! Now the degenerate peasantry of the district are much more inclined to ask than to give, and their blue eyes seem to have disappeared with their generosity.

But as it was a long time ago that the events of our story occurred, 'tis probable that the good Knight Ludwig of Hombourg was greeted upon his path by this fascinating peasantry; though we know not how he accepted their welcome. He continued his ride across the flat green country until he came to Rolandseck, whence he could command the Island of Nonnenwerth (that lies in the Rhine opposite that place), and all who went to it or passed from it.

Over the entrance of a little cavern in one of the rocks hanging above the Rhine-stream at Rolandseck, and covered with odoriferous cactuses and silvery magnolias, the traveller of the present day may perceive a rude broken image of a saint: that image represented the venerable Saint Buffo of Bonn, the patron of the Margrave; and Sir Ludwig, kneeling on the greensward, and reciting a censer, an

18

ave, and a couple of acolytes before it, felt encouraged to think that the deed he meditated was about to be performed under the very eyes of his friend's sanctified patron. His devotion done (and the knight of those days was as pious as he was brave), Sir Ludwig, the gallant Hombourger, exclaimed with a loud voice :—

'Ho! hermit! holy hermit, art thou in thy cell!'

'Who calls the poor servant of Heaven and Saint Buffo?' exclaimed a voice from the cavern; and presently, from beneath the wreaths of geranium and magnolia, appeared an intensely venerable, ancient, and majestic head—'twas that, we need not say, of Saint Buffo's solitary. A silver beard hanging to his knees gave his person an appearance of great respectability; his body was robed in simple brown serge, and girt with a knotted cord; his ancient feet were only defended from the prickles and stones by the rudest sandals, and his bald and polished head was bare.

'Holy hermit,' said the knight in a grave voice, 'make ready thy ministry, for there is some one about to die.'

'Where, son?'

'Here, father.'

'Is he here, now?'

'Perhaps,' said the stout warrior, crossing himself; 'but not so if right prevail.' At this moment he caught sight of a ferry-boat putting off from Nonnenwerth, with a knight on board. Ludwig knew at once, by the sinople reversed and the truncated gules on his surcoat, that it was Sir Gottfried of Godesberg.

'Be ready, father,' said the good knight, pointing towards the advancing boat; and waving his hand by way of respect to the reverend hermit, without a further word he vaulted into his saddle, and rode back for a few score of paces, when he wheeled round, and remained steady. His great lance and pennon rose in the air. His armour glistened in the sun; the chest and head of his battle-horse were similarly covered with steel. As Sir Gottfried, likewise armed and mounted (for his horse had been left at the ferry hard by), advanced up the road, he almost started at the figure before him— a glistening tower of steel.

'Are you the lord of this pass, Sir Knight?' said Sir Gottfried haughtily, 'or do you hold it against all comers, in honour of your lady-love?'

'I am not the lord of this pass. I do not hold it against all comers. I hold it but against one, and he is a liar and a traitor.'

'As the matter concerns me not, I pray you let me pass,' said Gottfried.

'The matter *does* concern thee, Gottfried of Godesberg. Liar and traitor! art thou coward, too?'

'Holy Saint Buffo! 'tis a fight!' exclaimed the old hermit (who, too, had been a gallant warrior in his day); and like the old war-horse that hears the trumpet's sound, and spite of his clerical profession, he prepared to look on at the combat with no ordinary eagerness, and sat down on the overhanging ledge of the rock, lighting his pipe, and affecting unconcern, but in reality most deeply interested in the event which was about to ensue.

As soon as the word 'coward' had been pronounced by Sir Ludwig, his opponent, uttering a curse far too horrible to be inscribed here, had wheeled back his powerful piebald, and brought his lance to the rest.

'Ha! Beauséant!' cried he. 'Allah humdillah!' 'Twas the battle-cry in Palestine of the irresistible Knights Hospitallers. 'Look to thyself, Sir Knight, and for mercy from Heaven. *I* will give thee none.'

'A Bugo for Katzenellenbogen!' exclaimed Sir Ludwig piously: that, too, was the well-known war-cry of his princely race.

'I will give the signal,' said the old hermit, waving his pipe. 'Knights, are you ready? One, two, three. *Los!*' (Let go.)

At the signal, the two steeds tore up the ground like whirlwinds; the two knights, two flashing perpendicular masses of steel, rapidly converged; the two lances met upon the two shields of either, and shivered, splintered, shattered into ten hundred thousand pieces, which whirled through the air here and there, among the rocks, or in the trees, or in the river. The two horses fell back trembling on their haunches, where they remained for half a minute or so.

'Holy Buffo! a brave stroke!' said the old hermit. 'Marry, but a splinter well-nigh took off my nose!' The honest hermit waved his pipe in delight, not perceiving that one of the splinters had carried off the head of it, and rendered his favourite amusement impossible. 'Ha! they are to it again! O my! how they go to with their great swords! Well stricken, grey! Well parried, piebald! Ha, that was a slicer! Go it, piebald! go it, grey!—go it, grey! go it, pie—— Peccavi! peccavi!' said the old man, here suddenly closing his eyes, and falling down on his knees. 'I forgot I was a man of peace.' And the next moment, uttering a hasty matin, he sprang down the ledge of rock, and was by the side of the combatants.

The battle was over. Good knight as Sir Gottfried was, his strength and skill had not been able to overcome Sir Ludwig the Hombourger, with RIGHT on his side. He was bleeding at every point of his armour: he had been run through the body several times, and a cut in tierce, delivered with tremendous dexterity, had cloven the crown of his helmet of Damascus steel, and passing through the cerebellum and sensorium, had split his nose almost in twain.

His mouth foaming—his face almost green—his eyes full of

GC.ᴿ

blood—his brains spattered over his forehead, and several of his teeth knocked out—the discomfited warrior presented a ghastly spectacle, as, reeling under the effects of the last tremendous blow which the Knight of Hombourg dealt, Sir Gottfried fell heavily from the saddle of his piebald charger ; the frightened animal whisked his tail wildly with a shriek and a snort, plunged out his hind legs, trampling for one moment upon the feet of the prostrate Gottfried, thereby causing him to shriek with agony, and then galloped away riderless.

Away! ay, away!—away amid the green vineyards and golden cornfields; away up the steep mountains, where he frightened the eagles in their eyries; away down the clattering ravines, where the flashing cataracts tumble; away through the dark pine-forests, where the hungry wolves are howling; away over the dreary wolds, where the wild wind walks alone; away through the plashing quagmires, where the will-o'-the-wisp slunk frightened among the reeds; away through light and darkness, storm and sunshine; away by tower and town, highroad and hamlet. Once a turnpike-man would have detained him; but, ha! ha! he charged the pike, and cleared it at a bound. Once the Cologne Diligence stopped the way: he charged the Diligence, he knocked off the cap of the conductor on the roof, and yet galloped wildly, madly, furiously, irresistibly on! Brave horse! gallant steed! snorting child of Araby! On went the horse, over mountains, rivers, turnpikes, apple-women; and never stopped until he reached a livery-stable in Cologne where his master was accustomed to put him up.

CHAPTER VI

BUT we have forgotten, meanwhile, the prostrate individual. Having examined the wounds in his side, legs, head, and throat, the old hermit (a skilful leech) knelt down by the side of the vanquished one and said, 'Sir Knight, it is my painful duty to state to you that you are in an exceedingly dangerous condition, and will not probably survive.'

'Say you so, Sir Priest? then 'tis time I make my confession. Hearken you, Priest, and you, Sir Knight, whoever you be.'

Sir Ludwig (who, much affected by the scene, had been tying his horse up to a tree) lifted his visor and said, 'Gottfried of Godesberg! I am the friend of thy kinsman, Margrave Karl, whose happiness thou hast ruined ; I am the friend of his chaste and virtuous lady, whose fair fame thou hast belied ; I am the godfather of young Count Otto, whose heritage thou wouldst have appropriated. Therefore I met thee in deadly fight, and overcame thee, and have well-nigh finished thee. Speak on.'

'I have done all this,' said the dying man, 'and here, in my last hour, repent me. The Lady Theodora is a spotless lady ; the youthful Otto the true son of his father—Sir Hildebrandt is not his father, but his *uncle*.'

'Gracious Buffo!' 'Celestial Bugo!' here said the hermit and the Knight of Hombourg simultaneously, clasping their hands.

'Yes, his uncle ; but with the *bar-sinister* in his 'scutcheon. Hence he could never be acknowledged by the family ; hence, too, the Lady Theodora's spotless purity (though the young people had been brought up together) could never be brought to own the relationship.'

'May I repeat your confession ?' asked the hermit.

'With the greatest pleasure in life : carry my confession to the Margrave, and pray him give me pardon. Were there—a notary-public present,' slowly gasped the knight, the film of dissolution glazing over his eyes, 'I would ask—you—two—gentlemen to witness it. I would gladly—sign the deposition—that is, if I could wr-wr-wr-wr-ite!' A faint shuddering smile—a quiver, a gasp, a gurgle—the blood gushed from his mouth in black volumes. . . .

'He will never sin more,' said the hermit solemnly.

'May Heaven assoilzie him!' said Sir Ludwig. 'Hermit, he was a gallant knight. He died with harness on his back, and with truth on his lips : Ludwig of Hombourg would ask no other death. . . .'

An hour afterwards the principal servants at the Castle of Godesberg were rather surprised to see the noble Lord Louis trot into the courtyard of the castle, with a companion on the crupper of his saddle. 'Twas the venerable Hermit of Rolandseck, who, for the sake of greater celerity, had adopted this undignified conveyance, and whose appearance and little dumpy legs might well create hilarity among the 'pampered menials' who are always found lounging about the houses of the great. He skipped off the saddle with considerable lightness, however ; and Sir Ludwig, taking the reverend man by the arm, and frowning the jeering servitors into awe, bade one of them lead him to the presence of His Highness the Margrave.

'What has chanced?' said the inquisitive servitor. 'The riderless horse of Sir Gottfried was seen to gallop by the outer wall anon. The Margrave's Grace has never quitted your Lordship's chamber, and sits as one distraught.'

'Hold thy prate, knave, and lead us on!' And so saying, the Knight and his Reverence moved into the well-known apartment, where, according to the servitor's description, the wretched Margrave sat like a stone.

Ludwig took one of the kind broken-hearted man's hands, the hermit seized the other, and began (but on account of his great age, with a prolixity which we shall not endeavour to imitate) to narrate the events which we have already described. Let the dear reader fancy, the while his Reverence speaks, the glazed eyes of the Margrave gradually lighting up with attention ; the flush of joy which mantles in his countenance—the start—the throb—the almost delirious outburst of hysteric exultation with which, when the whole truth was made known, he clasped the two messengers of glad tidings to his breast, with an energy that almost choked the aged recluse! 'Ride, ride this instant to the Margravine—say I have wronged her, that it is all right, that she may come back—that I forgive her—that I apologise, if you will' —and a secretary forthwith despatched a note to that effect, which was carried off by a fleet messenger.

'Now write to the Superior of the monastery at Cologne, and bid him send me back my boy, my darling, my Otto—my Otto of roses!' said the fond father, making the first play upon words he had ever attempted in his life. But what will not paternal love effect? The secretary (smiling at the joke) wrote another letter, and another fleet messenger was despatched on another horse.

'And now,' said Sir Ludwig playfully, 'let us to lunch. Holy hermit, are you for a snack?'

The hermit could not say nay on an occasion so festive, and the three gentles seated themselves to a plenteous repast; for which

the remains of the feast of yesterday offered, it need not be said, ample means.

'They will be home by dinner-time,' said the exulting father. 'Ludwig! reverend hermit! we will carry on till then.' And the cup passed gaily round, and the laugh and jest circulated, while the three happy friends sat confidently awaiting the return of the Margravine and her son.

But alas! said we not rightly at the commencement of a former chapter, that betwixt the lip and the raised wine-cup there is often many a spill? that our hopes are high, and often, too often, vain? About three hours after the departure of the first messenger, he returned, and with an exceedingly long face knelt down and presented to the Margrave a billet to the following effect :—

'CONVENT OF NONNENWERTH : Friday Afternoon.

'SIR,—I have submitted too long to your ill-usage, and am disposed to bear it no more. I will no longer be made the butt of your ribald satire, and the object of your coarse abuse. Last week you threatened me with your cane ! On Tuesday last you threw a wine-decanter at me, which hit the butler, it is true, but the intention was evident. This morning, in the presence of all the servants, you called me by the most vile abominable name, which Heaven forbid I should repeat ! You dismissed me from your house under a false accusation. You sent me to this odious convent to be immured for life. Be it so ! I will not come back, because, forsooth, you relent. Anything is better than a residence with a wicked, coarse, violent, intoxicated, brutal monster like yourself. I remain here for ever, and blush to be obliged to sign myself   THEODORA VON GODESBERG.

'<i>P.S.</i>—I hope you do not intend to keep all my best gowns, jewels, and wearing-apparel ; and make no doubt you dismissed me from your house in order to make way for some vile hussy, whose eyes I would like to tear out,   T. V. G.'

CHAPTER VII

THE SENTENCE

THIS singular document, illustrative of the passions of women at all times, and particularly of the manners of the early ages, struck dismay into the heart of the Margrave.

'Are her Ladyship's insinuations correct?' asked the hermit in a severe tone. 'To correct a wife with a cane is a venial, I may say a justifiable practice; but to fling a bottle at her is ruin, both to the liquor and to her.'

'But she sent a carving-knife at me first,' said the heart-broken husband. 'O jealousy, cursed jealousy, why, why did I ever listen to thy green and yellow tongue?'

'They quarrelled; but they loved each other sincerely,' whispered Sir Ludwig to the hermit; who began to deliver forthwith a lecture upon family discord and marital authority, which would have sent his two hearers to sleep, but for the arrival of the second messenger, whom the Margrave had despatched to Cologne for his son. This herald wore a still longer face than that of his comrade who preceded him.

'Where is my darling?' roared the agonised parent. 'Have ye brought him with ye?'

'N—no,' said the man, hesitating.

'I will flog the knave soundly when he comes,' cried the father, vainly endeavouring, under an appearance of sternness, to hide his inward emotion and tenderness.

'Please, your Highness,' said the messenger, making a desperate effort, 'Count Otto is not at the convent.'

'Know ye, knave, where he is?'

The swain solemnly said, 'I do. He is *there*.' He pointed as he spake to the broad Rhine, that was seen from the casement, lighted up by the magnificent hues of sunset.

'*There!* How mean ye *there?*' gasped the Margrave, wrought to a pitch of nervous fury.

'Alas! my good lord, when he was in the boat which was to

conduct him to the convent, he—he jumped suddenly from it, and is dr-dr-owned.'

'Carry that knave out and hang him!' said the Margrave, with a calmness more dreadful than any outburst of rage. 'Let every man of the boat's crew be blown from the mouth of the cannon on the tower—except the coxswain, and let him be——'

What was to be done with the coxswain, no one knows ; for at that moment, and overcome by his emotion, the Margrave sank down lifeless on the floor.

CHAPTER VIII

THE CHILDE OF GODESBERG

It must be clear to the dullest intellect (if amongst our readers we dare venture to presume that a dull intellect should be found) that the cause of the Margrave's fainting fit, described in the last chapter, was a groundless apprehension on the part of that too solicitous and credulous nobleman regarding the fate of his beloved child. No, young Otto was *not* drowned. Was ever hero of romantic story done to death so early in the tale? Young Otto was *not* drowned. Had such been the case, the Lord Margrave would infallibly have died at the close of the last chapter; and a few gloomy sentences at its close would have denoted how the lovely Lady Theodora became insane in the convent, and how Sir Ludwig determined, upon the demise of the old hermit (consequent upon the shock of hearing the news), to retire to the vacant hermitage, and assume the robe, the beard, the mortifications of the late venerable and solitary ecclesiastic. Otto was *not* drowned, and all those personages of our history are consequently alive and well.

The boat containing the amazed young Count—for he knew not the cause of his father's anger, and hence rebelled against the unjust sentence which the Margrave had uttered—had not rowed many miles, when the gallant boy rallied from his temporary surprise and despondency, and determined not to be a slave in any convent of any order: determined to make a desperate effort for escape. At a moment when the men were pulling hard against the tide, and Kuno, the coxswain, was looking carefully to steer the barge between some dangerous rocks and quicksands, which are frequently met with in the majestic though dangerous river, Otto gave a sudden spring from the boat, and with one single flounce was in the boiling, frothing, swirling eddy of the stream.

Fancy the agony of the crew at the disappearance of their young lord! All loved him; all would have given their lives for him; but as they did not know how to swim, of course they

declined to make any useless plunges in search of him, and stood
on their oars in mute wonder and grief.   *Once*, his fair head and
golden ringlets were seen to arise from the water; *twice*, puffing
and panting, it appeared for an instant again; *thrice*, it rose but
for one single moment: it was the last chance, and it sunk, sunk,
sunk.   Knowing the reception they would meet with from their
liege lord, the men naturally did not go home to Godesberg, but,
putting in at the first creek on the opposite bank, fled into the
Duke of Nassau's territory; where, as they have little to do with
our tale, we will leave them.

But they little knew how expert a swimmer was young Otto.
He had disappeared, it is true: but why? because he *had dived*.

He calculated that his conductors would consider him drowned,
and the desire of liberty lending him wings (or we had rather say
fins, in this instance), the gallant boy swam on beneath the water,
never lifting his head for a single moment between Godesberg and
Cologne—the distance being twenty-five or thirty miles.

Escaping from observation, he landed on the *Deutz* side of the
river, repaired to a comfortable and quiet hostel there, saying he
had had an accident from a boat, and thus accounting for the
moisture of his habiliments, and while these were drying before a
fire in his chamber, went snugly to bed, where he mused, not
without amaze, on the strange events of the day.   'This morning,'
thought he, 'a noble, and heir to a princely estate—this evening
an outcast, with but a few bank-notes which my mamma luckily

gave me on my birthday. What a strange entry into life is this for a young man of my family! Well, I have courage and resolution : my first attempt in life has been a gallant and successful one ; other dangers will be conquered by similar bravery.' And recommending himself, his unhappy mother, and his mistaken father to the care of their patron saint, Saint Buffo, the gallant-hearted boy fell presently into such a sleep, as only the young, the healthy, the innocent, and the extremely fatigued, can enjoy.

The fatigues of the day (and very few men but would be fatigued after swimming well-nigh thirty miles under water) caused young Otto to sleep so profoundly, that he did not remark how, after Friday's sunset, as a natural consequence, Saturday's Phœbus illumined the world, ay, and sunk at his appointed hour. The serving-maidens of the hostel, peeping in, marked him sleeping, and blessing him for a pretty youth, tripped lightly from the chamber ; the boots tried haply twice or thrice to call him (as boots will fain), but the lovely boy, giving another snore, turned on his side, and was quite unconscious of the interruption. In a word, the youth slept for six-and-thirty hours at an elongation ; and the Sunday sun was shining, and the bells of the hundred churches of Cologne were clinking and tolling in pious festivity, and the burghers and burgheresses of the town were trooping to vespers and morning service when Otto awoke.

As he donned his clothes of the richest Genoa velvet, the astonished boy could not at first account for his difficulty in putting them on. 'Marry,' said he, ' these breeches that my blessed mother ' (tears filled his fine eyes as he thought of her)—' that my blessed mother had made long on purpose, are now ten inches too short for me. Whir-r-r ! my coat cracks i' the back, as in vain I try to buckle it round me ; and the sleeves reach no farther than my elbows ! What is this mystery ? Am I grown fat and tall in a single night ? Ah ! ah ! ah ! ah ! I have it.'

The young and good-humoured Childe laughed merrily. He bethought him of the reason of his mistake : his garments had shrunk from being five-and-twenty miles under water.

But one remedy presented itself to his mind ; and that we need not say was to purchase new ones. Inquiring the way to the most genteel ready-made clothes' establishment in the city of Cologne, and finding it was kept in the Minoriten Strasse, by an ancestor of the celebrated Moses of London, the noble Childe hied him towards the emporium ; but you may be sure did not neglect to perform his religious duties by the way. Entering the cathedral, he made straight for the shrine of St. Buffo, and, hiding himself behind a pillar there (fearing he might be recognised by the Archbishop, or any of his father's numerous friends in Cologne), he proceeded with his devotions, as was the practice of the young nobles of the age.

But though exceedingly intent upon the service, yet his eye could not refrain from wandering a *little* round about him, and he remarked with surprise that the whole church was filled with archers ; and he remembered, too, that he had seen in the streets numerous other bands of men similarly attired in green. On asking at the cathedral porch the cause of this assemblage, one of the green ones said (in a jape), 'Marry, youngster, *you* must be *green*, not to know that we are all bound to the castle of his Grace Duke Adolf of Cleves, who gives an archery meeting once a year, and prizes for which we toxophilites muster strong.'

Otto, whose course hitherto had been undetermined, now immediately settled what to do. He straightway repaired to the ready-made emporium of Herr Moses, and bidding that gentleman furnish him with an archer's complete dress, Moses speedily selected a suit from his vast stock, which fitted the youth to a *t*, and we need not say was sold at an exceedingly moderate price. So attired (and bidding Herr Moses a cordial farewell), young Otto was a gorgeous, a noble, a soul-inspiring boy to gaze on. A coat and breeches of the most brilliant pea-green, ornamented with a profusion of brass buttons, and fitting him with exquisite tightness, showed off a figure unrivalled for slim symmetry. His feet were covered with peaked buskins of buff leather, and a belt round his slender waist, of the same material, held his knife, his tobacco-pipe and pouch, and his long shining dirk ; which, though the adventurous youth had as yet only employed it to fashion wicket-bails, or to cut bread-and-cheese, he was now quite ready to use against the enemy. His personal attractions were enhanced by a neat white hat, flung carelessly and fearlessly on one side of his open smiling countenance ; and his lovely hair, curling in ten thousand yellow ringlets, fell over his shoulder like golden epaulettes, and down his back as far as the waist-buttons of his coat. I warrant me, many a lovely Cölnerinn looked after the handsome Childe with anxiety, and dreamed that night of Cupid under the guise of 'a bonny boy in green.'

So accoutred, the youth's next thought was, that he must supply himself with a bow. This he speedily purchased at the most fashionable bowyer's, and of the best material and make. It was of ivory, trimmed with pink ribbon, and the cord of silk. An elegant quiver, beautifully painted and embroidered, was slung across his back with a dozen of the finest arrows, tipped

with steel of Damascus, formed of the branches of the famous
Upas tree of Java, and feathered with the wings of the ortolan.
These purchases being completed (together with that of a knap-
sack, dressing-case, change, etc.), our young adventurer asked
where was the hostel at which the archers were wont to assemble?
and being informed that it was at the sign of the 'Golden Stag,'
hied him to that house of entertainment, where, by calling for
quantities of liquor and beer, he speedily made the acquaintance
and acquired the goodwill of a company of his future comrades
who happened to be sitting in the coffee-room.

After they had eaten and drunken for all, Otto said, addressing
them, 'When go ye forth, gentles? I am a stranger here, bound
as you to the archery meeting of Duke Adolf. An ye will admit a
youth into your company, 'twill gladden me upon my lonely way?'

The archers replied, 'You seem so young and jolly, and you
spend your gold so very like a gentleman, that we'll receive you
in our band with pleasure. Be ready, for we start at half-past
two!' At that hour accordingly the whole joyous company
prepared to move, and Otto not a little increased his popularity
among them by stepping out and having a conference with the
landlord, which caused the latter to come into the room where the
archers were assembled previous to departure, and to say, 'Gentlemen, the bill is settled!'—words never ungrateful to an archer
yet: no, marry, nor to a man of any other calling that I wot of.

They marched joyously for several leagues, singing and joking,
and telling of a thousand feats of love and chase and war. While
thus engaged, some one remarked to Otto, that he was not
dressed in the regular uniform, having no feathers in his hat.

'I dare say I will find a feather,' said the lad, smiling.

Then another gibed because his bow was new.

'See that you can use your old one as well, Master Wolfgang,'
said the undisturbed youth. His answers, his bearing, his
generosity, his beauty, and his wit, inspired all his new toxo-
philite friends with interest and curiosity, and they longed to
see whether his skill with the bow corresponded with their
secret sympathies for him.

An occasion for manifesting this skill did not fail to present
itself soon—as indeed it seldom does to such a hero of romance
as young Otto was. Fate seems to watch over such: events
occur to them just in the nick of time; they rescue virgins just
as ogres are on the point of devouring them; they manage to be
present at Court and interesting ceremonies, and to see the most
interesting people at the most interesting moment; directly an
adventure is necessary for them, that adventure occurs: and I,

for my part, have often wondered with delight (and never could penetrate the mystery of the subject) at the way in which that humblest of romance heroes, Signor Clown, when he wants anything in the Pantomime, straightway finds it to his hand. How is it that—suppose he wishes to dress himself up like a woman, for instance, that minute a coalheaver walks in with a shovel-hat that answers for a bonnet: at the very next instant a butcher's lad passing with a string of sausages and a bundle of bladders unconsciously helps Master Clown to a necklace and a *tournure*, and so on through the whole toilet ? Depend upon it there is something we do not wot of in that mysterious over-coming of circumstances by great individuals : that apt and wondrous conjuncture of *the Hour and the Man ;* and so, for my part, when I heard the above remark of one of the archers, that Otto had never a feather in his bonnet, I felt sure that a heron would spring up in the next sentence to supply him with an *aigrette*.

And such indeed was the fact : rising out of a morass by which the archers were passing, a gallant heron, arching his neck, swelling his crest, placing his legs behind him, and his beak and red eyes against the wind, rose slowly, and offered the fairest mark in the world.

'Shoot, Otto,' said one of the archers. 'You would not shoot just now at a crow because it was a foul bird, nor at a hawk because it was a noble bird ; bring us down yon heron : it flies slowly.'

But Otto was busy that moment tying his shoe-string, and Rudolf, the third best of the archers, shot at the bird and missed it.

'Shoot, Otto,' said Wolfgang, a youth who had taken a liking to the young archer : 'the bird is getting further and further.'

But Otto was busy that moment whittling a willow-twig he had just cut. Max, the second best archer, shot and missed.

'Then,' said Wolfgang, 'I must try myself : a plague on you, young springald, you have lost a noble chance !'

Wolfgang prepared himself with all his care, and shot at the bird. 'It is out of distance,' said he, 'and a murrain on the bird !'

Otto, who by this time had done whittling his willow-stick (having carved a capital caricature of Wolfgang upon it), flung the twig down and said carelessly, 'Out of distance ! Pshaw ! We have two minutes yet,' and fell to asking riddles and cutting jokes ; to the which none of the archers listened, as they were all engaged, their noses in air, watching the retreating bird.

'Where shall I hit him ?' said Otto.

'Go to,' said Rudolf, 'thou canst see no limb of him : he is no bigger than a flea.'

'Here goes for his right eye !' said Otto ; and stepping forward

By C. M. YONGE and C. R. COLERIDGE

Strolling Players

By VARIOUS WRITERS

Hogan, M.P.

Flitters, Tatters, and the Counsellor

The New Antigone

Tim

Memories of Father Healy

CUTCLIFFE HYNE.—The "Paradise" Coal-Boat

CANON ATKINSON.—The Last of the Giant Killers

R. H. BARHAM. — The Ingoldsby Legends

HAWLEY SMART. — Breezie Langton

ANTHONY TROLLOPE.—The Three Clerks

SIR H. LYTTON BULWER.— Historical Characters

RICHARD JEFFERIES.—The Dewy Morn

FRANK BUCKLAND.—Curiosities of Natural History. 4 vols.

MRS. HUMPHRY WARD.— Miss Bretherton

D. C. MURRAY and H. HERMAN. — He fell among Thieves

LUCAS MALET.—Mrs. Lorimer

LANOE FALCONER.— Cecilia de Noël

M.M'LENNAN.—MuckleJock, and other Stories

MAJOR GAMBIER PARRY.— The Story of Dick

S. R. LYSAGHT.—The Marplot

SIR H. M. DURAND.—Helen Treveryan

MARCHESA THEODOLI.— Under Pressure

W. C. RHOADES.—John Trevennick

E. C. PRICE —In the Lion's Mouth

BLENNERHASSET AND SLEEMAN.—Adventures in Mashonaland

W. FORBES-MITCHELL. — Reminiscences of the Great Mutiny

REV. J. GILMORE. — Storm Warriors

LORD REDESDALE.—Tales of Old Japan

SIR S. BAKER.—True Tales for my Grandsons

HENRY KINGSLEY. — Tales of Old Travel

W. P. FRITH, R.A.—My Autobiography

CAMILLE ROUSSET. — Recollections of Marshal Macdonald

CHARLES WHITEHEAD.— Richard Savage

F. A. MIGNET.—Mary Queen of Scots

F. GUIZOT.—Oliver Cromwell

M. R. MITFORD.— Literary Recollections

REV. R. H. D. BARHAM.—Life of R. H. Barham

—— Life of Theodore Hook

Biographies of Eminent Persons   Vol. I.
    ,,   ,,   II.
    ,,   ,,   III.
    ,,   ,,   IV.
    ,,   ,,   V.

Annual Summaries. Vol. I.
    ,,   ,,   II.

Masson's French Dictionary

Shakespeare's Works. Vol. I.
    ,,   ,,   II.
    ,,   ,,   III.

MACMILLAN AND CO., LTD., LONDON

2 8.03

THREE-AND-SIXPENNY LIBRARY

W. M. THACKERAY—*continued*

Critical Papers in Literature and Art

The Fitzboodle Papers, Men's Wives, The Second Funeral of Napoleon, and other Sketches

Lovel the Widower, and other Stories

Lectures on the English Humorists of the Eighteenth Century, The Four Georges, Charity and Humour, etc.

Sketches and Travels in London, Mrs. Brown's Letters to a Young Man about Town, The Proser

Ballads and Verses, Miscellaneous Contributions to *Punch*

Other Volumes to follow

By JOHN TIMBS

Lives of Painters

Lives of Statesmen

Doctors and Patients

Wits and Humourists. 2 vols.

By E. WERNER

Success, and How he won it | Fickle Fortune

By MONTAGU WILLIAMS

Leaves of a Life | Later Leaves | Round London

By CHARLOTTE M. YONGE

The Heir of Redclyffe

Heartsease | Hopes and Fears

Dynevor Terrace

The Daisy Chain | The Trial

Pillars of the House. Vol. I.

　　　,,　　　,,　　II.

The Young Stepmother

Clever Woman of the Family

The Three Brides

My Young Alcides

The Caged Lion

The Dove in the Eagle's Nest

The Chaplet of Pearls

Lady Hester, and Danvers Papers

Magnum Bonum

Love and Life

Unknown to History

Stray Pearls

The Armourer's 'Prentices

The Two Sides of the Shield

Nuttie's Father

Scenes and Characters

Chantry House

A Modern Telemachus

Bywords

Beechcroft at Rockstone

More Bywords

A Reputed Changeling

The Little Duke

The Lances of Lynwood

The Prince and the Page

Two Penniless Princesses

That Stick

An Old Woman's Outlook

Grisly Grisell | The Release

The Long Vacation

BenBeriah | Henrietta's Wish

The Two Guardians

Countess Kate, and the Stokesley Secret

Modern Broods

MACMILLAN AND CO., LTD., LONDON

THREE=AND=SIXPENNY LIBRARY

By Mrs. PARR

Dorothy Fox | Loyalty George
Adam and Eve | Robin

By W. CLARK RUSSELL

Marooned | A Strange Elopement

By Sir WALTER SCOTT

The Large-type Illustrated Border Edition of THE WAVERLEY NOVELS
In 24 volumes

Waverley | Peveril of the Peak
Guy Mannering | Quentin Durward
The Antiquary | St. Ronan's Well
Rob Roy | Redgauntlet
Old Mortality | The Betrothed, and The
The Heart of Midlothian | Talisman
A Legend of Montrose, and | Woodstock
  the Black Dwarf | The Fair Maid of Perth
The Bride of Lammermoor | Anne of Geierstein
Ivanhoe   The Abbot | Count Robert of Paris, and
The Monastery Kenilworth | The Surgeon's Daughter
The Pirate | Castle Dangerous, Chronicles
The Fortunes of Nigel | of the Canongate, etc.

By J. H. SHORTHOUSE

John Inglesant | The Countess Eve
Sir Percival | A Teacher of the Violin
Little Schoolmaster Mark | Blanche, Lady Falaise

By W. M. THACKERAY

Reprints of the First Editions, with all the Original Illustrations,
Facsimiles of Wrappers, etc.

Vanity Fair
The History of Pendennis
The Newcomes
The Virginians
The History of Henry Esmond
Barry Lyndon and Catherine
Paris and Irish Sketch Books
Christmas Books
Burlesques, From Cornhill
  to Grand Cairo, and Juve-
  nilia

Book of Snobs, Miss Tickletoby's Lectures, History of
  the next French Revolution,
  A Little Dinner at Timmins',
  etc.
The Yellowplush Correspondence, Diary and Letters of
  James de la Pluche, History
  of Samuel Titmarsh and the
  Great Hoggarty Diamond,
  and Contributions to the
  Constitutional [and Public
  Ledger]

MACMILLAN AND CO., LTD., LONDON

THREE=AND=SIXPENNY LIBRARY

Charles Kingsley—continued

Sermons on National Subjects | Discipline, and other Sermons
Sermons for the Times | Westminster Sermons
Good News of God | All Saints' Day, and other
The Gospel of the Penta- | Sermons
teuch, etc. |

By MAARTEN MAARTENS

An Old Maid's Love | God's Fool
The Greater Glory | The Sin of Joost Avelingh
My Lady Nobody | Her Memory

By A. E. W. MASON

The Courtship of Morrice | The Philanderers
Buckler | Miranda of the Balcony

By F. D. MAURICE

Lincoln's Inn Sermons. Vol. I. | Prophets and Kings
,, ,, II. | Patriarchs and Lawgivers
,, ,, III. | Gospel of Kingdom of Heaven
,, ,, IV. | Gospel of St. John
,, ,, V. | Epistles of St. John
,, ,, VI. | Friendship of Books
Sermons Preached in Country | Prayer Book and Lord's
Churches. | Prayer
Christmas Day | Doctrine of Sacrifice
Theological Essays | Acts of the Apostles

By D. CHRISTIE MURRAY

Aunt Rachel | The Weaker Vessel
Schwartz | John Vale's Guardian

By W. E. NORRIS

Thirlby Hall | Bachelor's Blunder

By Mrs. OLIPHANT

Neighbours on the Green | Sir Tom
Joyce | The Heir-Presumptive, etc.
Kirsteen | A Country Gentleman
A Beleaguered City | A Son of the Soil
Hester | The Second Son
He that Will Not when He | The Wizard's Son
May | The Curate in Charge
The Railway Man | Lady William
Marriage of Elinor | Young Musgrave

MACMILLAN AND CO., LTD., LONDON

THREE-AND-SIXPENNY LIBRARY

MACMILLAN AND CO., LTD., LONDON

THREE=AND=SIXPENNY LIBRARY

By ROLF BOLDREWOOD

Robbery under Arms
The Miner's Right
The Squatter's Dream
A Sydney-side Saxon
A Colonial Reformer
Nevermore
A Modern Buccaneer
The Sealskin Cloak

Plain Living
The Crooked Stick
My Run Home
Old Melbourne Memories
War to the Knife
Romance of Canvas Town
Babes in the Bush
In Bad Company and other Stories

By ROSA NOUCHETTE CAREY

Nellie's Memories
Wee Wifie
Barbara Heathcote's Trial
Robert Ord's Atonement
Wooed and Married
Heriot's Choice
Queenie's Whim
Mary St. John
Not Like Other Girls
For Lilias
Uncle Max

Only the Governess
Lover or Friend?
Basil Lyndhurst
Sir Godfrey's Granddaughters
The Old, Old Story
Mistress of Brae Farm
Mrs. Romney, and But Men Must Work
Other People's Lives
Rue with a Difference
Herb of Grace

By EGERTON CASTLE

Consequences
The Bath Comedy
The Pride of Jennico

The Light of Scarthey
La Bella, and others
"Young April"

By HUGH CONWAY

A Family Affair

Living or Dead

By Mrs. CRAIK

Olive
The Ogilvies
Agatha's Husband
The Head of the Family
Two Marriages
The Laurel Bush
My Mother and I

Miss Tommy
King Arthur: Not a Love Story
About Money, and other Things
Concerning Men, and other Papers

By F. MARION CRAWFORD

Mr. Isaacs
Dr. Claudius
A Roman Singer
Zoroaster
A Tale of a Lonely Parish

Marzio's Crucifix
Paul Patoff
With the Immortals
Greifenstein | Sant' Ilario
Cigarette-Maker's Romance

MACMILLAN AND CO., LTD., LONDON

THE WORKS OF
CHARLES DICKENS

A Reprint of the First Edition, with the Illustrations, and
Introductions, Biographical and Bibliographical,
by CHARLES DICKENS the Younger.

Crown 8vo. **3/6** *each volume.*

THE PICKWICK PAPERS. With 50 Illustrations.

OLIVER TWIST. With 27 Illustrations.

NICHOLAS NICKLEBY. With 44 Illustrations.

MARTIN CHUZZLEWIT. With 41 Illustrations.

THE OLD CURIOSITY SHOP. With 97 Illustrations.

BARNABY RUDGE. With 76 Illustrations.

DOMBEY AND SON. With 40 Illustrations.

CHRISTMAS BOOKS. With 65 Illustrations.

SKETCHES BY BOZ. With 44 Illustrations.

AMERICAN NOTES and PICTURES FROM ITALY.
With 4 Illustrations.

DAVID COPPERFIELD. With 40 Illustrations.

BLEAK HOUSE. With 43 Illustrations.

LITTLE DORRIT. With 40 Illustrations.

THE LETTERS OF CHARLES DICKENS.

A TALE OF TWO CITIES. Illustrated.

MACMILLAN AND CO., LTD., LONDON.

THE WORKS OF THACKERAY

Reprints of the First Editions, with all the Original Illustrations, and with Facsimiles of Wrappers, etc.
Crown 8vo.   3s. 6d. each.

VANITY FAIR.	HISTORY OF PENDENNIS.
THE NEWCOMES.	HISTORY OF HENRY ESMOND.

THE VIRGINIANS.
BARRY LYNDON ; AND CATHERINE.
PARIS AND IRISH SKETCH BOOKS.
CHRISTMAS BOOKS
BURLESQUES ; FROM CORNHILL TO GRAND CAIRO;
AND JUVENILIA.

Volumes in the Press.

BOOK OF SNOBS ; MISS TICKLETOBY'S LECTURES ;
HISTORY OF THE NEXT FRENCH REVOLUTION, ETC.

THE YELLOWPLUSH CORRESPONDENCE ; DIARY
AND LETTERS OF JEAMES DE LA PLUCHE ; HISTORY OF
SAMUEL TITMARSH AND THE GREAT HOGGARTY
DIAMOND ; AND CONTRIBUTIONS TO THE CONSTITU-
TIONAL [AND PUBLIC LEDGER].

CRITICAL PAPERS IN LITERATURE.

CRITICAL PAPERS IN ART ; STUBBS'S CALENDAR ;
BARBER COX.

LOVEL THE WIDOWER, AND OTHER STORIES.

THE FITZ-BOODLE PAPERS ; MEN'S WIVES ; THE
SECOND FUNERAL OF NAPOLEON, AND OTHER SKETCHES.

LECTURES ON THE ENGLISH HUMOURISTS OF THE
EIGHTEENTH CENTURY ; THE FOUR GEORGES ; CHARITY
AND HUMOUR, ETC.

SKETCHES AND TRAVELS IN LONDON ; MR·
BROWN'S LETTERS TO A YOUNG MAN ABOUT TOWN ;
THE PROSER, ETC.

BALLADS AND VERSES ; A LITTLE DINNER AT
TIMMINS'S; MISCELLANEOUS CONTRIBUTIONS TO *PUNCH.*

THE ADVENTURES OF PHILIP, AND A SHABBY
GENTEEL STORY.

MACMILLAN AND CO., LTD., LONDON.

I tended her by night and day,
  But when the sportsman stray'd
Along the silent harvest-field,
  Death stole my village-maid.

Now winter's come, with hollow voice,
  I hear the howling wind
Ring through the savage naked woods,
  All gloomy like my mind.
O spring! come not again to me,
  By her I would be laid,
For what are birds or flow'rs to me,
  Without my village-maid.

T. M.

THE END

Printed by R. & R. CLARK, LIMITED, *Edinburgh*.

seems to say—cop. copy! cop. copy! but, by his own horns, he shall have none this time.—There! good ink—hiss on the fire awhile. Well?'—'If you please, sir, they say if you don't send more copy they'll not be able to get the work out, and if you please, they say the last you've sent's nonsense!'—'Indeed!' —'Yes, sir, they do.'—'Well, you must fetch me some ink; I've got none.'—'Why, if you please, when I come for the last copy you'd nearly a bottleful,—I shin'd it, sir!'—'Rascal, go along and fetch more, or I'll kick you downstairs! Cop. copy! cop. copy! by Jupiter, he shall have no more cop. copy to-night for his impudence. A villain!—to take notice of my ink. Now, I'll lock my door, creep into bed, and if he cries copy! copy! until his throat's sore, he shall have none until I've taken my rest.'

T. M.

ORIGINAL POETRY.

SONG.

I MET her in the early month
　Of blossom-laden spring;
When budding trees were lightly rob'd,
　And larks soar'd high to sing.
We wandered where the primrose grew,
　Deep in a silent glade,
And vow'd that naught save death should part
　Me and my village-maid.

When summer came with laughing days,
　And soft blue-hanging skies,
Which threw a gladness all around,
　As did her softer eyes;
Again we sought the twilight woods,
　Where hazels form'd a shade;
The ring-dove and the singing brook
　Pleas'd my sweet village-maid.

When autumn came in solemn gold,
　And yellow leaves were strown;
'Twas then death mark'd my village-maid,
　Alas! to be his own.

—yaw, yaw, yoyaw! What a wonderful system is man's,—no doing without sleep. Never did Satan arise with greater reluctance from his brimstone bed, to quell some riot infernal, than I rise now to furnish my devil with copy. Let's see,—I have not a line composed. Before me stands a pile of MS. which in time will out-top Olympus—it has all been published. As I opened my mouth just now to yawn, the printer's devil looked as if he would jump down my throat for 'more copy.' 'Wait a minute, my boy, while I write something. (*Aside.*) I wish your neck had been broken before you'd reach'd here.' Well, I must begin. 'The sun went down behind the dark-waving woods of Burton, amid masses of broken clouds, that roll'd wildly along, like war-steeds broken loose from the starry stables of heaven.'—'Here, my boy, take this.'—'Is this all, sir? I shall be back again in a minute for more.'—'Well, take that first, and begone; I shall have more ready ere you return.' There, thank God! I've got rid of that urchin once more. What were the ghosts that flitted with shadowy wings around King Richard's tent compared to this substantial devil? He was born with the word 'copy' upon his tongue. O for some pious divine to *lay* him, as they *lay* other devils when they arise,—in the Red Sea, or anywhere, so that I never see his demoniacal features in future. O mercy! here he comes again.—'More copy, sir, please!'—'The devil copy you! why, you must have lost the other; it never can have been set up in this time.'—'O dear, sir, when I got there, two on 'em wanted copy, and it seem'd no more to 'em than a nut would be to a whale for breakfast.'—'Where did I leave off, my boy, I have quite forgotten what I was writing.'—'If you please, sir, you left off at heaven, sir.'—'Humph! and I must begin again at the other place now you've come; I have no more knowledge as to what I was writing about than this pen. Well, yaw! yaw! yoyaw! the-e-y must have co-o-o-py,—there, I feel all the better for that. Heaven—well:'—'In heaven we shall have no crying out for copy (yaw—yaw!), in heaven we shall never feel sleepy, in heaven we shall have no proofs to correct, no punctuation to study, no silly *Tales of the Sea* to review, no Tories to attack,—no—no.'—'Here, my boy, tell the compositor to be particular in the pointing of this, as it's a climax!'—'Yes, sir.'

'O, what a blessing I've got rid of this ever-haunting spirit once more: yaw! yaw! yoyaw! yo-o-o-ah! there—hark! What again! I've only had time to place my feet comfortably upon the fender, (which once formed part of the tire of a waggon-wheel,) stretch my arms out three times, gape four, and rub my eyes five, before I again hear the devil upon the stairs. Every step he takes

MR. CROCKFORD.

GOOD readers, great Crockford you here may behold,
The fishmonger famous, whose fishes are gold;
His eye of a whiting, and mouth of a cod,
  Give a touch of his old fishy trade to his looks,
But they know, who can tell you a wink from a nod,
  That he now sticks to poultry, to pigeons, and rooks.
Yet he still makes a cast, and not seldom a haul,
  Still angles for flats, and still nets what he can;
And shows, every night, 'mid his shoal great and small,
  The trick how a gudgeon is made of a man.

L. E. U.

THE DEVIL TO PAY—A SKETCH.

I HAVE just now swallowed my supper, and am looking with
vacant eye upon the fire,—the only little rest which my jaded
mind has enjoyed for the last twenty-four hours. Hark! I
know his foot,—it is the printer's devil come again for 'more copy':

THE HISTORY OF THE FISH

THE HOG-BACKED TROUT

in the English manner (which his godfather having learnt in Palestine, had taught him), he brought his bowstring to his ear, took a good aim, allowing for the wind, and calculating the parabola to a nicety. Whizz! his arrow went off.

He took up the willow-twig again and began carving a head of Rudolf at the other end, chatting and laughing, and singing a ballad the while.

The archers, after standing a long time looking skywards with their noses in the air, at last brought them down from the perpendicular to the horizontal position, and said, 'Pooh, this lad is a humbug! The arrow's lost; let's go!'

'*Heads!*' cried Otto, laughing. A speck was seen rapidly descending from the heavens; it grew to be as big as a crown-piece, then as a partridge, then as a tea-kettle, and flop! down fell a magnificent heron to the ground, flooring poor Max in its fall.

'Take the arrow out of his eye, Wolfgang,' said Otto, without looking at the bird: 'wipe it and put it back into my quiver.'

The arrow indeed was there, having penetrated right through the pupil.

'Are you in league with Der Freischütz?' said Rudolf, quite amazed.

Otto laughing whistled the 'Huntsman's Chorus,' and said, 'No, my friend. It was a lucky shot: only a lucky shot. I was taught shooting, look you, in the fashion of merry England, where the archers are archers indeed.'

And so he cut off the heron's wing for a plume for his hat; and the archers walked on, much amazed, and saying, 'What a wonderful country that merry England must be!'

Far from feeling any envy at their comrade's success, the jolly archers recognised his superiority with pleasure; and Wolfgang and Rudolf especially held out their hands to the younker, and besought the honour of his friendship. They continued their walk all day, and when night fell made choice of a good hostel, you may be sure, where over beer, punch, champagne, and every luxury, they drank to the health of the Duke of Cleves, and indeed each other's healths all round. Next day they resumed their march, and continued it without interruption, except to take in a supply of victuals here and there (and it was found on these occasions that Otto, young as he was, could eat four times as much as the oldest archer present, and drink to correspond); and these continued refreshments having given them more than ordinary strength, they determined on making rather a long march of it, and did not halt till after nightfall at the gates of the little town of Windeck.

What was to be done? the town gates were shut. 'Is there

no hostel, no castle where we can sleep?' asked Otto of the sentinel at the gate. 'I am so hungry that in lack of better food I think I could eat my grandmamma.'

The sentinel laughed at this hyperbolical expression of hunger, and said, 'You had best go sleep at the Castle of Windeck yonder;' adding, with a peculiarly knowing look, 'Nobody will disturb you there.'

At that moment the moon broke out from a cloud, and showed on a hill hard by a castle indeed—but the skeleton of a castle. The roof was gone, the windows were dismantled, the towers were tumbling, and the cold moonlight pierced it through and through. One end of the building was, however, still covered in, and stood looking still more frowning, vast, and gloomy, even than the other part of the edifice.

'There is a lodging, certainly,' said Otto to the sentinel, who pointed towards the castle with his bartizan; 'but tell me, good fellow, what are we to do for a supper?'

'Oh, the castellan of Windeck will entertain you,' said the man-at-arms with a grin, and marched up the embrasure; the while the archers, taking counsel among themselves, debated whether or not they should take up their quarters in the gloomy and deserted edifice.

'We shall get nothing but an owl for supper there,' said young Otto. 'Marry, lads, let us storm the town; we are thirty gallant fellows, and I have heard the garrison is not more than three hundred.' But the rest of the party thought such a way of getting supper was not a very cheap one, and, grovelling knaves, preferred rather to sleep ignobly and without victuals, than dare the assault with Otto, and die, or conquer something comfortable.

One and all then made their way towards the castle. They entered its vast and silent halls, frightening the owls and bats that fled before them with hideous hootings and flappings of wings, and passing by a multiplicity of mouldy stairs, dank reeking roofs, and rickety corridors, at last came to an apartment which, dismal and dismantled as it was, appeared to be in rather better condition than the neighbouring chambers, and they therefore selected it as their place of rest for the night. They then tossed up which should mount guard. The first two hours of watch fell to Otto, who was to be succeeded by his young though humble friend Wolfgang; and, accordingly, the Childe of Godesberg, drawing his dirk, began to pace upon his weary round; while his comrades, by various gradations of snoring, told how profoundly they slept, spite of their lack of supper.

'Tis needless to say what were the thoughts of the noble Childe

as he performed his two hours' watch ; what gushing memories
poured into his full soul ; what 'sweet and bitter' recollections
of home inspired his throbbing heart ; and what manly aspirations
after fame buoyed him up. 'Youth is ever confident,' says the
bard. Happy, happy season ! The moonlit hours passed by on
silver wings, the twinkling stars looked friendly down upon him.
Confiding in their youthful sentinel, sound slept the valorous
toxophilites, as up and down, and there and back again, marched
on the noble Childe. At length his repeater told him, much to
his satisfaction, that it was half-past eleven, the hour when his

watch was to cease ; and so, giving a playful kick to the slumbering Wolfgang, that good-humoured fellow sprung up from his lair,
and, drawing his sword, proceeded to relieve Otto.

The latter laid him down for warmth's sake on the very spot
which his comrade had left, and for some time could not sleep.
Realities and visions then began to mingle in his mind, till he
scarce knew which was which. He dozed for a minute ; then he
woke with a start ; then he went off again ; then woke up again.
In one of these half-sleeping moments he thought he saw a figure,
as of a woman in white, gliding into the room, and beckoning Wolfgang from it. He looked again. Wolfgang was gone. At that
moment twelve o'clock clanged from the town, and Otto started up.

CHAPTER IX

THE LADY OF WINDECK

As the bell with iron tongue called midnight, Wolfgang the Archer, pacing on his watch, beheld before him a pale female figure. He did not know whence she came : but there suddenly she stood close to him. Her blue, clear, glassy eyes were fixed upon him. Her form was of faultless beauty ; her face pale as the marble of the fairy statue, ere yet the sculptor's love had given it life. A smile played upon her features, but it was no warmer than the reflection of a moonbeam on a lake ; and yet it was wondrous beautiful. A fascination stole over the senses of young Wolfgang. He stared at the lovely apparition with fixed eyes and distended jaws. She looked at him with ineffable archness. She lifted one beautifully rounded alabaster arm, and made a sign as if to beckon him towards her. Did Wolfgang—the young and lusty Wolfgang —follow ? Ask the iron whether it follows the magnet ?—ask the pointer whether it pursues the partridge through the stubble ? —ask the youth whether the lollypop-shop does not attract him ? Wolfgang *did* follow. An antique door opened, as if by magic. There was no light, and yet they saw quite plain ; they passed through the innumerable ancient chambers, and yet they did not wake any of the owls and bats roosting there. We know not through how many apartments the young couple passed ; but at last they came to one where a feast was prepared ; and on an antique table, covered with massive silver, covers were laid for two. The lady took her place at one end of the table, and with her sweetest nod beckoned Wolfgang to the other seat. He took it. The table was small, and their knees met. He felt as cold in his legs as if he were kneeling against an ice-well.

'Gallant archer,' said she, 'you must be hungry after your day's march. What supper will you have ? Shall it be a delicate lobster salad ? or a dish of elegant tripe and onions ? or a slice of boar's-head and truffles ? or a Welsh rabbit *à la cave au cidre ?* or

38

a beefsteak and shallot? or a couple of *rognons à la brochette?* Speak, brave bowyer: you have but to order.'

As there was nothing on the table but a covered silver dish, Wolfgang thought that the lady who proposed such a multiplicity of delicacies to him was only laughing at him; so he determined to try her with something extremely rare.

'Fair princess,' he said, 'I should like very much a pork chop and some mashed potatoes.'

She lifted the cover: there was such a pork chop as Simpson never served, with a dish of mashed potatoes that would have formed at least six portions in our degenerate days in Rupert Street.

When he had helped himself to these delicacies, the lady put the cover on the dish again, and watched him eating with interest. He was for some time too much occupied with his own food to remark that his companion did not eat a morsel; but big as it was, his chop was soon gone; the shining silver of his plate was scraped quite clean with his knife, and heaving a great sigh, he confessed a humble desire for something to drink.

'Call for what you like, sweet sir,' said the lady, lifting up a silver filigree bottle, with an india-rubber cork, ornamented with gold.

'Then,' said Master Wolfgang—for the fellow's tastes were, in sooth, very humble—'I call for half-and-half.' According to his wish, a pint of that delicious beverage was poured from the bottle, foaming, into his beaker.

Having emptied this at a draught, and declared that on his conscience it was the best tap he ever knew in his life, the young man felt his appetite renewed; and it is impossible to say how many different dishes he called for. Only enchantment, he was afterwards heard to declare (though none of his friends believed him), could have given him the appetite he possessed on that extraordinary night. He called for another pork chop and potatoes, then for pickled salmon; then he thought he would try a devilled turkey wing. 'I adore the devil,' said he.

'So do I,' said the pale lady, with unwonted animation; and the dish was served straightway. It was succeeded by black-puddings, tripe, toasted cheese, and—what was most remarkable —every one of the dishes which he desired came from under the same silver cover: which circumstance, when he had partaken of about fourteen different articles, he began to find rather mysterious.

'Oh,' said the pale lady, with a smile, 'the mystery is easily accounted for: the servants hear you, and the kitchen is *below.*' But this did not account for the manner in which more half-and-half, bitter ale, punch (both gin and rum), and even oil and vinegar, which he took with cucumber to his salmon, came out of the self-same bottle from which the lady had first poured out his pint of half-and-half.

'There are more things in heaven and earth, Voracio,' said his arch entertainer, when he put this question to her, 'than are dreamt of in your philosophy': and, sooth to say, the archer was by this time in such a state, that he did not find anything wonderful more.

'Are you happy, dear youth?' said the lady, as, after his collation, he sank back in his chair.

'Oh, miss, ain't I!' was his interrogative and yet affirmative reply.

'Should you like such a supper every night, Wolfgang?' continued the pale one.

'Why, no,' said he; 'no, not exactly; not *every* night: *some* nights I should like oysters.'

'Dear youth,' said she, 'be but mine, and you may have them all the year round!' The unhappy boy was too far gone to suspect anything, otherwise this extraordinary speech would have told him that he was in suspicious company. A person who can offer oysters all the year round can live to no good purpose.

'Shall I sing you a song, dear archer?' said the lady.

'Sweet love!' said he, now much excited, 'strike up and I will join the chorus.'

She took down her mandolin, and commenced a ditty. 'Twas a sweet and wild one. It told how a lady of high lineage cast her eyes on a peasant page; it told how nought could her love assuage, her suitor's wealth and her father's rage! it told how the youth did his foes engage; and at length they went off in the Gretna stage, the high-born dame and the peasant page. Wolfgang beat time, waggled his head, sung woefully out of tune as the song proceeded; and if he had not been too intoxicated with love and other excitement, he would have remarked how the pictures on the wall, as the lady sang, began to waggle their heads too, and nod and grin to the music. The song ended. 'I am the lady of high lineage: Archer, will you be the peasant page?'

'I'll follow you to the devil!' said Wolfgang.

'Come,' replied the lady, glaring wildly on him, 'come to the chapel; we'll be married this minute!'

She held out her hand—Wolfgang took it. It was cold, damp, —deadly cold; and on they went to the chapel.

As they passed out, the two pictures over the wall, of a gentleman and lady, tripped lightly out of their frames, skipped noiselessly down to the ground, and making the retreating couple a profound curtsey and bow, took the places which they had left at the table.

Meanwhile the young couple passed on towards the chapel, threading innumerable passages, and passing through chambers of great extent. As they came along, all the portraits on the wall stepped out of their frames to follow them. One ancestor, of whom there was only a bust, frowned in the greatest rage, because, having no legs, his pedestal would not move; and several sticking-plaster profiles of the former Lords of Windeck looked quite black at being, for similar reasons, compelled to keep their places. However, there was a goodly procession formed behind Wolfgang and his bride; and by the time they reached the church, they had near a hundred followers.

The church was splendidly illuminated; the old banners of the old knights glittered as they do at Drury Lane. The organ set up of itself to play the 'Bridesmaids' Chorus.' The choir-chairs were filled with people in black.

'Come, love,' said the pale lady.

'I don't see the parson,' exclaimed Wolfgang, spite of himself rather alarmed.

'Oh, the parson! that's the easiest thing in the world! I say, bishop!' said the lady, stooping down.

Stooping down—and to what? Why, upon my word and honour, to a great brass plate on the floor, over which they were passing, and on which was engraven the figure of a bishop—and a very ugly bishop, too—with crosier and mitre, and lifted finger, on which sparkled the episcopal ring. 'Do, my dear lord, come and marry us,' said the lady, with a levity which shocked the feelings of her bridegroom.

The bishop got up; and directly he rose, a dean, who was sleeping under a large slate near him, came bowing and cringing up to him; while a canon of the cathedral (whose name was Schidnischmidt) began grinning and making fun at the pair. The ceremony was begun, and

As the clock struck twelve, young Otto bounded up, and re-marked the absence of his companion Wolfgang. The idea he had had, that his friend disappeared in company with a white-robed female, struck him more and more. 'I will follow them,' said he; and, calling to the next on the watch (old Snozo, who was right unwilling to forego his sleep), he rushed away by the door through which he had seen Wolfgang and his temptress take their way.

That he did not find them was not his fault. The castle was vast, the chamber dark. There were a thousand doors, and what wonder that, after he had once lost sight of them, the intrepid Childe should not be able to follow in their steps? As might be expected, he took the wrong door, and wandered for at least three hours about the dark enormous solitary castle, calling out Wolfgang's name to the careless and indifferent echoes, knocking his young shins against the ruins scattered in the darkness, but still with a spirit entirely undaunted, and a firm resolution to aid his absent comrade. Brave Otto! thy exertions were rewarded at last!

For he lighted at length upon the very apartment where Wolfgang had partaken of supper, and where the old couple who had been in the picture-frames, and turned out to be the lady's father and mother, were now sitting at the table.

'Well, Bertha has got a husband at last,' said the lady.

'After waiting four hundred and fifty-three years for one, it was quite time,' said the gentleman. (He was dressed in powder and a pigtail, quite in the old fashion.)

'The husband is no great things,' continued the lady, taking snuff. 'A low fellow, my dear; a butcher's son, I believe. Did you see how the wretch ate at supper? To think my daughter should have to marry an archer!'

'There are archers and archers,' said the old man. 'Some archers are snobs, as your Ladyship states; some, on the contrary, are gentlemen by birth, at least, though not by breeding. Witness young Otto, the Landgrave of Godesberg's son, who is listening at the door like a lacquey, and whom I intend to run through the——'

'Law, Baron!' said the lady.

'I will, though,' replied the Baron, drawing an immense sword, and glaring round at Otto; but though at the sight of that sword and that scowl a less valorous youth would have taken to his heels, the undaunted Childe advanced at once into the apartment. He wore round his neck a relic of Saint Buffo (the tip of the saint's ear, which had been cut off at Constantinople). 'Fiends! I command you to retreat!' said he, holding up this sacred charm, which his mamma had fastened on him; and at the sight of it, with an unearthly yell the ghosts of the Baron and the Baroness sprang back into their picture-frames, as clown goes through a clock in a pantomime.

He rushed through the open door by which the unlucky Wolfgang had passed with his demoniacal bride, and went on and on through the vast gloomy chambers lighted by the ghastly moonshine: the noise of the organ in the chapel, the lights in the kaleidoscopic windows, directed him towards that edifice. He rushed to the door: 'twas barred! He knocked: the beadles were deaf. He applied his inestimable relic to the lock, and—whizz! crash! clang! bang! whang!—the gate flew open! the organ went off in a fugue—the lights quivered over the tapers,

and then went off towards the ceiling—the ghosts assembled rushed away with a skurry and a scream—the bride howled, and vanished—the fat bishop waddled back under his brass plate—the dean flounced down into his family vault—and the canon Schidnischmidt, who was making a joke, as usual, on the bishop, was obliged to stop at the very point of his epigram, and to disappear into the void whence he came.

Otto fell fainting at the porch, while Wolfgang tumbled lifeless down at the altar-steps ; and in this situation the archers, when they arrived, found the two youths. They were resuscitated, as we scarce need say ; but when, in incoherent accents, they came to tell their wondrous tale, some sceptics among the archers said —' Pooh ! they were intoxicated ! ' while others, nodding their older heads, exclaimed—' *They have seen the Lady of Windeck !* ' and recalled the stories of many other young men, who, inveigled by her devilish arts, had not been so lucky as Wolfgang, and had disappeared—for ever !

This adventure bound Wolfgang heart and soul to his gallant preserver ; and the archers—it being now morning, and the cocks crowing lustily round about—pursued their way without further delay to the castle of the noble patron of toxophilites, the gallant Duke of Cleves.

CHAPTER X

THE BATTLE OF THE BOWMEN

ALTHOUGH there lay an immense number of castles and abbeys between Windeck and Cleves, for every one of which the guide-books have a legend and a ghost, who might, with the commonest stretch of ingenuity, be made to waylay our adventurers on the road ; yet, as the journey would be thus almost interminable, let us cut it short by saying that the travellers reached Cleves without any further accident, and found the place thronged with visitors for the meeting next day.

And here it would be easy to describe the company which arrived, and make display of antiquarian lore. Now we would represent a cavalcade of knights arriving, with their pages carrying their shining helms of gold, and the stout esquires, bearers of lance and banner. Anon would arrive a fat abbot on his ambling pad, surrounded by the white-robed companions of his convent. Here should come the gleemen and jongleurs, the minstrels, the mountebanks, the particoloured gipsies, the dark-eyed, nut-brown Zigeunerinnen ; then a troop of peasants chanting Rhine-songs, and leading in their ox-drawn carts the peach-cheeked girls from the vine-lands. Next we would depict the litters blazoned with armorial bearings, from between the broidered curtains of which peeped out the swan-like necks and the haughty faces of the blonde ladies of the castles. But for these descriptions we have not space ; and the reader is referred to the account of the tournament in the ingenious novel of *Ivanhoe*, where the above phenomena are described at length. Suffice it to say, that Otto and his companions arrived at the town of Cleves, and, hastening to a hostel, reposed themselves after the day's march, and prepared them for the encounter of the morrow.

That morrow came : and as the sports were to begin early, Otto and his comrades hastened to the field, armed with their best bows and arrows, you may be sure, and eager to distinguish themselves ; as were the multitude of other archers assembled. They were from all neighbouring countries—crowds of English, as you may fancy, armed with Murray's guide-books, troops of chattering Frenchmen, Frankfort Jews with roulette-tables, and Tyrolese with gloves and trinkets—all hied towards the field where the butts were set up, and the archery practice was to be held. The Childe and his brother archers were, it need not be said, early on the ground.

But what words of mine can describe the young gentleman's emotion when, preceded by a band of trumpets, bagpipes, ophicleides, and other wind instruments, the Prince of Cleves appeared with the Princess Helen, his daughter? And ah! what expressions of my humble pen can do justice to the beauty of that young lady? Fancy every charm which decorates the person, every virtue which ornaments the mind, every accomplishment which renders charming mind and charming person doubly charming, and then you will have but a faint and feeble idea of the beauties of Her Highness the Princess Helen. Fancy a complexion such as they say (I know not with what justice) Rowland's Kalydor imparts to the users of that cosmetic; fancy teeth to which orient pearls are like Wallsend coals; eyes, which were so blue, tender, and bright, that while they ran you through with their lustre, they healed you with their kindness; a neck and waist, so ravishingly slender and graceful, that the least that is said about them the better; a foot which fell upon the flowers no heavier than a dewdrop—and this charming person set off by the most elegant toilet that ever milliner devised! The lovely Helen's hair (which was as black as the finest varnish for boots) was so long, that it was borne on a cushion several yards behind her by the maidens of her train; and a hat, set off with moss-roses, sunflowers, bugles, birds-of-paradise, gold lace, and pink ribbon, gave her a *distingué* air, which would have set the editor of the *Morning Post* mad with love.

It had exactly the same effect upon the noble Childe of Godesberg, as leaning on his ivory bow, with his legs crossed, he stood and gazed on her, as Cupid gazed on Psyche. Their eyes met: it was all over with both of them. A blush came at one and the same minute budding to the cheek of either. A simultaneous throb beat in those young hearts! They loved each other for ever from that instant. Otto still stood, cross-legged, enraptured, leaning on his ivory bow; but Helen, calling to a maiden for her pocket-handkerchief, blew her beautiful Grecian nose in order to hide her agitation. Bless ye, bless ye, pretty ones! I am old now; but not so old but that I kindle at the tale of love. Theresa MacWhirter too has lived and loved. Heigho!

Who is yon chief that stands behind the truck whereon are

seated the Princess and the stout old lord her father? Who is he whose hair is of the carroty hue—whose eyes, across a snubby bunch of a nose, are perpetually scowling at each other; who has a humpback, and a hideous mouth, surrounded with bristles, and crammed full of jutting yellow odious teeth? Although he wears a sky-blue doublet laced with silver, it only serves to render his vulgar punchy figure doubly ridiculous; although his nether garment is of salmon-coloured velvet, it only draws the more attention to his legs, which are disgustingly crooked and bandy. A rose-coloured hat, with towering pea-green ostrich-plumes, looks absurd on his bull-head; and though it is time of peace, the wretch is armed with a multiplicity of daggers, knives, yataghans, dirks, sabres, and scimitars, which testify his truculent and bloody disposition. 'Tis the terrible Rowski de Donnerblitz, Margrave of Eulenschreckenstein. Report says he is a suitor for the hand of the lovely Helen. He addresses various speeches of gallantry to her, and grins hideously as he thrusts his disgusting head over her lily shoulder. But she turns away from him! turns and shudders—ay, as she would at a black dose!

Otto stands gazing still, and leaning on his bow. 'What is the prize?' asks one archer of another. There are two prizes—a velvet cap, embroidered by the hand of the Princess, and a chain of massive gold, of enormous value. Both lie on cushions before her.

'I know which I shall choose, when I win the first prize,' says a swarthy, savage, and bandy-legged archer, who bears the owl gules on a black shield, the cognisance of the Lord Rowski de Donnerblitz.

'Which, fellow?' says Otto, turning fiercely upon him.

'The chain, to be sure!' says the leering archer. 'You do not suppose I am such a flat as to choose that velvet gimcrack there?' Otto laughed in scorn, and began to prepare his bow. The trumpets sounding proclaimed that the sports were about to commence.

Is it necessary to describe them? No: that has already been done in the novel of *Ivanhoe* before mentioned. Fancy the archers clad in Lincoln green, all coming forward in turn, and firing at the targets. Some hit, some missed; those that missed were fain to retire amidst the jeers of the multitudinous spectators. Those that hit began new trials of skill; but it was easy to see, from the first, that the battle lay between Squintoff (the Rowski archer) and the young hero with the golden hair and the ivory bow. Squintoff's fame as a marksman was known throughout Europe; but who was his young competitor? Ah! there was *one* heart in the assembly that beat most anxiously to know. 'Twas Helen's.

The crowning trial arrived. The bull's-eye of the target, set up at three-quarters of a mile distance from the archers, was so small, that it required a very clever man indeed to see, much more to hit it ; and as Squintoff was selecting his arrow for the final trial, the Rowski flung a purse of gold towards his archer, saying—'Squintoff, an ye win the prize, the purse is thine.' 'I may as well pocket it at once, your honour,' said the bowman, with a sneer at Otto. 'This young chick, who has been lucky as yet, will hardly hit such a mark as that.' And, taking his aim, Squintoff discharged his arrow right into the very middle of the bull's-eye.

'Can you mend that, young springald?' said he, as a shout rent the air at his success, as Helen turned pale to think that the champion of her secret heart was likely to be overcome, and as Squintoff, pocketing the Rowski's money, turned to the noble boy of Godesberg.

'Has anybody got a pea?' asked the lad. Everybody laughed at his droll request ; and an old woman, who was selling porridge in the crowd, handed him the vegetable which he demanded. It was a dry and yellow pea. Otto, stepping up to the target, caused Squintoff to extract his arrow from the bull's-eye, and placed in the orifice made by the steel point of the shaft, the pea which he had received from the old woman. He then came back to his place. As he prepared to shoot, Helen was so overcome by emotion, that 'twas thought she would have fainted. Never, never had she seen a being so beautiful as the young hero now before her.

He looked almost divine. He flung back his long clusters of hair from his bright eyes and tall forehead ; the blush of health mantled on his cheek, from which the barber's weapon had never shorn the down. He took his bow, and one of his most elegant arrows, and poising himself lightly on his right leg, he flung himself forward, raising his left leg on a level with his ear. He looked like Apollo, as he stood balancing himself there. He discharged his dart from the thrumming bowstring : it clove the blue air—whizz !

'*He has split the pea!*' said the Princess, and fainted. The Rowski, with one eye, hurled an indignant look at the boy, while with the other he levelled (if aught so crooked can be said to level anything) a furious glance at his archer.

The archer swore a sulky oath. 'He is the better man!' said he. 'I suppose, young chap, you take the gold chain?'

'The gold chain!' said Otto. 'Prefer a gold chain to a cap

worked by that august hand? Never!' And advancing to the balcony where the Princess, who now came to herself, was sitting, he kneeled down before her, and received the velvet cap; which, blushing as scarlet as the cap itself, the Princess Helen placed on his golden ringlets. Once more their eyes met—their hearts thrilled. They had never spoken, but they knew they loved each other for ever.

'Wilt thou take service with the Rowski of Donnerblitz?' said that individual to the youth. 'Thou shalt be captain of my archers in place of yon blundering nincompoop, whom thou hast overcome.'

'Yon blundering nincompoop is a skilful and gallant archer,' replied Otto haughtily; 'and I will *not* take service with the Rowski of Donnerblitz.'

'Wilt thou enter the household of the Prince of Cleves?' said the father of Helen, laughing, and not a little amused at the haughtiness of the humble archer.

'I would die for the Duke of Cleves and *his family*,' said Otto, bowing low. He laid a particular and a tender emphasis on the word family. Helen knew what he meant. *She* was the family. In fact, her mother was no more, and her papa had no other offspring.

'What is thy name, good fellow,' said the Prince, 'that my steward may enrol thee?'

'Sir,' said Otto, again blushing, 'I am OTTO THE ARCHER.'

CHAPTER XI

HE archers who had travelled in company with young Otto, gave a handsome dinner in compliment to the success of our hero; at which his friend distinguished himself as usual in the eating and drinking department. Squint-off, the Rowski bowman, declined to attend; so great was the envy of the brute at the youthful hero's superiority. As for Otto himself, he sat on the right hand of the chairman; but it was remarked that he could not eat. Gentle reader of my page! thou knowest why full well. He was too much in love to have any appetite; for though I myself, when labouring under that passion, never found my consumption of victuals diminish, yet remember our Otto was a hero of romance, and they *never* are hungry when they're in love.

The next day, the young gentleman proceeded to enrol himself in the corps of Archers of the Prince of Cleves, and with him came his attached squire, who vowed he never would leave him. As Otto threw aside his own elegant dress, and donned the livery of the House of Cleves, the noble Childe sighed not a little. 'Twas a splendid uniform, 'tis true, but still it *was* a livery, and one of his proud spirit ill bears another's cognisances. 'They are the colours of the Princess, however,' said he, consoling himself; 'and what suffering would I not undergo for *her?*' As for Wolfgang, the squire, it may well be supposed that the good-natured low-born fellow had no such scruples; but he was glad enough to exchange

50

for the pink hose, the yellow jacket, the pea-green cloak, and orange-tawny hat, with which the Duke's steward supplied him, the homely patched doublet of green which he had worn for years past.

'Look at yon two archers,' said the Prince of Cleves to his guest the Rowski of Donnerblitz, as they were strolling on the battlements after dinner, smoking their cigars as usual. His Highness pointed to our two young friends, who were mounting guard for the first time. 'See yon two bowmen—mark their bearing! One is the youth who beat thy Squintoff, and t'other, an I mistake not, won the third prize at the butts. Both wear the same uniform —the colours of my house—yet, wouldst not swear that the one was but a churl, and the other a noble gentleman?'

'Which looks like the nobleman?' said the Rowski, as black as thunder.

'*Which?* why, young Otto, to be sure,' said the Princess Helen eagerly. The young lady was following the pair; but under pretence of disliking the odour of the cigar, she had refused the Rowski's proffered arm, and was loitering behind with her parasol.

Her interposition in favour of her young *protégé* only made the black and jealous Rowski more ill-humoured. 'How long is it, Sir Prince of Cleves,' said he, 'that the churls who wear your livery permit themselves to wear the ornaments of noble knights? Who but a noble dare wear ringlets such as yon springald's? Ho, archer!' roared he, 'come hither, fellow.' And Otto stood before him. As he came, and presenting arms stood respectfully before the Prince and his savage guest, he looked for one moment at the lovely Helen—their eyes met, their hearts beat simultaneously: and, quick, two little blushes appeared in the cheek of either. I have seen one ship at sea answering another's signal so.

While they are so regarding each other, let us just remind our readers of the great estimation in which the hair was held in the North. Only nobles were permitted to wear it long. When a man disgraced himself, a shaving was sure to follow. Penalties were inflicted upon villains or vassals who sported ringlets. See the works of Aurelius Tonsor; Hirsutus de Nobilitate Capillari; Rolandus de Oleo Macassari; Schnurrbart; Frisirische Alterthum-skunde, etc.

'We must have those ringlets of thine cut, good fellow,' said the Duke of Cleves good-naturedly, but wishing to spare the feelings of his gallant recruit. ''Tis against the regulation cut of my archer guard.'

'Cut off my hair!' cried Otto, agonised.

'Ay, and thine ears with it, yokel,' roared Donnerblitz.

'Peace, noble Eulenschreckenstein,' said the Duke with dignity: 'let the Duke of Cleves deal as he will with his own men-at-arms. And you, young sir, unloose the grip of thy dagger.'

Otto, indeed, had convulsively grasped his snickersnee, with intent to plunge it into the heart of the Rowski; but his politer feelings overcame him. 'The Count need not fear, my Lord,' said he: 'a lady is present.' And he took off his orange-tawny cap and bowed low. Ah! what a pang shot through the heart of Helen, as she thought that those lovely ringlets must be shorn from that beautiful head!

Otto's mind was, too, in commotion. His feelings as a gentleman—let us add, his pride as a man—for who is not, let us ask, proud of a good head of hair?—waged war within his soul. He expostulated with the Prince. 'It was never in my contemplation,' he said, 'on taking service, to undergo the operation of hair-cutting.'

'Thou art free to go or stay, Sir Archer,' said the Prince pettishly. 'I will have no churls imitating noblemen in my service: I will bandy no conditions with archers of my guard.'

'My resolve is taken,' said Otto, irritated too in his turn. 'I will——'

'What?' cried Helen, breathless with intense agitation.

'I will *stay*,' answered Otto. The poor girl almost fainted with joy. The Rowski frowned with demoniac fury, and grinding his teeth and cursing in the horrible German jargon, stalked away. 'So be it,' said the Prince of Cleves, taking his daughter's arm— 'and here comes Snipwitz, my barber, who shall do the business for you.' With this the Prince too moved on, feeling in his heart not a little compassion for the lad; for Adolf of Cleves had been handsome in his youth, and distinguished for the ornament of which he was now depriving his archer.

Snipwitz led the poor lad into a side-room, and there—in a word—operated upon him. The golden curls—fair curls that his mother had so often played with!—fell under the shears and round the lad's knees, until he looked as if he was sitting in a bath of sunbeams.

When the frightful act had been performed, Otto, who entered the little chamber in the tower ringleted like Apollo, issued from it as cropped as a charity-boy.

See how melancholy he looks, now that the operation is over! —And no wonder. He was thinking what would be Helen's opinion of him, now that one of his chief personal ornaments was gone. 'Will she know me?' thought he; 'will she love me after this hideous mutilation?'

Yielding to these gloomy thoughts, and, indeed, rather unwilling to be seen by his comrades, now that he was so disfigured, the young gentleman had hidden himself behind one of the buttresses of the wall, a prey to natural despondency ; when he saw something which instantly restored him to good spirits. He saw the lovely Helen coming towards the chamber where the odious barber had performed upon him—coming forward timidly, looking round her anxiously, blushing with delightful agitation,—and presently

seeing, as she thought, the coast clear, she entered the apartment. She stooped down, and ah ! what was Otto's joy when he saw her pick up a beautiful golden lock of his hair, press it to her lips, and then hide it in her bosom ! No carnation ever blushed so redly as Helen did when she came out after performing this feat. Then she hurried straightway to her own apartments in the castle, and Otto, whose first impulse was to come out from his hiding-place, and, falling at her feet, call heaven and earth to witness to his passion, with difficulty restrained his feelings and let her pass ; but the love-stricken young hero was so delighted with this evident proof of reciprocated attachment, that all regret at losing his ringlets at once left him, and he vowed he would sacrifice not only his hair, but his head, if need were, to do her service.

That very afternoon, no small bustle and conversation took place in the castle, on account of the sudden departure of the Rowski of Eulenschreckenstein, with all his train and equipage. He went away in the greatest wrath, it was said, after a long and loud conversation with the Prince. As that potentate conducted his guest to the gate, walking rather demurely and shamefacedly by his side, as he gathered his attendants in the court, and there mounted his charger, the Rowski ordered his trumpets to sound, and scornfully flung a largesse of gold among the servitors and men-at-arms of the House of Cleves, who were marshalled in the court. 'Farewell, Sir Prince,' said he to his host: 'I quit you now suddenly; but remember, it is not my last visit to the Castle of Cleves.' And ordering his band to play 'See the Conquering Hero comes,' he clattered away through the drawbridge. The Princess Helen was not present at his departure; and the venerable Prince of Cleves looked rather moody and chapfallen when his guest left him. He visited all the castle defences pretty accurately that night, and inquired of his officers the state of the ammunition, provisions, etc. He said nothing; but the Princess Helen's maid did: and everybody knew that the Rowski had made his proposals, had been rejected, and, getting up in a violent fury, had called for his people, and sworn by his great gods that he would not enter the castle again until he rode over the breach, lance in hand, the conqueror of Cleves and all belonging to it.

No little consternation was spread through the garrison at the news: for everybody knew the Rowski to be one of the most intrepid and powerful soldiers in all Germany—one of the most skilful generals. Generous to extravagance to his own followers, he was ruthless to the enemy: a hundred stories were told of the dreadful barbarities exercised by him in several towns and castles which he had captured and sacked. And poor Helen had the pain of thinking, that in consequence of her refusal she was dooming all the men, women, and children of the principality to indiscriminate and horrible slaughter.

The dreadful surmises regarding a war received in a few days dreadful confirmation. It was noon, and the worthy Prince of Cleves was taking his dinner (though the honest warrior had had little appetite for that meal for some time past), when trumpets were heard at the gate; and presently the herald of the Rowski of Donnerblitz, clad in a tabard on which the arms of the Count were blazoned, entered the dining-hall. A page bore a steel gauntlet on

a cushion ; Bleu Sanglier had his hat on his head. The Prince of
Cleves put on his own, as the herald came up to the chair of state
where the sovereign sat.

'Silence for Bleu Sanglier,' cried the Prince gravely. 'Say
your say, Sir Herald.'

'In the name of the high and mighty Rowski, Prince of
Donnerblitz, Margrave of Eulenschreckenstein, Count of Kröten-
wald, Schnauzestadt, and Galgenhügel, Hereditary Grand Cork-
screw of the Holy Roman Empire—to you, Adolf the Twenty-third,
Prince of Cleves, I, Bleu Sanglier, bring war and defiance.
Alone, and lance to lance, or twenty to twenty in field or in
fort, on plain or on mountain, the noble Rowski defies you.
Here, or wherever he shall meet you, he proclaims war to the
death between you and him. In token whereof, here is his
glove.' And taking the steel glove from the page, Bleu Boar
flung it clanging on the marble floor.

The Princess Helen turned deadly pale : but the Prince, with a
good assurance, flung down his own glove, calling upon some one to
raise the Rowski's : which Otto accordingly took up and presented,
to him, on his knee.

'Boteler, fill my goblet,' said the Prince to that functionary,
who, clothed in tight black hose, with a white kerchief, and a
napkin on his dexter arm stood obsequiously by his master's chair.
The goblet was filled with Malvoisie : it held about three quarts ;
a precious golden hanap carved by the cunning artificer, Benvenuto
the Florentine.

'Drink, Bleu Sanglier,' said the Prince, 'and put the goblet
in thy bosom. Wear this chain, furthermore, for my sake.' And
so saying, Prince Adolf flung a precious chain of emeralds round the
herald's neck. 'An invitation to battle was ever a welcome call to
Adolf of Cleves.' So saying, and bidding his people take good care
of Bleu Sanglier's retinue, the Prince left the hall with his daughter.
All were marvelling at his dignity, courage, and generosity.

But, though affecting unconcern, the mind of Prince Adolf was
far from tranquil. He was no longer the stalwart knight who, in
the reign of Stanislaus Augustus, had, with his naked fist, beaten
a lion to death in three minutes : and alone had kept the postern
of Peterwaradin for two hours against seven hundred Turkish
janissaries, who were assailing it. Those deeds which had made
the heir of Cleves famous were done thirty years syne. A free
liver since he had come into his principality, and of a lazy turn,
he had neglected the athletic exercises which had made him in
youth so famous a champion, and indolence had borne its usual
fruits. He tried his old battle-sword—that famous blade with

which, in Palestine, he had cut an elephant-driver in two pieces, and split asunder the skull of the elephant which he rode. Adolf of Cleves could scarcely now lift the weapon over his head. He tried his armour. It was too tight for him. And the old soldier burst into tears when he found he could not buckle it. Such a man was not fit to encounter the terrible Rowski in single combat.

Nor could he hope to make head against him for any time in the field. The Prince's territories were small; his vassals proverbially lazy and peaceable; his treasury empty. The dismallest prospects were before him: and he passed a sleepless night writing to his friends for succour, and calculating with his secretary the small amount of the resources which he could bring to aid him against his advancing and powerful enemy.

Helen's pillow that evening was also unvisited by slumber. She lay awake thinking of Otto,—thinking of the danger and the ruin her refusal to marry had brought upon her dear papa. Otto, too, slept not: but *his* waking thoughts were brilliant and heroic: the noble Childe thought how he should defend the Princess, and win *los* and honour in the ensuing combat.

CHAPTER XII

THE CHAMPION

AND now the noble Cleves began in good earnest to prepare his
castle for the threatened siege. He gathered in all the available
cattle round the property, and the pigs round many miles; and a
dreadful slaughter of horned and snouted animals took place,—
the whole castle resounding with the lowing of the oxen and the
squeaks of the gruntlings, destined to provide food for the
garrison. These, when slain (her gentle spirit, of course, would
not allow of her witnessing that disagreeable operation), the lovely
Helen, with the assistance of her maidens, carefully salted and
pickled. Corn was brought in in great quantities, the Prince
paying for the same when he had money, giving bills when he
could get credit, or occasionally, marry, sending out a few stout
men-at-arms to forage, who brought in wheat without money or
credit either. The charming Princess, amidst the intervals of
her labours, went about encouraging the garrison, who vowed to
a man they would die for a single sweet smile of hers; and in
order to make their inevitable sufferings as easy as possible to

the gallant fellows, she and the apothecaries got ready a plenty of efficacious simples, and scraped a vast quantity of lint to bind their warriors' wounds withal. All the fortifications were strengthened; the fosses carefully filled with spikes and water; large stones placed over the gates, convenient to tumble on the heads of the assaulting parties; and cauldrons prepared, with furnaces to melt up pitch, brimstone, boiling oil, etc., wherewith hospitably to receive them. Having the keenest eye in the whole garrison, young Otto was placed on the topmost tower, to watch for the expected coming of the beleaguering host.

They were seen only too soon. Long ranks of shining spears were seen glittering in the distance, and the army of the Rowski soon made its appearance in battle's magnificently stern array. The tents of the renowned chief and his numerous warriors were pitched out of arrow-shot of the castle, but in fearful proximity; and when his army had taken up its position, an officer with a flag of truce and a trumpet was seen advancing to the castle gate. It was the same herald who had previously borne his master's defiance to the Prince of Cleves. He came once more to the castle gate, and there proclaimed that the noble Count of Eulenschreckenstein was in arms without, ready to do battle with the Prince of Cleves, or his champion; that he would remain in arms for three days, ready for combat. If no man met him at the end of that period, he would deliver an assault, and would give quarter to no single soul in the garrison. So saying, the herald nailed his lord's gauntlet on the castle gate. As before, the Prince flung him over another glove from the wall; though how he was to defend himself from such a warrior, or get a champion, or resist the pitiless assault that must follow, the troubled old nobleman knew not in the least.

The Princess Helen passed the night in the chapel, vowing tons of wax candles to all the patron saints of the House of Cleves, if they would raise her up a defender.

But how did the noble girl's heart sink—how were her notions of the purity of man shaken within her gentle bosom, by the dread intelligence which reached her the next morning, after the defiance of the Rowski! At roll-call it was discovered that he on whom she principally relied—he whom her fond heart had singled out as her champion, had proved faithless!

Otto, the degenerate Otto, had fled! His comrade, Wolfgang, had gone with him. A rope was found dangling from the casement of their chamber, and they must have swum the moat and passed over to the enemy in the darkness of the previous night. 'A pretty lad was this fair-spoken archer of thine!' said the

Prince her father to her; 'and a pretty kettle of fish hast thou cooked for the fondest of fathers.' She retired weeping to her apartment. Never before had that young heart felt so wretched.

That morning, at nine o'clock, as they were going to breakfast, the Rowski's trumpets sounded. Clad in complete armour, and mounted on his enormous piebald charger, he came out of his pavilion, and rode slowly up and down in front of the castle. He was ready there to meet a champion.

Three times each day did the odious trumpet sound the same notes of defiance. Thrice daily did the steel-clad Rowski come forth challenging the combat. The first day passed, and there was no answer to his summons. The second day came and went, but no champion had risen to defend. The taunt of his shrill clarion remained without answer; and the sun went down upon the wretchedest father and daughter in all the land of Christendom.

The trumpets sounded an hour after sunrise, an hour after noon, and an hour before sunset. The third day came, but with it brought no hope. The first and second summons met no response. At five o'clock the old Prince called his daughter and blessed her. 'I go to meet this Rowski,' said he. 'It may be we shall meet no more, my Helen—my child—the innocent cause of all this grief. If I shall fall to-night· the Rowski's victim, 'twill be that life is nothing without honour.' And so saying, he put into her hands a dagger, and bade her sheathe it in her own breast so soon as the terrible champion had carried the castle by storm.

This Helen most faithfully promised to do; and her aged father retired to his armoury, and donned his ancient war-worn corselet. It had borne the shock of a thousand lances ere this, but it was now so tight as almost to choke the knightly wearer.

The last trumpet sounded—tantara! tantara!—its shrill call rang over the wide plains, and the wide plains gave back no answer. Again!—but when its notes died away, there was only a mournful, an awful silence. 'Farewell, my child,' said the Prince, bulkily lifting himself into his battle-saddle. 'Remember the dagger. Hark! the trumpet sounds for the third time. Open, warders! Sound, trumpeters! and good Saint Bendigo guard the right.'

But Puffendorff, the trumpeter, had not leisure to lift the trumpet to his lips: when, hark! from without there came another note of another clarion!—a distant note at first, then swelling fuller. Presently, in brilliant variations, the full rich notes of the 'Huntsman's Chorus' came clearly over the breeze;

and a thousand voices of the crowd gazing over the gate exclaimed, 'A champion ! a champion !'

And, indeed, a champion *had* come. Issuing from the forest came a knight and squire : the knight gracefully cantering an elegant cream-coloured Arabian of prodigious power—the squire mounted on an unpretending grey cob ; which, nevertheless, was an animal of considerable strength and sinew. It was the squire who blew the trumpet, through the bars of his helmet ; the knight's visor was completely down. A small prince's coronet of gold, from which rose three pink ostrich feathers, marked the warrior's rank : his blank shield bore no cognisance. As gracefully poising his lance he rode into the green space where the Rowski's tents were pitched, the hearts of all present beat with anxiety, and the poor Prince of Cleves, especially, had considerable doubts about his new champion. 'So slim a figure as that can never compete with Donnerblitz,' said he, moodily, to his daughter ; 'but whoever he be, the fellow puts a good face on it, and rides like a man. See, he has touched the Rowski's shield with the point of his lance ! By Saint Bendigo, a perilous venture !'

The unknown knight had indeed defied the Rowski to the death, as the Prince of Cleves remarked from the battlement where he and his daughter stood to witness the combat ; and so, having defied his enemy, the Incognito galloped round under the castle wall, bowing elegantly to the lovely Princess there, and then took his ground and waited for the foe. His armour blazed in the sunshine as he sat there, motionless, on his cream-coloured steed. He looked like one of those fairy knights one has read of —one of those celestial champions who decided so may victories before the invention of gunpowder.

The Rowski's horse was speedily brought to the door of his pavilion ; and that redoubted warrior, blazing in a suit of magnificent brass armour, clattered into his saddle. Long waves of blood-red feathers bristled over his helmet, which was further ornamented by two huge horns of the aurochs. His lance was painted white and red, and he whirled the prodigious beam in the air and caught it with savage glee. He laughed when he saw the slim form of his antagonist ; and his soul rejoiced to meet the coming battle. He dug his spurs into the enormous horse he rode : the enormous horse snorted, and squealed, too, with fierce pleasure. He jerked and curvetted him with a brutal playfulness, and after a few minutes turning and wheeling, during which everybody had leisure to admire the perfection of his equitation, he cantered round to a point exactly opposite his enemy, and pulled up his impatient charger.

The old Prince on the battlement was so eager for the combat, that he seemed quite to forget the danger which menaced himself, should his slim champion be discomfited by the tremendous Knight of Donnerblitz. 'Go it!' said he, flinging his truncheon into the ditch; and at the word, the two warriors rushed with whirling rapidity at each other.

And now ensued a combat so terrible, that a weak female hand, like that of her who pens this tale of chivalry, can never hope to do justice to the terrific theme. You have seen two engines on the Great Western line rush past each other with a pealing scream? So rapidly did the two warriors gallop towards one another; the feathers of either streamed yards behind their backs as they converged. Their shock as they met was as that of two cannon-balls; the mighty horses trembled and reeled with the concussion; the lance aimed at the Rowski's helmet bore off the coronet, the horns, the helmet itself, and hurled them to an incredible distance: a piece of the Rowski's left ear was carried off on the point of the nameless warrior's weapon. How had he fared? His adversary's weapon had glanced harmless along the blank surface of his polished buckler: and the victory so far was with him.

The expression of the Rowski's face, as, bareheaded, he glared on his enemy with fierce bloodshot eyeballs, was one worthy of a demon. The imprecatory expressions which he made use of can never be copied by a feminine pen.

His opponent magnanimously declined to take advantage of the opportunity thus offered him of finishing the combat by splitting his opponent's skull with his curtal-axe, and, riding back to his starting-place, bent his lance's point to the ground, in token that he would wait until the Count of Eulenschreckenstein was helmeted afresh.

'Blessed Bendigo!' cried the Prince, 'thou art a gallant lance: but why didst not rap the Schelm's brain out?'

'Bring me a fresh helmet!' yelled the Rowski. Another casque was brought to him by his trembling squire.

As soon as he had braced it, he drew his great flashing sword from his side, and rushed at his enemy, roaring hoarsely his cry of battle. The unknown knight's sword was unsheathed in a moment, and at the next the two blades were clanking together the dreadful music of the combat!

The Donnerblitz wielded his with his usual savageness and activity. It whirled round his adversary's head with frightful rapidity. Now it carried away a feather of his plume; now it shore off a leaf of his coronet. The flail of the thresher does not fall more swiftly upon the corn. For many minutes it was the Unknown's only task to defend himself from the tremendous activity of the enemy.

But even the Rowski's strength would slacken after exertion. The blows began to fall less thick anon, and the point of the unknown knight began to make dreadful play. It found and penetrated every joint of the Donnerblitz armour. Now it nicked him in the shoulder, where the vambrace was buckled to the corselet; now it bored a shrewd hole under the light brassart, and blood followed; now, with fatal dexterity, it darted through the visor, and came back to the recover deeply tinged with blood. A scream of rage followed the last thrust; and no wonder:—it had penetrated the Rowski's left eye.

His blood was trickling through a dozen orifices; he was almost choking in his helmet with loss of breath, and loss of blood, and rage. Gasping with fury, he drew back his horse, flung his great sword at his opponent's head, and once more plunged at him, wielding his curtal-axe.

Then you should have seen the unknown knight employing the same dreadful weapon! Hitherto he had been on his defence; now he began the attack; and the gleaming axe whirred in his hand like a reed, but descended like a thunderbolt! 'Yield! yield! Sir Rowski,' shouted he in a calm clear voice.

A blow dealt madly at his head was the reply. 'Twas the last blow that the Count of Eulenschreckenstein ever struck in battle! The curse was on his lips as the crushing steel descended into his brain, and split it in two. He rolled like a log from his horse: his enemy's knee was in a moment on his chest, and the dagger of mercy at his throat, as the knight once more called upon him to yield.

But there was no answer from within the helmet. When it was withdrawn, the teeth were crunched together; the mouth that should have spoken, grinned a ghastly silence: one eye still glared with hate and fury, but it was glazed with the film of death!

The red orb of the sun was just then dipping into the Rhine. The unknown knight, vaulting once more into his saddle, made a graceful obeisance to the Prince of Cleves and his daughter, without a word, and galloped back into the forest, whence he had issued an hour before sunset.

CHAPTER XIII

THE MARRIAGE

THE consternation which ensued on the death of the Rowski speedily sent all his camp-followers, army, etc., to the rightabout. They struck their tents at the first news of his discomfiture ; and each man laying hold of what he could, the whole of the gallant force which had marched under his banner in the morning had disappeared ere the sun rose.

On that night, as it may be imagined, the gates of the Castle of Cleves were not shut. Everybody was free to come in. Wine-butts were broached in all the courts ; the pickled meat prepared in such lots for the siege was distributed among the people, who crowded to congratulate their beloved sovereign on his victory ; and the Prince, as was customary with that good man, who never lost an opportunity of giving a dinner-party, had a splendid entertainment made ready for the upper classes, the whole concluding with a tasteful display of fireworks.

In the midst of these entertainments, our old friend the Count of Hombourg arrived at the castle. The stalwart old warrior swore by Saint Bugo that he was grieved the killing of the Rowski had been taken out of his hand. The laughing Cleves vowed by Saint Bendigo, Hombourg could never have finished off his enemy so satisfactorily as the unknown knight had just done.

But who was he ? was the question which now agitated the bosom of these two old nobles. How to find him—how to reward the champion and restorer of the honour and happiness of Cleves ? They agreed over supper that he should be sought for everywhere. Beadles were sent round the principal cities within fifty miles, and the description of the knight advertised in the *Journal de Francfort* and the *Allgemeine Zeitung*. The hand of the Princess Helen was solemnly offered to him in these advertisements, with the reversion of the Prince of Cleves's splendid though somewhat dilapidated property.

'But we don't know him, my dear papa,' faintly ejaculated

that young lady. 'Some impostor may come in a suit of plain armour, and pretend that he was the champion who overcame the Rowski (a prince who had his faults certainly, but whose attachment for me I can never forget) ; and how are you to say whether he is the real knight or not ? There are so many deceivers in this world,' added the Princess, in tears, 'that one can't be too cautious now.' The fact is, that she was thinking of the desertion of Otto in the morning ; by which instance of faithlessness her heart was well-nigh broken.

As for that youth and his comrade Wolfgang, to the astonishment of everybody at their impudence, they came to the archers' mess that night, as if nothing had happened ; got their supper, partaking both of meat and drink most plentifully ; fell asleep when their comrades began to describe the events of the day, and the admirable achievements of the unknown warrior ; and, turning into their hammocks, did not appear on parade in the morning until twenty minutes after the names were called.

When the Prince of Cleves heard of the return of these deserters, he was in a towering passion. 'Where were you, fellows,' shouted he, 'during the time my castle was at its utmost need ?'

Otto replied, ' We were out on particular business.'

'Does a soldier leave his post on the day of battle, sir ?' exclaimed the Prince. 'You know the reward of such—Death ! and death you merit. But you are a soldier only of yesterday, and yesterday's victory has made me merciful. Hanged you shall not be, as you merit—only flogged, both of you. Parade the men, Colonel Tickelstern, after breakfast, and give these scoundrels five hundred apiece.'

You should have seen how young Otto bounded, when this information was thus abruptly conveyed to him. 'Flog *me !*' cried he. 'Flog Otto of——'

'Not so, my father,' said the Princess Helen, who had been standing by during the conversation, and who had looked at Otto all the while with the most ineffable scorn. 'Not so : although these *persons* have forgotten their duty' (she laid a particularly sarcastic emphasis on the word persons), 'we have had no need of their services, and have luckily found *others* more faithful. You promised your daughter a boon, papa : it is the pardon of these two *persons*. Let them go, and quit a service they have disgraced : a mistress—that is, a master—they have deceived.'

'Drum 'em out of the castle, Tickelstern ; strip their uniforms from their backs, and never let me hear of the scoundrels again.' So saying, the old Prince angrily turned on his heel to breakfast, leaving the two young men to the fun and derision of their surrounding comrades.

The noble Count of Hombourg, who was taking his usual airing on the ramparts before breakfast, came up at this juncture, and asked what was the row? Otto blushed when he saw him, and turned away rapidly; but the Count, too, catching a glimpse of him, with a hundred exclamations of joyful surprise seized upon the lad, hugged him to his manly breast, kissed him most affectionately, and almost burst into tears as he embraced him. For, in sooth, the good Count had thought his godson long ere this at the bottom of the silver Rhine.

The Prince of Cleves, who had come to the breakfast-parlour window (to invite his guest to enter, as the tea was made), beheld this strange scene from the window, as did the lovely tea-maker likewise, with breathless and beautiful agitation. The old Count and the archer strolled up and down the battlements in deep conversation. By the gestures of surprise and delight exhibited by the former, 'twas easy to see the young archer was conveying some very strange and pleasing news to him; though the nature of the conversation was not allowed to transpire.

'A godson of mine,' said the noble Count, when interrogated over his muffins. 'I know his family; worthy people; sad scapegrace; ran away; parents longing for him; glad you did not flog him; devil to pay,' and so forth. The Count was a man of few words, and told his tale in this brief artless manner. But why, at its conclusion, did the gentle Helen leave the room, her eyes filled with tears? She left the room once more to kiss a certain lock of yellow hair she had pilfered. A dazzling delicious thought, a strange wild hope, arose in her soul!

When she appeared again, she made some side-handed inquiries regarding Otto (with that gentle artifice oft employed by women); but he was gone. He and his companion were gone. The Count of Hombourg had likewise taken his departure, under pretext of particular business. How lonely the vast castle seemed to Helen, now that *he* was no longer there. The transactions of the last few days; the beautiful archer-boy; the offer from the Rowski (always an event in a young lady's life); the siege of the castle; the death of her truculent admirer: all seemed like a fevered dream to her: all was passed away, and had left no trace behind. No trace?—yes! one: a little insignificant lock of golden hair, over which the young creature wept so much that she put it out of curl; passing hours and hours in the summer-house where the operation had been performed.

On the second day (it is my belief she would have gone into a

F

consumption and died of languor, if the event had been delayed a
day longer) a messenger, with a trumpet, brought a letter in haste
to the Prince of Cleves, who was, as usual, taking refreshment.
'To the High and Mighty Prince,' etc., the letter ran.   'The
Champion who had the honour of engaging on Wednesday last
with his late Excellency the Rowski of Donnerblitz, presents his
compliments to H.S.H. the Prince of Cleves.   Through the
medium of the public prints the C. has been made acquainted with
the flattering proposal of His Serene Highness relative to a union

between himself (the Champion) and Her Serene Highness the
Princess Helen of Cleves.   The Champion accepts with pleasure
that polite invitation, and will have the honour of waiting upon
the Prince and Princess of Cleves about half-an-hour after the
receipt of this letter.'
    'Tol lol de rol, girl,' shouted the Prince with heartfelt joy.
(Have you not remarked, dear friend, how often in novel-books,
and on the stage, joy is announced by the above burst of insensate
monosyllables?)   'Tol lol de rol.   Don thy best kirtle, child;
thy husband will be here anon.'   And Helen retired to arrange

her toilet for this awful event in the life of a young woman. When she returned, attired to welcome her defender, her young cheek was as pale as the white satin slip and orange sprigs she wore.

She was scarce seated on the daïs by her father's side, when a huge flourish of trumpets from without proclaimed the arrival of *the Champion.* Helen felt quite sick : a draught of ether was necessary to restore her tranquillity.

The great door was flung open. He entered,—the same tall warrior, slim and beautiful, blazing in shining steel. He approached the Prince's throne, supported on each side by a friend likewise in armour. He knelt gracefully on one knee.

'I come,' said he, in a voice trembling with emotion, 'to claim, as per advertisement, the hand of the lovely Lady Helen.' And he held out a copy of the *Allgemeine Zeitung* as he spoke.

'Art thou noble, Sir Knight ?' asked the Prince of Cleves.

'As noble as yourself,' answered the kneeling steel.

'Who answers for thee ?'

'I, Karl, Margrave of Godesberg, his father !' said the knight on the right hand, lifting up his visor.

'And I—Ludwig, Count of Hombourg, his godfather !' said the knight on the left, doing likewise.

The kneeling knight lifted up his visor now, and looked on Helen.

'*I knew it was,*' said she, and fainted as she saw Otto the Archer.

But she was soon brought to, gentles, as I have small need to tell ye. In a very few days after, a great marriage took place at Cleves, under the patronage of Saint Bugo, Saint Buffo, and Saint Bendigo. After the marriage ceremony, the happiest and handsomest pair in the world drove off in a chaise-and-four, to pass the honeymoon at Kissingen. The Lady Theodora, whom we left locked up in her convent a long while since, was prevailed upon to come back to Godesberg, where she was reconciled to her husband. Jealous of her daughter-in-law, she idolised her son, and spoiled all her little grandchildren. And so all are happy, and my simple tale is done.

I read it in an old old book, in a mouldy old circulating library. 'Twas written in the French tongue, by the noble Alexandre Dumas ; but 'tis probable that he stole it from some other, and that the other had filched it from a former tale-teller. For nothing is new under the sun. Things die and are reproduced only. And so it is that the forgotten tale of the great Dumas reappears under the signature of   THERESA MACWHIRTER.

WHISTLEBINKIE, N.B. : *December* 1.

REBECCA AND ROWENA.

A ROMANCE UPON ROMANCE

By Mr. M. A. TITMARSH.

WITH ILLUSTRATIONS BY RICHARD DOYLE

PREFACE

THOSE readers who saw in *Frazer's Magazine*, some three years since, the proposals for a continuation of Ivanhoe, which were issued by the undersigned, very likely imagined, that like a thousand magnificent railroad projects and other schemes then rife, my plan for a Walter-Scott-continuation and Isaac-of-York-and-Ivanhoe Junction, was never to be brought to completion. But passing many hours on a sofa of late, recovering from a fever, and ordered by DR. ELLIOTSON (whose skill and friendship rescued me from it) ON NO ACCOUNT to put pen to paper, I, of course, wished to write immediately,—for which I humbly ask the Doctor's pardon.

It need scarcely be said, that the humble artist who usually illustrates my works fell ill at the same time with myself, and on trial his hand shook so that it was found impossible he could work for the present volume. But this circumstance no one but the Author (who disapproves of odious comparisons) will regret, as it has called in the aid of my friend MR. RICHARD DOYLE to illustrate the tale.

Receive it kindly, you gentle readers of novels, who love poetical justice ; and you honest children of large and small growth, who still have a relish for a little play and nonsense, and the harmless jingle of the cap and bells.

M. A. TITMARSH.

KENSINGTON,
    December 20*th*, 1849.

REBECCA AND ROWENA

CHAPTER I

THE OVERTURE—COMMENCEMENT OF THE BUSINESS

ELL-BELOVED novel-readers and gentle patronesses of romance, assuredly it has often occurred to every one of you, that the books we delight in have very unsatisfactory conclusions, and end quite prematurely with page 320 of the third volume. At that epoch of the history it is well known that the hero is seldom more than thirty years old, and the heroine by consequence some seven or eight years younger; and I would ask any of you whether it is fair to suppose that people after the above age have nothing worthy of note in their lives, and cease to exist as they drive away from Saint George's, Hanover Square? You, dear young ladies, who get your knowledge of

life from the circulating library, may be led to imagine that when the marriage business is done, and Emilia is whisked off in the new travelling carriage, by the side of the enraptured Earl ; or Belinda, breaking away from the tearful embraces of her excellent mother, dries her own lovely eyes upon the throbbing waistcoat of her bridegroom—you may be apt, I say, to suppose that all is over then ; that Emilia and the Earl are going to be happy for the rest of their lives in his Lordship's romantic castle in the north, and Belinda and her young clergyman to enjoy uninterrupted bliss in their rose-trellised parsonage in the west of England : but some there be among the novel-reading classes— old experienced folks—who know better than this. Some there be who have been married, and found that they have still something to see and to do, and to suffer mayhap ; and that adventures, and pains, and pleasures, and taxes, and sunrises and settings, and the business and joys and griefs of life go on after as before the nuptial ceremony.

Therefore I say, it is an unfair advantage, which the novelist takes of hero and heroine, as of his inexperienced reader, to say good-bye to the two former, as soon as ever they are made husband and wife ; and have often wished that additions should be made to all works of fiction, which have been brought to abrupt terminations in the manner described ; and that we should hear what occurs to the sober married man, as well as to the ardent bachelor ; to the matron, as well as to the blushing spinster. And in this respect I admire (and would desire to imitate) the noble and prolific French author, Alexandre Dumas, Marquis Davy de la Pailleterie, who carries his heroes from early youth down to the most venerable old age ; and does not let them rest, until they are so old, that it is full time the poor fellows should get a little peace and quiet. A hero is much too valuable a gentleman to be put upon the retired list, in the prime and vigour of his youth ; and I wish to know, what lady among us would like to be put on the shelf, and thought no longer interesting, because she has a family growing up, and is four or five and thirty years of age ? I have known ladies at sixty, with hearts as tender, and ideas as romantic, as any young misses of sixteen. Let us have middle aged novels then, as well as your extremely juvenile legends : let the young ones be warned, that the old folks have a right to be interesting : and that a lady may continue to have a heart, although she is somewhat stouter than she was when a schoolgirl, and a man his feelings, although he gets his hair from Truefitt's.

Thus I would desire, that the biographies of many of our most illustrious personages of romance, should be continued by fitting hands, and that they should be heard of, until at least a decent age.—Look at Mr. James's heroes : they invariably marry young. Look at Mr. Dickens's, they disappear from the scene when they are mere chits. I trust these authors, who are still alive, will see the propriety of telling us something more about people in whom we took a considerable interest, and who must be at present strong and hearty, and in the full vigour of health and intellect. And in the tales of the great Sir Walter (may honour be to his name), I am sure there are a number of people who are untimely carried away from us ; and of whom we ought to hear more.

My dear Rebecca, daughter of Isaac of York, has always, in my mind, been one of these ; nor can I ever believe that such a woman, so admirable, so tender, so heroic, so beautiful, could disappear altogether before such another woman as Rowena, that vapid, flaxen-headed creature, who is, in my humble opinion, unworthy of Ivanhoe, and unworthy of her place as heroine. Had both of them got their rights, it ever seemed to me that Rebecca would have had the husband, and Rowena would have gone off to a convent and shut herself up, where I, for one, would never have taken the trouble of inquiring for her.

But after all she married Ivanhoe. What is to be done ? There is no help for it. There it is in black and white at the end of the third volume of Sir Walter Scott's chronicle, that the couple were joined together in matrimony. And must the Disinherited Knight, whose blood has been fired by the suns of Palestine, and whose heart has been warmed in the company of the tender and beautiful Rebecca, sit down contented for life by the side of such a frigid piece of propriety as that icy, faultless, prim, niminy-piminy Rowena ? Forbid it fate, forbid it poetical justice ! There is a simple plan for setting matters right, and giving all parties their due, which is here submitted to the novel-reader. Ivanhoe's history *must* have had a continuation ; and it is this, which ensues. I may be wrong in some particulars of the narrative,—as what writer will not be ?—but of the main incidents of the history, I have in my own mind no sort of doubt, and confidently submit them to that generous public which likes to see virtue righted, true love rewarded, and the brilliant Fairy descend out of the blazing chariot at the end of the pantomime, and make Harlequin and Columbine happy. What, if reality be not so, gentlemen and ladies ; and if, after dancing a variety of jigs and antics, and jumping in and out of endless trap-doors and windows, through life's shifting scenes, no fairy comes down to make *us* comfortable at the close of the performance ? Ah ! let us give our honest novel-folks the benefit of their position, and not be envious of their good luck.

No person who has read the preceding volumes of this history, as the famous chronicler of Abbotsford has recorded them, can doubt for a moment what was the result of the marriage between Sir Wilfrid of Ivanhoe and the Lady Rowena. Those who have marked her conduct during her maidenhood, her distinguished politeness, her spotless modesty of demeanour, her unalterable coolness under all circumstances, and her lofty and gentlewoman-like bearing, must be sure that her married conduct would equal her spinster behaviour, and that Rowena the wife would be a pattern of correctness for all the matrons of England.

Such was the fact. For miles around Rotherwood her character for piety was known. Her castle was a rendezvous for all the clergy and monks of the district, whom she fed with the richest viands, while she pinched herself upon pulse and water. There was not an invalid in the three Ridings, Saxon or Norman, but the palfrey of the Lady Rowena might be seen journeying to his door, in company with Father Glauber her almoner, and Brother Thomas of Epsom, her leech. She lighted up all the churches in Yorkshire with wax-candles, the offerings of her piety. The bells of her chapel began to ring at two o'clock in the morning; and all the domestics of Rotherwood were called upon to attend at matins, at complins, at nones, at vespers, and at sermon. I need not say that fasting was observed with all the rigours of the Church; and that those of the servants of the Lady Rowena were looked upon with most favour whose hair shirts were the roughest, and who flagellated themselves with the most becoming perseverance.

Whether it was that this discipline cleared poor Wamba's wits or cooled his humour, it is certain that he became the most melancholy fool in England, and if ever he ventured upon a pun to the shuddering, poor servitors, who were mumbling their dry crusts below the salt, it was such a faint and stale joke, that nobody dared to laugh at the inuendoes of the unfortunate wag, and a sickly smile was the best applause he could muster. Once, indeed, when Guffo, the goose-boy (a half-witted, poor wretch), laughed outright at a lamentably stale pun which Wamba palmed upon him at supper-time (it was dark, and the torches being brought in, Wamba said, 'Guffo, they can't see their way in the argument, and are going *to throw a little light upon the subject*'), the Lady Rowena, being disturbed in a theological controversy with Father Willibald (afterwards canonised as St. Willibald, of Bareacres, hermit and confessor), called out to know what was the cause of the unseemly interruption, and Guffo and Wamba being pointed out as the culprits, ordered them straightway into the court-yard, and three dozen to be administered to each of them.

'I got you out of Front-de-Bœuf's castle,' said poor Wamba, piteously, appealing to Sir Wilfrid of Ivanhoe, 'and canst thou not save me from the lash ?'

'Yes, from Front-de-Bœuf's castle, *where you were locked up with the Jewess in the tower !*' said Rowena, haughtily replying to the timid appeal of her husband; 'Gurth, give him four dozen !'

And this was all poor Wamba got by applying for the mediation of his master.

In fact, Rowena knew her own dignity so well as a princess of the royal blood of England, that Sir Wilfrid of Ivanhoe, her consort, could scarcely call his life his own, and was made, in all things, to feel the inferiority of his station. And which of us is there acquainted with the sex that has not remarked this propensity in lovely woman, and how often the wisest in the council are made to be as fools at *her* board, and the boldest in the battle-field are craven when facing her distaff ?

'*Where you were locked up with the Jewess in the tower,*' was a remark, too, of which Wilfrid keenly felt, and, perhaps, the reader will understand, the significancy. When the daughter of Isaac of York brought her diamonds and rubies—the poor, gentle victim !—and, meekly laying them at the feet of the conquering Rowena, departed into foreign lands to tend the sick of her people, and to brood over the bootless passion which consumed her own pure heart, one would have thought that the heart of the royal lady would have melted before such beauty and humility, and that she would have been generous in the moment of her victory.

But did you ever know a right-minded woman pardon another for being handsome and more love-worthy than herself? The Lady Rowena did certainly say with mighty magnanimity to the Jewish maiden, 'Come and live with me as a sister,' as the former part of this history shows ; but Rebecca knew in her heart that her ladyship's proposition was what is called *bosh* (in that noble Eastern language with which Wilfrid the Crusader was familiar), or fudge, in plain Saxon ; and retired, with a broken, gentle spirit, neither able to bear the sight of her rival's happiness nor willing to disturb it by the contrast of her own wretchedness. Rowena, like the most high-bred and virtuous of women, never forgave Isaac's daughter her beauty, nor her flirtation with Wilfrid (as the Saxon lady chose to term it) ; nor, above all, her admirable diamonds and jewels, although Rowena was actually in possession of them.

In a word, she was always flinging Rebecca into Ivanhoe's teeth. There was not a day in his life but that unhappy warrior was made to remember that a Hebrew damsel had been in love with him, and that a Christian lady of fashion could never forgive the insult. For instance, if Gurth, the swine-herd, who was now promoted to be a gamekeeper and verderer, brought the account of a famous wild boar in the wood, and proposed a hunt, Rowena would say, 'Do, Sir Wilfrid, persecute those poor pigs—you know your friends the Jews can't abide them!' Or when, as it oft would happen, our lion-hearted monarch, Richard, in order to get a loan or a benevolence from the Jews, would roast a few of the Hebrew capitalists, or extract some of the principal rabbis' teeth, Rowena would exult and say, ' Serve them right, the misbelieving wretches ! England can never be a happy country until every one of these monsters is exterminated !' Or else, adopting a strain of still more savage sarcasm, would exclaim, 'Ivanhoe, my dear, more persecution for the Jews ! Hadn't you better interfere, my love ? His Majesty will do anything for you ; and, you know, the Jews were *always such favourites of yours,*' or words to that effect. But, nevertheless, her ladyship never lost an opportunity of wearing Rebecca's jewels at court, whenever the Queen held a drawing-room ; or at the York assizes and ball, when she appeared there, not of course because she took any interest in such things, but because she considered it her duty to attend as one of the chief ladies of the county.

Thus Sir Wilfrid of Ivanhoe, having attained the height of his wishes, was, like many a man when he has reached that dangerous elevation, disappointed. Ah, dear friends, it is but too often so in life ! Many a garden, seen from a distance, looks fresh and green, which, when beheld closely, is dismal and weedy ; the shady walks melancholy and grass-grown ; the bowers you would fain repose in, cushioned with stinging nettles. I have ridden in a caique upon the waters of the Bosphorus, and looked upon the capital of the Soldan of Turkey. As seen from those blue waters, with palace and pinnacle, with gilded dome and towering cypress, it seemeth a very Paradise of Mahound ; but, enter the city, and it is but a beggarly labyrinth of rickety huts and dirty alleys, where the ways are steep and the smells are foul, tenanted by mangy dogs and ragged beggars—a dismal illusion ! Life is such, ah, well-a-day ! It is only hope which is real, and reality is a bitterness and a deceit.

Perhaps a man, with Ivanhoe's high principles, would never bring himself to acknowledge this fact ; but others did for him. He grew thin, and pined away as much as if he had been in a fever under the scorching sun of Ascalon. He had no appetite for his meals ; he slept ill, though he was yawning all day. The jangling of the doctors and friars whom Rowena brought together did not in the least enliven him, and he would sometimes give proofs of somnolency during their disputes, greatly to the consternation of his lady. He hunted a good deal, and, I very much fear, as Rowena rightly remarked, that he might have an excuse for being absent from home. He began to like wine, too, who had been as sober as a hermit; and when he came back from Athelstane's (whither he would repair not unfrequently), the unsteadiness of his gait and the unnatural brilliancy of his eye were remarked by his lady, who, you may be sure, was sitting up for him. As for Athelstane, he swore by St. Wullstan that he was glad to have escaped a marriage with such a pattern of propriety; and honest Cedric the Saxon (who had been very speedily driven out of his daughter-in-law's castle) vowed by St. Waltheof that his son had bought a dear bargain.

So Sir Wilfrid of Ivanhoe became almost as tired of England as his royal master Richard was (who always quitted the country when he had squeezed from his loyal nobles, commons, clergy, and Jews all the money which he could get), and when the lion-hearted Prince began to make war against the French king, in Normandy and Guienne, Sir Wilfrid pined like a true servant to be in company of the good champion, alongside of whom he had shivered so many lances, and dealt such woundy blows of sword and battle-axe on the plains of Jaffa, or the breaches of Acre. Travellers were welcome at Rotherwood that brought news from the camp of the good king: and I warrant me that the knight listened with all his might when Father Drono, the chaplain, read in the *St. James's Chronykyll* (which was the paper of news he of Ivanhoe took in) of 'another glorious triumph'—'Defeat of the French near Blois' —'Splendid victory at Epte, and narrow escape of the French king,' the which deeds of arms the learned scribes had to narrate.

However such tales might excite him during the reading, they left the knight of Ivanhoe only the more melancholy after listening: and the more moody as he sate in his great hall silently draining his Gascony wine. Silently sate he and looked at his coats of mail, hanging vacant on the wall, his banner covered with spider-webs and his sword and axe rusting there. 'Ah, dear axe,' sighed he (into his drinking-horn)—'ah, gentle steel! that was a merry time when I sent thee crashing into the pate of the Emir Abdul Melik as he rode on the right of Saladin. Ah, my sword, my dainty headsman, my sweet split-rib, my razor of infidel beards; is the rust to eat thine edge off, and am I never more to wield thee in battle? What is the use of a shield on a wall, or a lance that has a cobweb for a pennon? O, Richard, my good king, would I could hear once more thy voice in the front of the onset!

Bones of Brian the Templar, would ye could rise from your grave at Templestowe, and that we might break another spear for honour and—and——' * * *

And *Rebecca*, he would have said—but the knight paused here in rather a guilty panic; and her Royal Highness the Princess Rowena (as she chose to style herself at home) looked so hard at him out of her china-blue eyes, that Sir Wilfrid felt as if she was reading his thoughts, and was fain to drop his own eyes into his flagon.

In a word, his life was intolerable. The dinner hour of the twelfth century, it is known, was very early : in fact people dined at ten o'clock in the morning : and after dinner, Rowena sate mum under her canopy, embroidered with the arms of Edward the Confessor, working with her maidens at the most hideous pieces of tapestry, representing the tortures and martyrdoms of her favourite saints, and not allowing a soul to speak above his breath, except when she chose to cry out in her own shrill voice when a handmaid made a wrong stitch, or let fall a ball of worsted. It was a dreary life. Wamba, we have said, never ventured to crack a joke, save in a whisper, when he was ten miles from home; and then Sir Wilfrid Ivanhoe was too weary and blue-devilled to laugh : but hunted in silence, moodily bringing down deer and wild boar with shaft and quarrel.

Then he besought Robin of Huntingdon, the jolly outlaw, nathless, to join him, and go to the help of their fair sire King Richard, with a score or two of lances. But the Earl of Huntingdon was a very different character from Robin Hood the forester. There was no more conscientious magistrate in all the county than his lordship : he was never known to miss church or quarter-sessions ; he was the strictest game proprietor in all the Riding, and sent scores of poachers to Botany Bay. 'A man who has a stake in the country, my good Sir Wilfrid,' Lord Huntingdon said, with rather a patronising air (his lordship had grown immensely fat since the King had taken him into grace, and required a horse as strong as an elephant to mount him), 'a man with a stake in the country ought to stay *in* the country. Property has its duties as well as its privileges, and a person of my rank is bound to live on the land from which he gets his living.'

'Amen !' sang out the Reverend —— Tuck, his lordship's domestic chaplain, who had also grown as sleek as the Abbot of Jorvaulx, who was as prim as a lady in his dress, wore bergamot in his handkerchief, and had his poll shaved, and his beard curled every day. And so sanctified was his Reverence grown, that he thought it was a shame to kill the pretty deer (though he ate of them still hugely, both in pasties and with French beans and currant jelly), and being shown a quarter-staff upon a certain occasion, handled it curiously, and asked 'what that ugly great stick was?'

Lady Huntingdon, late Maid Marian, had still some of her old fun and spirits, and poor Ivanhoe begged and prayed that she would come and stay at Rotherwood occasionally, and *égayer* the general dulness of that castle. But her ladyship said that Rowena gave herself such airs, and bored her so intolerably with stories of King Edward the Confessor, that she preferred any place rather than Rotherwood, which was as dull as if it had been at the top of Mount Athos.

The only person who visited it was Athelstane. 'His Royal Highness the Prince,' Rowena of course called him, whom the lady received with royal honours. She had the guns fired, and the footmen turned out with presented arms when he arrived; helped him to all Ivanhoe's favourite cuts of the mutton or the turkey, and forced her poor husband to light him to the state bedroom, walking backwards, holding a pair of wax candles. At this hour of bedtime the Thane used to be in such a condition that he saw two pair of candles and a couple of Ivanhoes reeling before him— let us hope it was not Ivanhoe that was reeling, but only his kinsman's brains muddled with the quantities of drink which it was his daily custom to consume. Rowena said it was the crack which the wicked Bois Guilbert, 'the Jewess's *other* lover, Wilfrid, my dear,' gave him on his royal skull, which caused the Prince to be disturbed so easily; but added, that drinking became a person of royal blood, and was but one of the duties of his station.

Sir Wilfrid of Ivanhoe saw it would be of no avail to ask this man to bear him company on his projected tour abroad; but still he himself was every day more and more bent upon going, and he long cast about for some means of breaking to his Rowena his firm resolution to join the King. He thought she would certainly fall ill if he communicated the news too abruptly to her; he would pretend a journey to York to attend a grand jury; then a call to London on law business or to buy stock; then he would slip over to Calais by the packet by degrees, as it were; and so be with the King before his wife knew that he was out of sight of Westminster Hall.

'Suppose your honour says you are going, as your honour would say Bo to a goose, plump, short, and to the point,' said Wamba, the jester, who was Sir Wilfrid's chief counsellor and attendant, 'depend on't Her Highness would bear the news like a Christian woman.'

'Tush, malapert! I will give thee the strap,' said Sir Wilfrid, in a fine tone of high tragedy indignation; 'thou knowest not the delicacy of the nerves of high-born ladies. An she faint not, write me down Hollander.'

'I will wager my bauble against an Irish billet of exchange that she will let your honour go off readily : that is, if you press not the matter too strongly,' Wamba answered, knowingly; and this Ivanhoe found to his discomfiture : for one morning at break-fast, adopting a *dégagé* air, as he sipped his tea, he said, 'My love, I was thinking of going over to pay His Majesty a visit in Normandy :' upon which, laying down her muffin (which, since the royal Alfred baked those cakes, had been the chosen breakfast cate of noble Anglo-Saxons, and which a kneeling page tendered to her on a salver, chased by the Florentine Benvenuto Cellini),— 'When do you think of going, Wilfrid, my dear ?'—the lady said, and the moment the tea-things were removed, and the tables and their trestles put away, she set about mending his linen, and getting ready his carpet-bag.

So Sir Wilfrid was as disgusted at her readiness to part with him as he had been weary of staying at home, which caused Wamba the fool to say, 'Marry, gossip, thou art like the man on ship-board, who, when the boatswain flogged him, did cry out "Oh!" wherever the rope's end fell on him : which caused Master Boatswain to say, "Plague on thee, fellow, and a pize on thee, knave, wherever I hit thee there is no pleasing thee."'

'And truly there are some backs which Fortune is always be-labouring,' thought Sir Wilfrid, with a groan, 'and mine is one that is ever sore.'

So, with a moderate retinue, whereof the knave Wamba made one, and a large woollen comforter round his neck, which his wife's own white fingers had woven, Sir Wilfrid of Ivanhoe left home to join the King, his master. Rowena, standing on the steps, poured out a series of prayers and blessings, most edifying to hear, as her lord mounted his charger, which his squires led to the door. 'It was the duty of the British female of rank,' she said, 'to suffer all, *all* in the cause of her Sovereign. *She* would not fear loneli-ness during the campaign : she would bear up against widowhood, desertion, and an unprotected situation.'

'My cousin Athelstane will protect thee,' said Ivanhoe, with profound emotion, as the tears trickled down his basnet; and bestowing a chaste salute upon the steel-clad warrior, Rowena modestly said, 'She hoped His Highness would be so kind.'

Then Ivanhoe's trumpet blew; then Rowena waved her pocket-handkerchief; then the household gave a shout; then the pursuivant of the good knight, Sir Wilfrid the Crusader, flung out his banner (which was argent a gules cramoisy with three Moors impaled sable); then Wamba gave a lash on his mule's haunch, and Ivanhoe, heaving a great sigh, turned the tail of his war-horse upon the castle of his fathers.

As they rode along the forest they met Athelstane, the Thane, powdering along the road in the direction of Rotherwood on his great dray-horse of a charger. 'Good-bye, good luck to you, old brick,' cried the Prince, using the vernacular Saxon; 'pitch into those Frenchmen; give it 'em over the face and eyes; and I'll stop at home and take care of Mrs. I.'

'Thank you, kinsman,' said Ivanhoe, looking, however, not particularly well pleased; and the chiefs shaking hands, the train of each took its different way—Athelstane's to Rotherwood, Ivanhoe's towards his place of embarkation.

The poor knight had his wish, and yet his face was a yard long, and as yellow as a lawyer's parchment; and having longed to quit home any time these three years past, he found himself envying Athelstane, because, forsooth, he was going to Rotherwood: which symptoms of discontent being observed by the witless Wamba, caused that absurd madman to bring his rebeck over his shoulder from his back, and to sing—

ATRA CURA

> Before I lost my five poor wits,
> I mind me of a Romish clerk,
> Who sang how Care, the phantom dark,
> Beside the belted horseman sits.
> Methought I saw the griesly sprite
> Jump up but now behind my Knight.'

'Perhaps thou didst, knave,' said Ivanhoe, looking over his shoulder; and the knave went on with his jingle.

> And though he gallop as he may,
> I mark that cursed monster black
> Still sits behind his honour's back,
> Tight squeezing of his heart alway.
> Like two black Templars sit they there,
> Beside one crupper, Knight and Care.
>
> No knight am I with pennoned spear,
> To prance upon a bold destrere:
> I will not have black Care prevail
> Upon my long-eared charger's tail,
> For lo, I am a witless fool,
> And laugh at Grief and ride a mule.

And his bells rattled as he kicked his mule's sides.

'Silence, fool!' said Sir Wilfrid of Ivanhoe, in a voice both majestic and wrathful. 'If thou knowest not care and grief, it is because thou knowest not love, whereof they are the companions. Who can love without an anxious heart? How shall there be joy at meeting, without tears at parting?' (I did not see that his honour or my lady shed many anon, thought Wamba the fool; but he was only a zany, and his mind was not right.) 'I would not exchange my very sorrows for thine indifference,' the knight continued. 'Where there is a sun there must be a shadow. If the shadow offend me, shall I put out my eyes and live in the dark? No! I am content with my fate, even such as it is. The Care of which thou speakest, hard though it may vex him, never yet rode down an honest man. I can bear him on my shoulders, and make my way through the world's press in spite of him; for my arm is strong, and my sword is keen, and my shield has no stain on it; and my heart, though it is sad, knows no guile.' And here, taking a locket out of his waistcoat (which was made of chain-mail), the knight kissed the token, put it back under the waistcoat again, heaved a profound sigh, and stuck spurs into his horse.

As for Wamba, he was munching a black pudding whilst Sir Wilfrid was making the above speech (which implied some secret grief on the knight's part, that must have been perfectly unintelligible to the fool), and so did not listen to a single word of Ivanhoe's pompous remarks. They travelled on by slow stages through the whole kingdom, until they came to Dover, whence they took shipping for Calais. And in this little voyage, being exceedingly sea-sick, and besides elated at the thought of meeting his Sovereign, the good knight cast away that profound melancholy which had accompanied him during the whole of his land journey.

CHAPTER II

THE LAST DAYS OF THE LION

FROM Calais Sir Wilfrid of Ivanhoe took the diligence across country to Limoges, sending on Gurth, his squire, with the horses and the rest of his attendants, with the exception of Wamba, who travelled not only as the knight's fool but as his valet, and who, perched on the roof of the carriage, amused himself by blowing tunes upon the *conducteur's* French horn. The good King Richard was, as Ivanhoe learned, in the Limousin, encamped before a little place called Chalus ; the lord whereof, though a vassal of the King's, was holding the castle against his Sovereign with a resolution and valour which caused a great fury and annoyance on the part of the Monarch with the Lion Heart. For, brave and magnanimous as he was, the Lion-hearted one did not love to be baulked any more than another ; and, like the royal animal whom he was said to resemble, he commonly tore his adversary to pieces, and then, perchance, had leisure to think how brave the latter had been. The Count of Chalus had found, it was said, a pot of money ; the royal Richard wanted it. As the Count denied that he had it, why did he not open the gates of his castle at once ? It was a clear proof that he was guilty ; and the King was determined to punish this rebel, and have his money and his life too.

He had naturally brought no breaching guns with him, because those instruments were not yet invented; and though he had assaulted the place a score of times with the utmost fury, His Majesty had been beaten back on every occasion, until he was so savage that it was dangerous to approach the British Lion. The Lion's wife, the lovely Berengaria, scarcely ventured to come near him. He flung the joint-stools in his tent at the heads of the Officers of State, and kicked his aides-de-camp round his pavilion ; and, in fact, a maid of honour, who brought a sack-posset unto His Majesty from the Queen, after he came in from the assault, came spinning like a football out of the royal tent just as Ivanhoe entered it.

'Send me my Austrian drum-major to flog that woman,' roared out the infuriate King. 'By the bones of St. Barnabas she has burned the sack! By St. Wittikind, I will have her flayed alive. Ha, St. George! ha, St. Richard! whom have we here?' And he lifted up his demi-culverin, or curtal axe, a weapon weighing about thirteen hundredweight, and was about to fling it at the intruder's head, when the latter, kneeling gracefully on one knee, said calmly, 'It is I, my good liege, Wilfrid of Ivanhoe.'

'What, Wilfrid of Templestowe, Wilfrid the married man, Wilfrid the hen-pecked!' cried the King with a sudden burst of good-humour, flinging away the culverin from him, as though it had been a reed (it lighted three hundred yards off, on the foot of Hugo de Bunyon, who was smoking a cigar at the door of his tent, and caused that redoubted warrior to limp for some days after). 'What, Wilfrid, my gossip? Art come to see the Lion's den? There are bones in it, man, bones and carcases, and the Lion is angry,' said the King, with a terrific glare of his eyes, 'but tush! we will talk of that anon. Ho! bring two gallons of hypocras for the King, and the good knight, Wilfrid of Ivanhoe. Thou art come in time, Wilfrid, for by St. Richard, and St. George, we will give a grand assault to-morrow. There will be bones broken, ha!'

'I care not, my liege,' said Ivanhoe, pledging the Sovereign respectfully, and tossing off the whole contents of the bowl of hypocras to His Highness's good health,—and he at once appeared to be taken into high favour, not a little to the envy of many of the persons surrounding the King.

As His Majesty said, there was fighting and feasting in plenty before Chalus. Day after day the besiegers made assaults upon the castle, but it was held so stoutly by the Count of Chalus and his gallant garrison, that each afternoon beheld the attacking parties returning disconsolately to their tents, leaving behind them many of their own slain, and bringing back with them store of broken heads and maimed limbs, received in the unsuccessful onset. The valour displayed by Ivanhoe, in all these contests, was prodigious; and the way in which he escaped death from the discharges of mangonels, catapults, battering-rams, twenty-four pounders, boiling oil, and other artillery, with which the besieged received their enemies, was remarkable. After a day's fighting, Gurth and Wamba used to pick the arrows out of their intrepid master's coat-of-mail, as if they had been so many almonds in a pudding. 'Twas well for the good knight, that under his first coat of armour he wore a choice suit of Toledan steel, perfectly impervious to arrow shots, and given to him by a certain Jew, named Isaac of York, to whom he had done some considerable services a few years back.

A COURT BALL

If King Richard had not been in such a rage at the repeated failures of his attacks upon the castle, that all sense of justice was blinded in the lion-hearted monarch, he would have been the first to acknowledge the valour of Sir Wilfrid of Ivanhoe, and would have given him a Peerage and the Grand Cross of the Bath at least a dozen times in the course of the siege : for Ivanhoe led more than a dozen storming parties, and with his own hand killed as many men (viz. two thousand three hundred and fifty-one) within six, as were slain by the lion-hearted monarch himself. But His Majesty was rather disgusted than pleased by his faithful servant's prowess ; and all the courtiers, who hated Ivanhoe for his superior valour and dexterity (for he would kill you off a couple of hundred of them of Chalus, whilst the strongest champions of the King's host could not finish more than their two dozen of a day), poisoned the royal mind against Sir Wilfrid, and made the King look upon his feats of arms with an evil eye. Roger de Backbite sneeringly told the King that Sir Wilfrid had offered to bet an equal bet that he would kill more men than Richard himself in the next assault : Peter de Toadhole said that Ivanhoe stated everywhere, that His Majesty was not the man he used to be ; that pleasures and drink had enervated him ; that he could neither ride, nor strike a blow with sword or axe, as he had been enabled to do in the old times in Palestine : and finally, in the twenty-fifth assault, in which they had very nearly carried the place, and in which onset Ivanhoe slew seven, and His Majesty six, of the sons of the Count de Chalus, its defender, Ivanhoe almost did for himself, by planting his banner before the King's upon the wall ; and only rescued himself from utter disgrace by saving His Majesty's life several times in the course of this most desperate onslaught.

Then the luckless knight's very virtues (as, no doubt, my respected readers know) made him enemies amongst the men—nor was Ivanhoe liked by the women frequenting the camp of the gay King Richard. His young Queen, and a brilliant court of ladies, attended the pleasure-loving monarch. His Majesty would transact business in the morning, then fight severely from after breakfast till about three o'clock in the afternoon ; from which time, until after midnight, there was nothing but jigging and singing, feasting and revelry, in the royal tents. Ivanhoe, who was asked as a matter of ceremony, and forced to attend these entertainments, not caring about the blandishments of any of the ladies present, looked on at their ogling and dancing with a countenance as glum as an undertaker's, and was a perfect wet-blanket in the midst of the festivities. His favourite resort and conversation were with a remarkably austere hermit, who lived in the neighbourhood of

Chalus, and with whom Ivanhoe loved to talk about Palestine, and
the Jews, and other grave matters of import, better than to mingle
in the gayest amusements of the court of King Richard.   Many a
night, when the Queen and the ladies were dancing quadrilles and
polkas (in which His Majesty, who was enormously stout as well
as tall, insisted upon figuring, and in which he was about as
graceful as an elephant dancing a hornpipe), Ivanhoe would steal
away from the ball, and come and have a night's chat under the
moon with his reverend friend.   It pained him to see a man of
the King's age and size dancing about with the young folks.   They
laughed at His Majesty whilst they flattered him : the pages and
maids of honour mimicked the royal mountebank almost to his
face ; and, if Ivanhoe ever could have laughed, he certainly would
one night, when the King, in light-blue satin inexpressibles, with
his hair in powder, chose to dance the Minuet de la Cour with the
little Queen Berengaria.

Then, after dancing, His Majesty must needs order a guitar,
and begin to sing.   He was said to compose his own songs—words
and music—but those who have read Lord Campobello's *Lives of
the Lord Chancellors*, are aware that there was a person by the
name of Blondel, who, in fact, did all the musical part of the
King's performances ; and, as for the words, when a King writes
verses, we may be sure there will be plenty of people to admire
his poetry.   His Majesty would sing you a ballad, of which he
had stolen every idea, to an air which was ringing on all the
barrel-organs of Christendom, and, turning round to his courtiers,
would say, ' How do you like that ?   I dashed it off this morning.'
Or, ' Blondel, what do you think of this movement in B flat ?' or
what not ; and the courtiers and Blondel, you may be sure, would
applaud with all their might, like hypocrites as they were.

One evening—it was the evening of the 27th March 1199,
indeed—His Majesty, who was in the musical mood, treated the
court with a quantity of his so-called compositions, until the people
were fairly tired of clapping with their hands, and laughing in their
sleeves.   First he sang an *original* air and poem, beginning

> Cherries nice, cherries nice, nice, come choose
> Fresh and fair ones, who'll refuse ? etc.

The which he was ready to take his affidavit he had composed
the day before yesterday.   Then he sang an *original* heroic melody,
of which the chorus was

> Rule Britannia, Britannia rules the sea,
> For Britons never, never, never slaves shall be, etc.

The courtiers applauded this song as they did the other, all except

KING RICHARD IN MUSICAL MOOD

Ivanhoe, who sate without changing a muscle of his features, until the King questioned him, when the knight with a bow said 'he thought he had heard something very like the air and the words elsewhere.' His Majesty scowled at him a savage glance from under his red bushy eyebrows; but Ivanhoe had saved the royal life that day, and the King, therefore, with difficulty controlled his indignation.

'Well,' said he, 'by St. Richard and St. George, but ye never heard *this* song, for I composed it this very afternoon as I took my bath after the mêlée. Did I not, Blondel?'

Blondel, of course, was ready to take an affidavit that His Majesty had done as he said, and the King, thrumming on his guitar with his great red fingers and thumbs, began to sing out of tune, and as follows :—

COMMANDERS OF THE FAITHFUL

The Pope he is a happy man,
His Palace is the Vatican :
And there he sits and drains his can,
The Pope he is a happy man.
I often say when I'm at home,
I'd like to be the Pope of Rome.

And then there's Sultan Saladin,
That Turkish Soldan full of sin ;
He has a hundred wives at least,
By which his pleasure is increased ;
I've often wished, I hope no sin,
That I were Sultan Saladin.

But no, the Pope no wife may chose,
And so I would not wear his shoes ;
No wine may drink the proud Paynim,
And so I'd rather not be him ;
My wife, my wine, I love I hope,
And would be neither Turk nor Pope.

Encore ! Encore ! Bravo ! Bis ! Everybody applauded the King's song with all his might; everybody except Ivanhoe, who preserved his abominable gravity : and when asked aloud by Roger de Backbite whether he had heard that too? said firmly, 'Yes, Roger de Backbite ; and so hast thou if thou darest but tell the truth.'

'Now, by St. Cicely, may I never touch gittern again,' bawled the King in a fury, 'if every note, word, and thought be not mine ; may I die in to-morrow's onslaught if the song be not my song. Sing thyself, Wilfrid of the Lanthorn Jaws ; thou couldst sing a good song in old times :' and with all his might, and with a forced

laugh, the King, who loved brutal practical jests, flung his guitar
at the head of Ivanhoe.

Sir Wilfrid caught it gracefully with one hand, and, making an
elegant bow to the Sovereign, began to chant as follows :—

KING CANUTE

King Canute was weary-hearted ; he had reigned for years a score ;
Battling, struggling, pushing, fighting, killing much and robbing more,
And he thought upon his actions, walking by the wild sea-shore.

'Twixt the Chancellor and Bishop walked the King with steps sedate,
Chamberlains and grooms came after, silver sticks and gold sticks great,
Chaplains, aides-de-camp, and pages,—all the officers of state.

Sliding after like his shadow, pausing when he chose to pause ;
If a frown his face contracted, straight the courtiers dropped their jaws ;
If to laugh the King was minded, out they burst in loud hee-haws.

But that day a something vexed him, that was clear to old and young,
Thrice his Grace had yawned at table, when his favourite gleeman sung,
Once the Queen would have consoled him, but he bade her hold her tongue.

'Something ails my gracious Master,' cried the Keeper of the Seal,
'Sure, my lord, it is the lampreys, served at dinner, or the veal !'
'Psha !' exclaimed the angry Monarch, 'Keeper, 'tis not that I feel.

''Tis the *heart*, and not the dinner, fool, that doth my rest impair ;
Can a King be great as I am, prithee, and yet know no care ?
Oh, I'm sick, and tired, and weary.' Some one cried, 'The King's
    arm-chair !'

Then towards the lackeys turning, quick my lord the Keeper nodded,
Straight the King's great chair was brought him, by two footmen
    able-bodied ;
Languidly he sank into it ; it was comfortably wadded.

'Leading on my fierce companions,' cried he, 'over storm and brine,
I have fought and I have conquered ! Where was glory like to mine ?'
Loudly all the courtiers echoed : 'Where is glory like to thine ?'

'What avail me all my kingdoms ? Weary am I now, and old ;
Those fair sons I have begotten, long to see me dead and cold ;
Would I were, and quiet buried, underneath the silent mould !

'Oh, remorse, the writhing serpent ! at my bosom tears and bites ;
Horrid, horrid things I look on, though I put out all the lights ;
Ghosts of ghastly recollections troop about my bed of nights.

'Cities burning, convents blazing, red with sacrilegious fires ;
Mothers weeping, virgins screaming, vainly for their slaughtered sires—'
'Such a tender conscience,' cries the Bishop, 'every one admires.

'But for such unpleasant bygones, cease, my gracious Lord, to search,
They're forgotten and forgiven by our holy Mother Church ;
Never, never does she leave her benefactors in the lurch.

'Look! the land is crowned with minsters, which your Grace's bounty
    raised ;
Abbeys filled with holy men, where you and Heaven are daily praised ;
You, my lord, to think of dying ? on my conscience, I'm amazed !'

'Nay, I feel,' replied King Canute, 'that my end is drawing near.'
'Don't say so,' exclaimed the courtiers (striving each to squeeze a tear),
'Sure your Grace is strong and lusty, and may live this fifty year.'

'Live these fifty years !' the Bishop roared, with actions made to suit,
'Are you mad, my good Lord Keeper, thus to speak of King Canute ?
Men have lived a thousand years, and sure His Majesty will do't.

'Adam, Enoch, Lamech, Canan, Mahaleel, Methusela,
Lived nine hundred years apiece, and mayn't the King as well as they ?'
'Fervently,' exclaimed the Keeper, 'fervently I trust he may.'

'*He* to die ?' resumed the Bishop. 'He a mortal like to *us?*
Death was not for him intended, though *communis omnibus ;*
Keeper, you are irreligious, for to talk and cavil thus.

'With his wondrous skill in healing ne'er a doctor can compete,
Loathsome lepers, if he touch them, start up clean upon their feet ;
Surely he could raise the dead up, did His Highness think it meet.

'Did not once the Jewish captain stay the sun upon the hill,
And, the while he slew the foemen, bid the silver moon stand still ?
So, no doubt, could gracious Canute, if it were his sacred will.'

'Might I stay the sun above us, good Sir Bishop ?' Canute cried ;
'Could I bid the silver moon to pause upon her heavenly ride ?
If the moon obeys my orders, sure I can command the tide.

'Will the advancing waves obey me, Bishop, if I make the sign ?'
Said the Bishop, bowing lowly, 'Land and sea, my lord, are thine.'
Canute turned towards the ocean—'Back !' he said, 'thou foaming brine.

'From the sacred shore I stand on, I command thee to retreat ;
Venture not, thou stormy rebel, to approach thy master's seat ;
Ocean, be thou still ! I bid thee come not nearer to my feet !'

But the sullen ocean answered with a louder, deeper roar,
And the rapid waves drew nearer, falling sounding on the shore ;
Back the Keeper and the Bishop, back the King and courtiers bore.

And he sternly bade them never more to kneel to human clay,
But alone to praise and worship That which earth and seas obey,
And his golden crown of empire never wore he from that day.
King Canute is dead and gone : Parasites exist alway.

At this ballad, which, to be sure, was awfully long, and as
grave as a sermon, some of the courtiers tittered, some yawned,
and some affected to be asleep and snore outright. But Roger de
Backbite, thinking to curry favour with the King by this piece of
vulgarity, His Majesty fetched him a knock on the nose and a buffet

on the ear, which, I warrant me, wakened Master Roger ; to whom the King said, ' Listen and be civil, slave ; Wilfrid is singing about thee.—Wilfrid, thy ballad is long, but it is to the purpose, and I have grown cool during thy homily. Give me thy hand, honest friend. Ladies, good-night. Gentlemen, we give the grand assault to-morrow ; when I promise thee, Wilfrid, thy banner shall not be before mine '—and the King, giving his arm to Her Majesty, retired into the private pavilion.

CHAPTER III

WHILST the royal Richard and his Court were feasting in the camp outside the walls of Chalus, they of the castle were in the most miserable plight that may be conceived. Hunger, as well as the fierce assaults of the besiegers, had made dire ravages in the place. The garrison's provisions of corn and cattle, their very horses, dogs, and donkeys had been eaten up—so that it might well be said by Wamba 'that famine, as well as slaughter, had *thinned* the garrison.' When the men of Chalus came on the walls to defend it against the scaling parties of King Richard— they were like so many skeletons in armour—they could hardly pull their bow-strings at last, or pitch down stones on the heads of His Majesty's party, so weak had their arms become ; and the gigantic Count of Chalus, a warrior as redoubtable for his size and strength as Richard Plantagenet himself, was scarcely able to lift up his battle-axe upon the day of that last assault, when Sir Wilfrid of Ivanhoe ran him through the * * but we are advancing matters.

What should prevent me from describing the agonies of hunger which the Count (a man of large appetite) suffered in company with his heroic sons and garrison ?—Nothing, but that Dante has already done the business in the notorious history of Count Ugolino, so that my efforts might be considered as mere imitations. Why should I not, if I were minded to revel in horrifying details, show you how the famished garrison drew lots, and ate themselves during the siege ; and how the unlucky lot falling upon the Countess of Chalus, that heroic woman, taking an affectionate leave of her family, caused her large cauldron in the castle kitchen to be set a-boiling, had onions, carrots and herbs, pepper and salt made ready, to make a savoury soup, as the French like it, and when all things were quite completed, kissed her children, jumped into the cauldron from off the kitchen stool, and so was stewed down in her flannel bed-gown ? Dear friends, it is not from want of imagination, or from having no turn for the terrible or pathetic, that I spare you these details. I could give you some description that would spoil your dinner and night's rest, and make your hair stand on end. But why harrow your feelings? Fancy all the tortures and horrors that possibly can occur in a beleaguered and famished castle : fancy the feelings of men who know that no more quarter will be given them than they would get if they were peaceful Hungarian citizens, kidnapped and brought to trial by His Majesty the Emperor of Austria, and then let us rush on to the breach and prepare once more to meet the assault of dreadful King Richard and his men.

On the 29th of March, in the year 1199, the good King, having copiously partaken of breakfast, caused his trumpets to blow, and advanced with his host upon the breach of the castle of Chalus. Arthur de Pendennis bore his banner ; Wilfrid of Ivanhoe fought on the King's right hand. Molyneux, Bishop of Bullocksmithy, doffed crosier and mitre for that day, and though fat and pursy, panted up the breach with the most resolute spirit, roaring out war-cries and curses, and wielding a prodigious mace of iron, with which he did good execution. Hugo de Backbite was forced to come in attendance upon the Sovereign, but took care to keep in the rear of his august master, and to shelter behind his huge triangular shield as much as possible. Many lords of note followed the King and bore the ladders ; and as they were placed against the wall, the air was perfectly dark with the showers of arrows which the French archers poured out at the besiegers ; and the cataract of stones, kettles, boot-jacks, chests of drawers, crockery, umbrellas, congreve-rockets, bombshells, bolts and arrows, and other missiles which the desperate garrison flung out on the storming-party. The King received a copper coal-scuttle right over his eyes, and a mahogany wardrobe was discharged at his morion, which would have felled an ox, and would have done for the King had not Ivanhoe warded it off skilfully. Still they advanced, the warriors falling around them like grass beneath the scythe of the mower.

The ladders were placed in spite of the hail of death raining round : the King and Ivanhoe were, of course, the first to mount them. Chalus stood in the breach, borrowing strength from despair ; and roaring out, 'Ha! Plantagenet, Saint Barbacue for Chalus!' he dealt the King a crack across the helmet with his battle-axe, which shore off the gilt lion and crown that surmounted the steel cap. The King bent and reeled back ; the besiegers were dismayed ; the garrison and the Count of Chalus set up a shout of triumph : but it was premature.

ASSAULT ON THE CASTLE OF CHALUS

KING RICHARD IN MURDEROUS MOOD

As quick as thought Ivanhoe was into the Count with a thrust in tierce, which took him just at the joint of the armour, and ran him through as clean as a spit does a partridge. Uttering a horrid shriek, he fell back writhing; the King recovering staggered up the parapet; the rush of knights followed, and the Union Jack was planted triumphantly on the walls, just as Ivanhoe,—but we must leave him for a moment.

'Ha, St. Richard!—ha, St. George!' the tremendous voice of the Lion-king was heard over the loudest roar of the onset. At every sweep of his blade a severed head flew over the parapet, a spouting trunk tumbled, bleeding, on the flags of the bartizan. The world hath never seen a warrior equal to that Lion-hearted Plantagenet, as he raged over the keep, his eyes flashing fire through the bars of his morion, snorting and chafing with the hot lust of battle. One by one *les enfans de Chalus* had fallen : there was only one left at last of all the brave race that had fought round the gallant Count :—only one, and but a boy, a fair-haired boy, a blue-eyed boy ! he had been gathering pansies in the fields but yesterday—it was but a few years, and he was a baby in his mother's arms ! What could his puny sword do against the most redoubted blade in Christendom ?—and yet Bohemond faced the great champion of England, and met him foot to foot ! Turn away, turn away, my dear young friends and kind-hearted ladies ! Do not look at that ill-fated poor boy ! his blade is crushed into splinters under the axe of the conqueror, and the poor child is beaten to his knee ! * * *

'Now, by St. Barbacue of Limoges,' said Bertrand de Gourdon, 'the butcher will never strike down yonder lambling ! Hold thy hand, Sir King, or, by St. Barbacue——'

Swift as thought the veteran archer raised his arblast to his shoulder, the whizzing bolt fled from the ringing string, and the next moment crushed quivering into the corslet of Plantagenet.

'Twas a luckless shot, Bertrand of Gourdon ! Maddened by the pain of the wound, the brute nature of Richard was aroused : his fiendish appetite for blood rose to madness, and grinding his teeth, and with a curse too horrible to mention, the flashing axe of the royal butcher fell down on the blond ringlets of the child, and the children of Chalus were no more ! * * *

I just throw this off by way of description, and to show what *might* be done if I chose to indulge in this style of composition, but as in the battles which are described by the kindly chronicler of one of whose works this present masterpiece is professedly a continuation, everything passes off agreeably ; the people are slain,

but without any unpleasant sensation to the reader; nay, some of
the most savage and blood-stained characters of history, such is the
indomitable good-humour of the great novelist, become amiable,
jovial companions, for whom one has a hearty sympathy—so, if
you please, we will have this fighting business at Chalus, and the
garrison and honest Bertrand of Gourdon, disposed of, the former,
according to the usage of the good old times, having been hung up
or murdered to a man, and the latter killed in the manner described
by the late Dr. Goldsmith in his History.

As for the Lion-hearted, we all very well know that the shaft
of Bertrand de Gourdon put an end to the royal hero—and that
from that 29th of March he never robbed or murdered any more.
And we have legends in recondite books of the manner of the
King's death.

'You must die, my son,' said the venerable Walter of Rouen,
as Berengaria was carried shrieking from the King's tent. 'Repent, Sir King, and separate yourself from your children!'

'It is ill jesting with a dying man,' replied the King. 'Children
have I none, my good lord bishop, to inherit after me.'

'Richard of England,' said the Archbishop, turning up his fine
eyes, 'your vices are your children. Ambition is your eldest child,
Cruelty is your second child, Luxury is your third child; and you
have nourished them from your youth up. Separate yourself from
these sinful ones, and prepare your soul, for the hour of departure
draweth nigh.'

Violent, wicked, sinful, as he might have been, Richard of
England met his death like a Christian man. Peace be to the
soul of the brave! When the news came to King Philip of
France, he sternly forbade his courtiers to rejoice at the death of
his enemy. 'It is no matter of joy but of dolour,' he said, 'that
the bulwark of Christendom and the bravest king of Europe is
no more.'

Meanwhile what has become of Sir Wilfrid of Ivanhoe, whom
we left in the act of rescuing his Sovereign by running the Count
of Chalus through the body?

As the good knight stooped down to pick his sword out of the
corpse of his fallen foe, some one coming behind him suddenly
thrust a dagger into his back at a place where his shirt of mail
was open (for Sir Wilfrid had armed that morning in a hurry,
and it was his breast, not his back, that he was accustomed
ordinarily to protect); and when poor Wamba came up on the
rampart, which he did when the fighting was over—being such a

BURLESQUES

FROM CORNHILL TO GRAND CAIRO

AND

JUVENILIA

fool that he could not be got to thrust his head into danger for glory's sake—he found his dear knight with the dagger in his back lying without life upon the body of the Count de Chalus whom he had anon slain.

Ah, what a howl poor Wamba set up when he found his master killed! How he lamented over the corpse of that noble knight and friend! What mattered it to him that Richard the King was borne wounded to his tent, and that Bertrand de Gourdon was flayed alive? At another time the sight of this spectacle might have amused the simple knave; but now all his thoughts were of his lord, so good, so gentle, so kind, so loyal, so frank with the great, so tender to the poor, so truthful of speech, so modest regarding his own merit, so true a gentleman, in a word, that anybody might, with reason, deplore him.

As Wamba opened the dear knight's corslet, he found a locket round his neck, in which there was some hair, not flaxen like that of my Lady Rowena, who was almost as fair as an Albino, but as black, Wamba thought, as the locks of the Jewish maiden whom the knight had rescued in the lists of Templestowe. A bit of Rowena's hair was in sir Wilfrid's possession, too, but that was in his purse along with his seal of arms, and a couple of groats; for the good knight never kept any money, so generous was he of his largesses when money came in.

Wamba took the purse, and seal, and groats, but he left the locket of hair round his master's neck, and when he returned to England never said a word about the circumstance. After all, how should he know whose hair it was? It might have been the knight's grandmother's hair for aught the fool knew; so he kept his counsel when he brought back the sad news and tokens to the disconsolate widow at Rotherwood.

The poor fellow would never have left the body at all, and indeed sate by it all night, and until the grey of the morning, when, seeing two suspicious-looking characters advancing towards him, he fled in dismay, supposing that they were marauders who were out searching for booty among the dead bodies; and having not the least courage, he fled from these, and tumbled down the breach, and never stopped running as fast as his legs would carry him until he reached the tents of his late beloved master.

The news of the knight's demise, it appeared, had been known at his quarters long before; for his servants were gone, and had ridden off on his horses; his chests were plundered, there was not so much as a shirt-collar left in his drawers, and the very bed and blankets had been carried away by these *faithful* attendants. Who had slain Ivanhoe? That remains a mystery to the present day; but Hugo de Backbite, whose nose he had pulled for defamation, and who was behind him in the assault at Chalus, was seen two years afterwards at the court of King John in an embroidered velvet waistcoat which Rowena could have sworn she had worked for Ivanhoe, and about which the widow would have made some little noise, but that—but that she was no longer a widow.

That she truly deplored the death of her lord, cannot be questioned, for she ordered the deepest mourning which any milliner in York could supply, and erected a monument to his memory as big as a minster. But she was a lady of such fine principles, that she did not allow her grief to overmaster her; and an opportunity speedily arising for uniting the two best Saxon families in England, by an alliance between herself and the gentleman who offered himself to her, Rowena sacrificed her inclination to remain single to her sense of duty; and contracted a second matrimonial engagement.

That Athelstane was the man, I suppose no reader familiar with life, and novels (which are a rescript of life, and are all strictly natural and edifying), can for a moment doubt. Cardinal Pandulfo tied the knot for them: and lest there should be any doubt about Ivanhoe's death (for his body was never sent home after all, nor seen after Wamba ran away from it), his Eminence procured a Papal decree annulling the former marriage, so that Rowena became Mrs. Athelstane with a clear conscience. And who shall be surprised if she was happier with the stupid and boozy Thane than with the gentle and melancholy Wilfrid? Did women never have a predilection for fools, I should like to know; or fall in love with donkeys, before the time of the amours of Bottom and Titania? 'Ah! Mary, had you not preferred an ass to a man, would you have married Jack Bray, when a Michael Angelo offered. Ah! Fanny, were you not a woman, would you persist in adoring Tom Hiccups, who beats you, and comes home tipsy from the Club?' Yes, Rowena cared a hundred times more about tipsy Athelstane than ever she had done for gentle Ivanhoe, and so great was her infatuation about the latter, that she would sit upon his knee in the presence of all her maidens, and let him smoke his cigars in the very drawing-room.

This is the epitaph she caused to be written by Father Drono (who piqued himself upon his Latinity), on the stone commemorating the death of her late lord:—

Hic est Guilfridus, belli dum vixit avidus;
Cum gladio et lancea, Normannia et quoque Francia
Verbera dura dabat: per Turcos multum equitabat:

Guilbertum occidit: atque Hierosolyma bidit.
Heu! nunc sub fossa sunt tanti militis ossa,
Uxor Athelstani est conjux castissima Thani.

And this is the translation which the doggrel knave Wamba made
of the Latin lines :

REQUIESCAT

Under the stone you behold,
Buried, and coffined, and cold,
Lieth Sir Wilfrid the Bold.

Always he marched in advance,
Warring in Flanders and France,
Doughty with sword and with lance.

Famous in Saracen fight,
Rode in his youth the good knight,
Scattering Paynims in flight.

Brian the Templar untrue,
Fairly in tourney he slew,
Saw Hierusalem too.

Now he is buried and gone,
Lying beneath the grey stone :
Where shall you find such a one ?

Long time his widow deplored,
Weeping the fate of her lord,
Sadly cut off by the sword.

When she was eased of her pain,
Came the good Lord Athelstane,
When her ladyship married again.

Athelstane burst into a loud laugh, when he heard it, at the
last line, but Rowena would have had the fool whipped, had not
the Thane interceded, and to him, she said, she could refuse
nothing.

CHAPTER IV

I TRUST nobody will suppose, from the events described in the last chapter, that our friend Ivanhoe is really dead. Because we have given him an epitaph or two and a monument, are these any reasons that he should be really gone out of the world? No: as in the pantomime, when we see Clown and Pantaloon lay out Harlequin and cry over him, we are always sure that Master Harlequin will be up at the next minute alert and shining in his glistening coat; and, after giving a box on the ears to the pair of them, will be taking a dance with Columbine, or leaping gaily through the clock-face, or into the three-pair-of-stairs window :— so Sir Wilfrid, the Harlequin of our Christmas piece, may be run through a little, or may make believe to be dead, but will assuredly rise up again when he is wanted, and show himself at the right moment.

The suspicious-looking characters from whom Wamba ran away were no cut-throats and plunderers, as the poor knave imagined, but no other than Ivanhoe's friend, the hermit, and a reverend brother of his, who visited the scene of the late battle in order to see if any Christians still survived there, whom they might shrive and get ready for Heaven, or to whom they might possibly offer the benefit of their skill as leeches. Both were prodigiously learned in the healing art; and had about them those precious elixirs which so often occur in romances, and with which patients are so miraculously restored. Abruptly dropping his master's head from his lap as he fled, poor Wamba caused the knight's pate to fall with rather a heavy thump to the ground, and if the knave had but stayed a minute longer, he would have heard Sir Wilfrid utter a deep groan. But though the fool heard him not, the holy hermits did; and to recognise the gallant Wilfrid, to withdraw the enormous dagger still sticking out of his back, to wash the wound with a portion of the precious elixir, and to pour a little of it down his throat, was with the excellent hermits the work of an instant;

108

which remedies being applied, one of the good men took the knight by the heels and the other by the head, and bore him daintily from the castle to their hermitage in a neighbouring rock. As for the Count of Chalus, and the remainder of the slain, the hermits were too much occupied with Ivanhoe's case to mind them, and did not, it appears, give them any elixir, so that, if they are really dead, they must stay on the rampart stark and cold; or if otherwise, when the scene closes upon them as it does now, they may get up, shake themselves, go to the slips and drink a pot of porter, or change their stage-clothes and go home to supper. My dear readers, you may settle the matter among yourselves as you like. If you wish to kill the characters really off, let them be dead, and have done with them : but, *entre nous*, I don't believe they are any more dead than you or I are, and sometimes doubt whether there is a single syllable of truth in this whole story.

Well, Ivanhoe was taken to the hermits' cell, and there doctored by the holy fathers for his hurts, which were of such a severe and dangerous order, that he was under medical treatment for a very considerable time. When he woke up from his delirium, and asked how long he had been ill, fancy his astonishment when he heard that he had been in the fever for six years ! He thought the reverend fathers were joking at first, but their profession forbade them from that sort of levity ; and besides, he could not possibly have got well any sooner, because the story would have been sadly put out had he appeared earlier. And it proves how good the fathers were to him, and how very nearly that scoundrel of a Hugh de Backbite's dagger had finished him, that he did not get well under this great length of time, during the whole of which the fathers tended him without ever thinking of a fee. I know of a kind physician in this town who does as much sometimes, but I won't do him the ill service of mentioning his name here.

Ivanhoe, being now quickly pronounced well, trimmed his beard, which by this time hung down considerably below his knees, and calling for his suit of chain armour, which before had fitted his elegant person as tight as wax, now put it on, and it bagged and hung so loosely about him, that even the good friars laughed at his absurd appearance. It was impossible that he should go about the country in such a garb as that : the very boys would laugh at him : so the friars gave him one of their old gowns, in which he disguised himself; and, after taking an affectionate farewell of his friends, set forth on his return to his native country. As he went along, he learned that Richard was dead, that John reigned, that Prince Arthur had been poisoned, and was of course

made acquainted with various other facts of public importance
recorded in Pinnock's Catechism and the Historic Page.

But these subjects did not interest him near so much as his
own private affairs ; and I can fancy that his legs trembled under
him, and his pilgrim's staff shook with emotion, as at length, after
many perils, he came in sight of his paternal mansion of Rotherwood, and saw once more the chimneys smoking, the shadows of
the oaks over the grass in the sunset, and the rooks winging over
the trees.   He heard the supper gong sounding : he knew his way
to the door well enough ; he entered the familiar hall with a
benedicite, and without any more words took his place.

*   *   *   *   *

You might have thought for a moment that the grey friar
trembled, and his shrunken cheek looked deadly pale ; but he
recovered himself presently, nor could you see his pallor for the
cowl which covered his face.

A little boy was playing on Athelstane's knee ; Rowena, smiling
and patting the Saxon Thane fondly on his broad bull-head, filled
him a huge cup of spiced wine from a golden jug.   He drained a
quart of the liquor, and, turning round, addressed the friar,—

'And so, grey frere, thou sawest good King Richard fall at
Chalus by the bolt of that felon bowman ?'

'We did, an it please you.   The brothers of our house attended
the good King in his last moments ; in truth, he made a Christian
ending !'

'And didst thou see the archer flayed alive ?   It must have
been rare sport,' roared Athelstane, laughing hugely at the joke.
'How the fellow must have howled !'

'My love !' said Rowena, interposing tenderly, and putting a
pretty white finger on his lip.

'I would have liked to see it too,' cried the boy.

'That's my own little Cedric, and so thou shalt.   And, friar,
didst see my poor kinsman Sir Wilfrid of Ivanhoe ?   They say he
fought well at Chalus !'

'My sweet lord,' again interposed Rowena, 'mention him not.'

'Why ?   Because thou and he were so tender in days of yore—
when you could not bear my plain face, being all in love with his
pale one ?'

'Those times are past now, dear Athelstane,' said his affectionate
wife, looking up to the ceiling.

'Marry, thou never couldst forgive him the Jewess, Rowena.'

'The odious hussy ! don't mention the name of the unbelieving
creature,' exclaimed the lady.

'Well, well, poor Will was a good lad—a thought melancholy

IVANHOE IN THE HALL OF HIS FATHERS

and milksop though.   Why, a pint of sack fuddled his poor brains.'

'Sir Wilfrid of Ivanhoe was a good lance,' said the friar.   'I have heard there was none better in Christendom.   He lay in our convent after his wounds, and it was there we tended him till he died.   He was buried in our north cloister.'

'And there's an end of him,' said Athelstane.   'But come, this is dismal talk.   Where's Wamba the jester?   Let us have a song.   Stir up, Wamba, and don't lie like a dog in the fire!   Sing us a song, thou crack-brained jester, and leave off whimpering for bygones.   Tush, man!   There be many good fellows left in this world.'

'There be buzzards in eagles' nests,' Wamba said, who was lying stretched before the fire, sharing the hearth with the Thane's dogs.   'There be dead men alive and live men dead.   There be merry songs and dismal songs.   Marry, and the merriest are the saddest sometimes.   I will leave off motley and wear black, gossip Athelstane.   I will turn howler at funerals, and then, perhaps, I shall be merry.   Motley is fit for mutes, and black for fools.   Give me some drink, gossip, for my voice is as cracked as my brain.'

'Drink and sing, thou beast, and cease prating,' the Thane said.

And Wamba, touching his rebeck wildly, sat up in the chimney-side and curled his lean shanks together and began :—

LOVE AT TWO SCORE

Ho! pretty page, with dimpled chin,
  That never has known the barber's shear,
All your aim is woman to win.
This is the way that boys begin.
  Wait till you've come to forty year!

Curly gold locks cover foolish brains,
  Billing and cooing is all your cheer,
Sighing and singing of midnight strains
Under Bonnybells' window-panes.
  Wait till you've come to forty year!

Forty times over let Michaelmas pass,
  Grizzling hair the brain doth clear;
Then you know a boy is an ass,
Then you know the worth of a lass,
  Once you have come to forty year.

Pledge me round, I bid ye declare,
  All good fellows whose beards are grey;
Did not the fairest of the fair
Common grow and wearisome, ere
  Ever a month was past away?

I

The reddest lips that ever have kissed,
    The brightest eyes that ever have shone,
May pray and whisper and we not list,
Or look away and never be missed,
    Ere yet ever a month was gone.

Gillian's dead, Heaven rest her bier,
    How I loved her twenty years' syne !
Marian's married, but I sit here,
Alive and merry at forty year,
    Dipping my nose in the Gascon wine.

'Who taught thee that merry lay, Wamba, thou son of
Witless ?' roared Athelstane, clattering his cup on the table and
shouting the chorus.

'It was a good and holy hermit, sir, the pious clerk of
Copmanhurst, that you wot of, who played many a prank with us
in the days that we knew King Richard.   Ah, noble sir, that was
a jovial time and a good priest.'

'They say the holy priest is sure of the next bishopric, my
love,' said Rowena.   'His Majesty hath taken him into much
favour.   My Lord of Huntingdon looked very well at the last
ball, though I never could see any beauty in the Countess—a
freckled, blowsy thing, whom they used to call Maid Marian ;
though, for the matter of that, what between her flirtations with
Major Littlejohn and Captain Scarlett, really——'

'Jealous again—haw ! haw !' laughed Athelstane.

'I am above jealousy, and scorn it,' Rowena answered, drawing
herself up very majestically.

'Well, well, Wamba's was a good song,' Athelstane said.

'Nay, a wicked song,' said Rowena, turning up her eyes as
usual.   'What ! rail at woman's love ?   Prefer a filthy wine-cup
to a true wife ?   Woman's love is eternal, my Athelstane.   He
who questions it would be a blasphemer were he not a fool.   The
well-born and well-nurtured gentlewoman loves once and once only.'

'I pray you, madam, pardon me, I—I am not well,' said the
grey friar, rising abruptly from his settle, and tottering down the
steps of the dais.   Wamba sprung after him, his bells jingling as
he rose, and casting his arms round the apparently fainting man,
he led him away into the court.   'There be dead men alive and
live men dead,' whispered he.   'There be coffins to laugh at and
marriages to cry over.   Said I not sooth, holy friar ?'   And when
they had got out into the solitary court, which was deserted by all
the followers of the Thane, who were mingling in the drunken
revelry in the hall, Wamba, seeing that none were by, knelt down,
and kissing the friar's garment, said, 'I knew thee, I knew thee,
my lord and my liege !'

'Get up,' said Wilfrid of Ivanhoe, scarcely able to articulate; 'only fools are faithful.'

And he passed on and into the little chapel where his father lay buried. All night long the friar spent there, and Wamba the Jester lay outside watching as mute as the saint over the porch.

When the morning came, Wamba was gone; and the knave being in the habit of wandering hither and thither as he chose, little notice was taken of his absence by a master and mistress who had not much sense of humour. As for Sir Wilfrid, a gentleman of his delicacy of feelings could not be expected to remain in a house where things so naturally disagreeable to him were occurring, and he quitted Rotherwood incontinently, after paying a dutiful visit to the tomb where his old father, Cedric, was buried, and hastened on to York, at which city he made himself known to the family attorney, a most respectable man, in whose hands his ready money was deposited, and took up a sum sufficient to fit himself out with credit, and a handsome retinue, as became a knight of consideration. But he changed his name, wore a wig and spectacles, and disguised himself entirely, so that it was impossible his friends or the public should know him, and thus metamorphosed, went about whithersoever his fancy led him. He was present at a public ball at York, which the Lord Mayor gave, danced Sir Roger de Coverley in the very same set with Rowena—(who was disgusted that Maid Marian took precedence of her)—he saw little Athelstane overeat himself at the supper, and pledged his big father in a cup of sack; he met the Reverend Mr. Tuck at a missionary meeting, where he seconded a resolution proposed by that eminent divine;—in fine, he saw a score of his old acquaintances, none of whom recognised in him the warrior of Palestine and Templestowe. Having a large fortune and nothing to do, he went about this country performing charities, slaying robbers, rescuing the distressed, and achieving noble feats of arms. Dragons and giants existed in his day no more, or be sure he would have had a fling at them: for the truth is, Sir Wilfrid of Ivanhoe was somewhat sick of the life which the hermits of Chalus had restored to him, and felt himself so friendless and solitary that he would not have been sorry to come to an end of it. Ah, my dear friends and intelligent British public, are there not others who are melancholy under a mask of gaiety, and who, in the midst of crowds, are lonely? Liston was a most melancholy man; Grimaldi had feelings; and there are others I wot of—but psha! —let us have the next chapter.

CHAPTER V

THE rascally manner in which the chicken-livered successor of Richard of the Lion-heart conducted himself to all parties, to his relatives, his nobles, and his people, is a matter notorious, and set forth clearly in the Historic Page : hence, although nothing, except perhaps success, can, in my opinion, excuse disaffection to the Sovereign, or appearance in armed rebellion against him, the loyal reader will make allowance for two of the principal personages of this narrative, who will have to appear in the present chapter in the odious character of rebels to their lord and king. It must be remembered, in partial exculpation of the fault of Ivanhoe and Rowena (a fault for which they were bitterly punished, as you shall presently hear), that the Monarch exasperated his subjects in a variety of ways,—that before he murdered his royal nephew, Prince Arthur, there was a great question whether he was the rightful King of England at all,—that his behaviour as an uncle, and a family man, was likely to wound the feelings of any lady and mother,—finally, that there were palliations for the conduct of Rowena and Ivanhoe, which it now becomes our duty to relate.

When his Majesty destroyed Prince Arthur, the Lady Rowena, who was one of the ladies of honour to the Queen, gave up her place at Court at once, and retired to her castle of Rotherwood. Expressions made use of by her, and derogatory to the character of the Sovereign, were carried to the Monarch's ears by some of those parasites, doubtless, by whom it is the curse of kings to be attended ; and John swore, by St. Peter's teeth, that he would be revenged upon the haughty Saxon lady,—a kind of oath which, though he did not trouble himself about all other oaths, he was never known to break. It was not for some years after he had registered this vow, that he was enabled to keep it.

Had Ivanhoe been present at Rouen when the King meditated his horrid designs against his nephew, there is little doubt that Sir Wilfrid would have prevented them, and rescued the boy : for

Ivanhoe was, we need scarcely say, a hero of romance; and it is the custom and duty of all gentlemen of that profession to be present on all occasions of historic interest, to be engaged in all conspiracies, royal interviews, and remarkable occurrences,—and hence Sir Wilfrid would certainly have rescued the young Prince, had he been anywhere in the neighbourhood of Rouen, where the foul tragedy occurred. But he was a couple of hundred leagues off, at Chalus, when the circumstance happened: tied down in his bed as crazy as a Bedlamite, and raving ceaselessly in the Hebrew tongue, which he had caught up during a previous illness in which he was tended by a maiden of that nation, about a certain Rebecca Ben Isaacs, of whom, being a married man, he never would have thought, had he been in his sound senses. During this delirium, what were Politics to him, or he to Politics? King John or King Arthur were entirely indifferent to a man who announced to his nurse-tenders, the good hermits of Chalus before mentioned, that he was the Marquis of Jericho, and about to marry Rebecca the Queen of Sheba. In a word, he only heard of what had occurred when he reached England, and his senses were restored to him. Whether was he happier, sound of brain and entirely miserable (as any man would be who found so admirable a wife as Rowena married again), or perfectly crazy, the husband of the beautiful Rebecca? I don't know which he liked best.

Howbeit the conduct of King John inspired Sir Wilfrid with so thorough a detestation of that Sovereign, that he never could be brought to take service under him; to get himself presented at St. James's, or in any way to acknowledge, but by stern acquiescence, the authority of the sanguinary successor of his beloved King Richard. It was Sir Wilfrid of Ivanhoe, I need scarcely say, who got the Barons of England to league together and extort from the King that famous instrument and palladium of our liberties at present in the British Museum, Great Russell Street, Bloomsbury —the MAGNA CHARTA. His name does not naturally appear in the list of Barons, because he was only a knight, and a knight in disguise too: nor does Athelstane's signature figure on that document. Athelstane, in the first place, could not write; nor did he care a pennypiece about politics, so long as he could drink his wine at home undisturbed, and have his hunting and shooting in quiet.

It was not until the King wanted to interfere with the sport of every gentleman in England (as we know by reference to the Historic Page that this odious monarch did), that Athelstane broke out into open rebellion, along with several Yorkshire squires and noblemen. It is recorded of the King, that he forbade every man to hunt his own deer ; and, in order to secure an obedience to his orders, this Herod of a monarch wanted to secure the eldest sons of all the nobility and gentry, as hostages for the good behaviour of their parents.

Athelstane was anxious about his game—Rowena was anxious about her son. The former swore that he would hunt his deer in spite of all Norman tyrants—the latter asked, should she give up her boy to the ruffian who had murdered his own nephew ?[1] The speeches of both were brought to the King at York ; and, furious, he ordered an instant attack upon Rotherwood, and that the lord and lady of that castle should be brought before him dead or alive.

Ah, where was Wilfrid of Ivanhoe, the unconquerable champion, to defend the castle against the royal party ? A few thrusts from his lance would have spitted the leading warriors of the King's host : a few cuts from his sword would have put John's forces to rout. But the lance and sword of Ivanhoe were idle on this occasion. 'No, be hanged to me !' said the knight bitterly, '*this* is a quarrel in which I can't interfere. Common politeness forbids. Let yonder ale-swilling Athelstane defend his—ha, ha—*wife ;* and my Lady Rowena guard her—ha, ha, ha—*son.*' And he laughed wildly and madly ; and the sarcastic way in which he choked and gurgled out the words ' wife ' and ' son ' would have made you shudder to hear.

When he heard, however, that, on the fourth day of the siege, Athelstane had been slain by a cannon ball (and this time for good, and not to come to life again as he had done before), and that the widow (if so the innocent bigamist may be called) was conducting the defence of Rotherwood herself with the greatest intrepidity, showing herself upon the walls with her little son (who bellowed like a bull, and did not like the fighting at all), pointing the guns and encouraging the garrison in every way—better feelings returned to the bosom of the knight of Ivanhoe, and summoning his men, he armed himself quickly, and determined to go forth to the rescue.

He rode without stopping for two days and two nights in the direction of Rotherwood, with such swiftness and disregard for refreshment, indeed, that his men dropped one by one upon the road, and he arrived alone at the lodge-gate of the park. The windows were smashed ; the door stove in ; the lodge, a neat little Swiss cottage, with a garden where the pinafores of Mrs. Gurth's children might have been seen hanging on the gooseberry bushes in

[1] See Hume, Giraldus Cambrensis, The Monk of Croyland, and Pinnock's Catechism.

more peaceful times, was now a ghastly heap of smoking ruins—cottage, bushes, pinafores, children lay mangled together, destroyed by the licentious soldiery of an infuriate monarch! Far be it from me to excuse the disobedience of Athelstane and Rowena to their Sovereign; but surely, surely this cruelty might have been spared.

Gurth, who was lodge-keeper, was lying dreadfully wounded and expiring at the flaming and violated threshold of his lately picturesque home. A catapult and a couple of mangonels had done his business. The faithful fellow, recognising his master, who had put up his visor and forgotten his wig and spectacles in the agitation of the moment, exclaimed, 'Sir Wilfrid! my dear master—praised be St. Waltheof—there may be yet time—my beloved mistr—master Athelst . . .' He sank back, and never spoke again.

Ivanhoe spurred on his horse Bavieca madly up the chestnut avenue. The castle was before him; the western tower was in flames; the besiegers were pressing at the southern gate; Athelstane's banner, the bull rampant, was still on the northern bartizan. 'An Ivanhoe, an Ivanhoe!' he bellowed out, with a shout that overcame all the din of battle—Nostre Dame a la rescousse—and to hurl his lance through the midriff of Reginald de Bracy, who was commanding the assault, who fell howling with anguish, to wave his battle-axe over his own head, and cut off those of thirteen men-at-arms, was the work of an instant. 'An Ivanhoe, an Ivanhoe!' he still shouted, and down went a man as sure as he said 'hoe!'

'Ivanhoe! Ivanhoe!' a shrill voice cried from the top of the northern bartizan. Ivanhoe knew it.

'Rowena! my love! I come!' he roared on his part. 'Villains! touch but a hair of her head, and I . . .'

Here, with a sudden plunge and a squeal of agony, Bavieca sprang forward wildly, and fell as wildly on her back, rolling over and over upon the knight. All was dark before him; his brain reeled; it whizzed; something came crashing down on his forehead. St. Waltheof, and all the saints of the Saxon calendar protect the knight! * * *

When he came to himself, Wamba and the lieutenant of his lances were leaning over him with a bottle of the hermit's elixir. 'We arrived here the day after the battle,' said the fool; 'marry, I have a knack of that.'

'Your worship rode so deucedly quick, there was no keeping up with your worship,' said the lieutenant.

'The day—after—the bat—' groaned Ivanhoe.—'Where is the Lady Rowena?'

'The castle has been taken and sacked,' the lieutenant said, —and pointed to what once *was* Rotherwood, but was now only a heap of smoking ruins.—Not a tower was left, not a roof, not a floor, not a single human being! Everything was flame and ruin, smash and murther!

Of course Ivanhoe fell back fainting again among the ninety-seven men-at-arms whom he had slain; and it was not until Wamba had applied a second, and uncommonly strong, dose of the elixir that he came to life again. The good knight was, however, from long practice, so accustomed to the severest wounds, that he bore them far more easily than common folk, and thus was enabled to reach York upon a litter, which his men constructed for him, with tolerable ease.

Rumour had as usual advanced him; and he heard at the hotel where he stopped, what had been the issue of the affair at Rotherwood. A minute or two after his horse was stabbed, and Ivanhoe knocked down, the western bartizan was taken by the storming party which invested it, and every soul slain, except Rowena and her boy, who were tied upon horses and carried away, under a secure guard, to one of the King's castles—nobody knew whither—and Ivanhoe was recommended by the hotel-keeper (whose house he had used in former times) to reassume his wig and spectacles, and not call himself by his own name any more, lest some of the King's people should lay hands on him. However, as he had killed everybody round about him, there was but little danger of his discovery; and the Knight of the Spectacles, as he was called, went about York quite unmolested, and at liberty to attend to his own affairs.

We wish to be brief in narrating this part of the gallant hero's existence; for his life was one of feeling rather than affection, and the description of mere sentiment is considered by many well-informed persons to be tedious. What *were* his sentiments, now it may be asked, under the peculiar position in which he found himself? He had done his duty by Rowena, certainly: no man could say otherwise. But as for being in love with her any more, after what had occurred, that was a different question. Well, come what would, he was determined still to continue doing his duty by her;—but as she was whisked away, the deuce knew whither, how could he do anything? So he resigned himself to the fact that she was thus whisked away.

He, of course, sent emissaries about the country to endeavour to find out where Rowena was; but these came back without any sort of intelligence; and it was remarked, that he still remained in a perfect state of resignation. He remained in this condition for a year, or more ; and it was said that he was becoming more cheerful, and he certainly was growing rather fat. The Knight of the Spectacles was voted an agreeable man in a grave way ; and gave some very elegant, though quiet parties, and was received in the best society of York.

It was just at assize-time, the lawyers and barristers had arrived, and the town was unusually gay ; when, one morning, the attorney, whom we have mentioned as Sir Wilfrid's man of business, and a most respectable man, called upon his gallant client at his lodgings, and said he had a communication of importance to make. Having to communicate with a client of rank, who was condemned to be hanged for forgery, Sir Hugo de Backbite, the attorney said, he had been to visit that party in the condemned cell ; and on the way through the yard, and through the bars of another cell, had seen and recognised an old acquaintance of Sir Wilfrid of Ivanhoe —and the lawyer held him out, with a particular look, a note, written on a piece of whity-brown paper.

What were Ivanhoe's sensations when he recognised the hand-writing of Rowena !—he tremblingly dashed open the billet, and read as follows :—

'MY DEAREST IVANHOE,—For I am thine now as erst, and my first love for ever—ever dear to me. Have I been near thee dying for a whole year, and didst thou make no effort to rescue thy Rowena ? Have ye given to others—I mention not their name nor their odious creed—the heart that ought to be mine ? I send thee my forgiveness from my dying pallet of straw.—I forgive thee the insults I have received, the cold and hunger I have endured, the failing health of my boy, the bitterness of my prison, thy infatuation about that Jewess, which made our married life miserable, and which caused thee, I am sure, to go abroad to look after her. I forgive thee all my wrongs, and fain would bid thee farewell. Mr. Smith hath gained over my gaoler—he will tell thee how I may see thee.—Come and console my last hour by promising that thou wilt care for my boy—*his* boy who fell like a hero (when thou wert absent) combating by the side of

ROWENA.

The reader may consult his own feelings, and say whether Ivanhoe was likely to be pleased or not by this letter : however, he inquired of Mr. Smith, the solicitor, what was the plan which that gentleman had devised for the introduction to Lady Rowena, and was informed that he was to get a barrister's gown and wig, when the gaoler would introduce him into the interior of the prison. These decorations, knowing several gentlemen of the Northern Circuit, Sir Wilfrid of Ivanhoe easily procured, and, with feelings of no small trepidation, reached the cell where, for the space of a year, poor Rowena had been immured.

If any person have a doubt of the correctness, of the historical exactness, of this narrative, I refer him to the *Biographie Universelle* (article 'Jean sans Terre'), which says, 'La femme d'un baron auquel on vint demander son fils, répondit, "Le roi pense-t-il que je confierai mon fils à un homme qui a égorgé son neveu de sa propre main ?" Jean fit enlever la mère et l'enfant, et la laissa *mourir de faim* dans les cachots.'

I picture to myself, with a painful sympathy, Rowena undergoing this disagreeable sentence. All her virtues, her resolution, her chaste energy and perseverance, shine with redoubled lustre, and, for the first time since the commencement of the history, I feel that I am partially reconciled to her. The weary year passes —she grows weaker and more languid, thinner and thinner ! At length Ivanhoe, in the disguise of a barrister of the Northern Circuit, is introduced to her cell, and finds his lady in the last stage of exhaustion, on the straw of her dungeon, with her little boy in her arms. She has preserved his life at the expense of her own, giving him the whole of the pittance which her gaolers allowed her, and perishing herself of inanition.

There is a scene ! I feel as if I had made it up, as it were, with this lady, and that we part in peace, in consequence of my providing her with so sublime a death-bed. Fancy Ivanhoe's entrance—their recognition—the faint blush upon her worn features—the pathetic way in which she gives little Cedric in charge to him, and his promises of protection.

'Wilfrid, my early loved,' slowly gasped she, removing her grey hair from her furrowed temples, and gazing on her boy fondly, as he nestled on Ivanhoe's knee—' promise me, by St. Waltheof of Templestowe—promise me one boon !'

'I do,' said Ivanhoe, clasping the boy, and thinking it was to that little innocent the promise was intended to apply.

'By St. Waltheof ?'

'By St. Waltheof !'

'Promise me, then,' gasped Rowena, staring wildly at him, 'that you never will marry a Jewess ?

'By St. Waltheof,' cried Ivanhoe, 'this is too much ! Rowena !' But he felt his hand grasped for a moment, the nerves then relaxed, the pale lip ceased to quiver—she was no more !

IVANHOE RANSOMS A JEW'S GRINDERS

CHAPTER VI

HAVING placed young Cedric at school at the Hall of Dotheboyes, in Yorkshire, and arranged his family affairs, Sir Wilfrid of Ivanhoe quitted a country which had no longer any charms for him, and in which his stay was rendered the less agreeable by the notion that King John would hang him, if ever he could lay hands on the faithful follower of King Richard and Prince Arthur.

But there was always in those days a home and occupation for a brave and pious knight. A saddle on a gallant war-horse, a pitched field against the Moors, a lance wherewith to spit a turbaned infidel, or a road to Paradise carved out by his scimetar, —these were the height of the ambition of good and religious warriors ; and so renowned a champion as Sir Wilfrid of Ivanhoe was sure to be well received wherever blows were stricken for the cause of Christendom. Even among the dark Templars, he who had twice overcome the most famous lance of their Order was a respected though not a welcome guest : but among the opposition company of the Knights of St. John, he was admired and courted beyond measure ; and always affectioning that Order, which offered him, indeed, its first rank and commanderies, he did much good service, fighting in their ranks for the glory of Heaven and St. Waltheof, and slaying many thousands of the heathen in Prussia, Poland, and those savage northern countries. The only fault that the great and gallant, though severe and ascetic Folko of Heydenbraten, the chief of the Order of St. John, found with the melancholy warrior, whose lance did such good service to the cause, was, that he did not persecute the Jews as so religious a knight should. He let off sundry captives of that persuasion whom he had taken with his sword and his spear, saved others from torture, and actually ransomed the two last grinders of a venerable rabbi (that Roger de Cartright, an English knight of the Order, was about to extort from the elderly Israelite) with a hundred crowns and a gimmal ring, which were all the property he possessed. Whenever he so ransomed or benefited one of this religion, he would moreover give them a little token or a message (were the good knight out of money), saying, 'Take this token, and remember this deed was done by Wilfrid the Disinherited, for the services whilome rendered to him by Rebecca, the daughter of Isaac of York ?' So among themselves, and in their meetings and synagogues, and in their restless travels from land to land, when they of Jewry cursed and reviled all Christians, as such abominable heathens will, they nevertheless excepted the name of the Desdichado, or the doubly-disinherited as he now was, the Desdichado-Doblado.

The account of all the battles, storms, and scaladoes in which Sir Wilfrid took part, would only weary the reader ; for the chopping off one heathen's head with an axe must be very like the decapitation of any other unbeliever. Suffice it to say, that whereever this kind of work was to be done, and Sir Wilfrid was in the way, he was the man to perform it. It would astonish you were you to see the account that Wamba kept of his master's achievements, and of Bulgarians, Bohemians, Croatians, slain or maimed by his hand : and as, in those days, a reputation for valour had an immense effect upon the soft hearts of women, and even the ugliest man, were he a stout warrior, was looked upon with favour by Beauty ; so Ivanhoe, who was by no means ill-favoured, though now becoming rather elderly, made conquests over female breasts as well as over Saracens, and had more than one direct offer of marriage made to him by princesses, countesses, and noble ladies possessing both charms and money, which they were anxious to place at the disposal of a champion so renowned. It is related that the Duchess Regent of Kartoffelberg offered him her hand, and the Ducal Crown of Kartoffelberg, which he had rescued from the unbelieving Prussians ; but Ivanhoe evaded the Duchess's offer by riding away from her capital secretly at midnight, and hiding himself in a convent of Knights Hospitallers, on the borders of Poland ; and it is a fact that the Princess Rosalia Seraphina of Pumpernickel, the most lovely woman of her time, became so frantically attached to him, that she followed him on a campaign, and was discovered with his baggage disguised as a horse-boy. But no princess, no beauty, no female blandishments had any charms for Ivanhoe : no hermit practised a more austere celibacy. The severity of his morals contrasted so remarkably with the lax and dissolute manner of the young lords and nobles in the courts which he frequented, that these young springalds would sometimes sneer and call him Monk and Milksop ; but his courage in the day of battle was so terrible and admirable, that I promise you the youthful libertines did not sneer *then ;* and the most reckless of

IVANHOE SLAYING THE MOORS

them often turned pale when they couched their lances to follow Ivanhoe. Holy Waltheof! it was an awful sight to see him with his pale, calm face, his shield upon his breast, his heavy lance before him, charging a squadron of heathen Bohemians, or a regiment of Cossacks! Wherever he saw the enemy, Ivanhoe assaulted him; and when people remonstrated with him, and said if he attacked such and such a post, breach, castle, or army, he would be slain, 'And suppose I be?' he answered, giving them to understand that he would as lief the Battle of Life were over altogether.

While he was thus making war against the northern infidels, news was carried all over Christendom of a catastrophe which had befallen the good cause in the south of Europe, where the Spanish Christians had met with such a defeat and massacre at the hands of the Moors as had never been known in the proudest days of Saladin.

Thursday, the 9th of Shaban, in the 605th year of the Hejira, is known all over the West as the *amun-al-ark*, the year of the battle of Alarcos, gained over the Christians by the Moslems of Andalus, on which fatal day Christendom suffered a defeat so signal, that it was feared the Spanish peninsula would be entirely wrested away from the dominion of the Cross. On that day the Franks lost 150,000 men and 30,000 prisoners. A man-slave sold among the unbelievers for a dirhem; a donkey, for the same; a sword, half a dirhem; a horse, five dirhems. Hundreds of thousands of these various sorts of booty were in the possession of the triumphant followers of Yakoob-al-Mansoor. Curses on his head! But he was a brave warrior, and the Christians before him seemed to forget that they were the descendants of the brave Cid, the *Kanbitoor*, as the Moorish hounds (in their jargon) denominated the famous Campeador.

A general move for the rescue of the faithful in Spain—a crusade against the infidels triumphing there, was preached throughout all Europe by all the most eloquent clergy: and thousands and thousands of valorous knights and nobles, accompanied by well-meaning varlets and vassals of the lower sort, trooped from all sides to the rescue. The straits of Gibel-al-Tariff, at which spot the Moor, passing from Barbary, first planted his accursed foot on the Christian soil, were crowded with the galleys of the Templars and the knights of St. John, who flung succours into the menaced kingdoms of the peninsula; the inland sea swarmed with their ships hasting from their forts and islands, from Rhodes and Byzantium, from Jaffa and Askalon. The Pyrenean peaks beheld

the pennons and glittered with the armour of the knights marching out of France into Spain ; and, finally, in a ship that set sail
direct from Bohemia, where Sir Wilfrid happened to be quartered
at the time when the news of the defeat of Alarcos came and
alarmed all good Christians, Ivanhoe landed at Barcelona, and
proceeded to slaughter the Moors forthwith.

He brought letters of introduction from his friend Folko of
Heydenbraten, the Grand Master of the Knights of Saint John,
to the venerable Baldomero de Garbanzos; Grand Master of the
renowned order of Saint Jago. The chief of Saint Jago's knights
paid the greatest respect to a warrior, whose fame was already so
widely known in Christendom ; and Ivanhoe had the pleasure of
being appointed to all the posts of danger and forlorn hopes that
could be devised in his honour. He would be called up twice or
thrice in a night to fight the Moors : he led ambushes, scaled
breaches, was blown up by mines, was wounded many hundred
times (recovering, thanks to the elixir, of which Wamba always
carried a supply) ; he was the terror of the Saracens, and the
admiration and wonder of the Christians.

To describe his deeds would, I say, be tedious ; one day's battle
was like that of another. I am not writing in ten volumes like
Monsieur Alexandre Dumas, or even in three like other great
authors. We have no room for the recounting of Sir Wilfrid's
deeds of valour. Whenever he took a Moorish town, it was remarked, that he went anxiously into the Jewish quarter, and
inquired amongst the Hebrews, who were in great numbers in
Spain, for Rebecca, the daughter of Isaac. Many Jews, according
to his wont, he ransomed, and created so much scandal by this
proceeding, and by the manifest favour which he showed to the
people of the nation, that the Master of Saint Jago remonstrated
with him, and it is probable he would have been cast into the
Inquisition and roasted, but that his prodigious valour and success
against the Moors counterbalanced his heretical partiality for the
children of Jacob.

It chanced that the good knight was present at the siege of
Xixona in Andalusia, entering the breach the first, according to his
wont, and slaying, with his own hand, the Moorish lieutenant of
the town, and several hundred more of its unbelieving defenders.
He had very nearly done for the Alfaqui, or governor, a veteran
warrior with a crooked scimetar and a beard as white as snow,
but a couple of hundred of the Alfaqui's bodyguard flung themselves between Ivanhoe and their chief, and the old fellow escaped
with his life, leaving a handful of his beard in the grasp of the
English knight. The strictly military business being done, and

A GAME AT CHESS

such of the garrison as did not escape put, as by right, to the sword, the good knight, Sir Wilfrid of Ivanhoe, took no further part in the proceedings of the conquerors of that ill-fated place. A scene of horrible massacre and frightful reprisals ensued, and the Christian warriors, hot with victory and flushed with slaughter, were, it is to be feared, as savage in their hour of triumph as ever their heathen enemies had been.

Among the most violent and least scrupulous was the ferocious knight of Saint Jago, Don Beltran de Cuchilla y Trabuco y Espada y Espelon. Raging through the vanquished city like a demon, he slaughtered indiscriminately all those infidels of both sexes whose wealth did not tempt him to a ransom, or whose beauty did not reserve them for more frightful calamities than death. The slaughter over, Don Beltran took up his quarters in the Albaycen, where the Alfaqui had lived who had so narrowly escaped the sword of Ivanhoe; but the wealth, the treasure, the slaves, and the family of the fugitive chieftain, were left in possession of the conqueror of Xixona. Among the treasures Don Beltran recognised with a savage joy the coat-armours and ornaments of many brave and unfortunate companions-in-arms who had fallen in the fatal battle of Alarcos. The sight of those bloody relics added fury to his cruel disposition, and served to steel a heart already but little disposed to sentiments of mercy.

Three days after the sack and plunder of the place, Don Beltran was seated in the hall-court lately occupied by the proud Alfaqui, lying in his divan, dressed in his rich robes, the fountains playing in the centre, the slaves of the Moor ministering to his scarred and rugged Christian conqueror. Some fanned him with peacocks' pinions, some danced before him, some sang Moors' melodies to the plaintive notes of a guzla, one—it was the only daughter of the Moor's old age, the young Zutulbe, a rosebud of beauty—sat weeping in a corner of the gilded hall, weeping for her slain brethren, the pride of Moslem chivalry, whose heads were blackening in the blazing sunshine on the portals without, and for her father, whose home had been thus made desolate.

He and his guest, the English knight Sir Wilfrid, were playing at chess, a favourite amusement with the chivalry of the period, when a messenger was announced from Valencia, to treat, if possible, for the ransom of the remaining part of the Alfaqui's family. A grim smile lighted up Don Beltran's features as he bade the black slave admit the messenger. He entered. By his costume it was at once seen that the bearer of the flag of truce was a Jew—the people were employed continually then as ambassadors between the two races at war in Spain.

'I come,' said the old Jew (in a voice which made Sir Wilfrid start), 'from my lord the Alfaqui to my noble señor, the invincible Don Beltran de Cuchilla, to treat for the ransom of the Moor's only daughter, the child of his old age and the pearl of his affection.'

'A pearl is a valuable jewel, Hebrew. What does the Moorish dog bid for her?' asked Don Beltran, still smiling grimly.

'The Alfaqui offers 100,000 dinars, twenty-four horses with their caparisons, twenty-four suits of plate-armour, and diamonds and rubies to the amount of 1,000,000 dinars.'

'Ho, slaves!' roared Don Beltran, 'show the Jew my treasury of gold. How many hundred thousand pieces are there?' And ten enormous chests were produced in which the accountant counted 1000 bags of 1000 dirhems each, and displayed several caskets of jewels containing such a treasure of rubies, smaragds, diamonds, and jacinths as made the eyes of the aged ambassador twinkle with avarice.

'How many horses are there in my stable?' continued Don Beltran; and Muley, the master of the horse, numbered three hundred fully caparisoned; and there was, likewise, armour of the richest sort for as many cavaliers, who followed the banner of this doughty captain.

'I want neither money nor armour,' said the ferocious knight; 'tell this to the Alfaqui, Jew. And I will keep the child, his daughter, to serve the messes for my dogs, and clean the platters for my scullions.'

'Deprive not the old man of his child,' here interposed the knight of Ivanhoe; 'bethink thee, brave Don Beltran, she is but an infant in years.'

'She is my captive, Sir Knight,' replied the surly Don Beltran; 'I will do with my own as becomes me.'

'Take 200,000 dirhems!' cried the Jew; 'more! anything! The Alfaqui will give his life for his child!'

'Come hither, Zutulbe!——come hither, thou Moorish pearl!' yelled the ferocious warrior; 'come closer, my pretty black-eyed houri of heathenesse! Hast heard the name of Beltran de Espada y Trabuco?'

'There were three brothers of that name at Alarcos, and my brothers slew the Christian dogs!' said the proud young girl, looking boldly at Don Beltran, who foamed with rage.

'The Moors butchered my mother and her little ones at midnight, in our castle of Murcia,' Beltran said.

'Thy father fled like a craven, as thou didst, Don Beltran!' cried the high-spirited girl.

'By Saint Jago, this is too much!' screamed the infuriated

nobleman ; and the next moment there was a shriek, and the maiden fell to the ground with Don Beltran's dagger in her side.

'Death is better than dishonour !' cried the child, rolling on the blood-stained marble pavement. 'I—I spit upon thee, dog of a Christian !' and with this, and with a savage laugh, she fell back and died.

'Bear back this news, Jew, to the Alfaqui,' howled the Don, spurning the beauteous corpse with his foot. 'I would not have ransomed her for all the gold in Barbary !' And shuddering, the old Jew left the apartment, which Ivanhoe quitted likewise.

When they were in the outer court, the knight said to the Jew, 'ISAAC OF YORK, dost thou not know me ?' and threw back his hood, and looked at the old man.

The old Jew stared wildly, rushed forward, as if to seize his hand, then started back, trembling convulsively, and clutching his withered hands over his face, said, with a burst of grief, 'Sir Wilfrid of Ivanhoe !—no, no !—I do not know thee !'

'Holy mother ! what has chanced ?' said Ivanhoe, in his turn becoming ghastly pale; 'where is thy daughter—where is Rebecca ?'

'Away from me !' said the old Jew, tottering, 'away ! REBECCA IS—DEAD !'

     *   *   *   *   *

When the Disinherited Knight heard that fatal announcement, he fell to the ground senseless, and was for some days as one perfectly distraught with grief. He took no nourishment and uttered no word. For weeks he did not relapse out of his moody silence, and when he came partially to himself again, it was to bid his people to horse, in a hollow voice, and to make a foray against the Moors. Day after day he issued out against these infidels, and did nought but slay and slay. He took no plunder as other knights did, but left that to his followers ; he uttered no war-cry, as was the manner of chivalry, and he gave no quarter, insomuch that the 'silent knight' became the dread of all the Paynims of Granada and Andalusia, and more fell by his lance than by that of any the most clamorous captain of the troops in arms against them. Thus the tide of battle turned, and the Arab historian El Makary recounts how, at the great battle of Al Akab, called by the Spaniards Las Navas, the Christians retrieved their defeat at Alarcos, and absolutely killed half a million of Mahometans. Fifty thousand of these, of course, Don Wilfrid took to his own lance ; and it was remarked that the melancholy warrior seemed somewhat more easy in spirits after that famous feat of arms.

CHAPTER VII

THE END OF THE PERFORMANCE

In a short time the redoubtable knight, Wilfrid of Ivanhoe, had killed off so many of the Moors, that though those unbelieving miscreants poured continual reinforcements into Spain from Barbary, they could make no head against the Christian forces, and in fact came into battle quite discouraged at the notion of meeting the dreadful silent knight. It was commonly believed amongst them, that the famous Malek Ric Richard of England, the conqueror of Saladin, had come to life again, and was battling in the Spanish hosts—that this, his second life was a charmed one, and his body inaccessible to blow of scimetar or thrust of spear—that after battle he ate the hearts and drank the blood of many young Moors for his supper: a thousand wild legends were told of Ivanhoe, indeed, so that the Morisco warriors came half-vanquished into the field, and fell an easy prey to the Spaniards, who cut away among them without mercy. And although none of the Spanish historians whom I have consulted make mention of Sir Wilfrid as the real author of the numerous triumphs which now graced the arms of the good cause, this is not in the least to be wondered at in a nation that has always been notorious for bragging, and for the non-payment of their debts of gratitude as of their other obligations, and that writes histories of the Peninsular war with the Emperor Napoleon, without making the slightest mention of his Grace the Duke of Wellington, or of the part taken by BRITISH VALOUR in that transaction. Well, it must be confessed, on the other hand, that we brag enough of our fathers' feats in those campaigns ; but this is not the subject at present under consideration.

To be brief, Ivanhoe made such short work with the unbelievers, that the monarch of Aragon, King Don Jayme, saw himself speedily enabled to besiege the city of Valencia, the last stronghold which the Moors had in his dominions, and garrisoned by many thousands of those infidels under the command of their King Aboo Abdallah Mahommed, son of Yakoob Almansoor. The Arabian historian El Makary gives a full account of the military precautions taken by Aboo Abdallah to defend his city, but as I do not wish to make a parade of my learning, or to write a costume novel, I shall pretermit any description of the city under its Moorish governors.

Besides the Turks who inhabited it, there dwelt within its walls great store of those of the Hebrew nation, who were always protected by the Moors during their unbelieving reign in Spain; and who were, as we very well know, the chief physicians, the chief bankers, the chief statesmen, the chief artists and musicians, the chief everything, under the Moorish kings. Thus it is not surprising that the Hebrews, having their money, their liberty, their teeth, their lives, secure under the Mahometan domination, should infinitely prefer it to the Christian sway, beneath which they were liable to be deprived of every one of these benefits.

Among these Hebrews of Valencia, lived a very ancient Israelite, —no other than Isaac of York, before mentioned, who came into Spain with his daughter, soon after Ivanhoe's marriage, in the third volume of the first part of this history. Isaac was respected by his people for the money which he possessed, and his daughter for her admirable good qualities, her beauty, her charities, and her remarkable medical skill.

The young Emir Aboo Abdallah was so struck by her charms, that though she was considerably older than his Highness, he offered to marry her, and instal her as Number 1 of his wives,—and Isaac of York would not have objected to the union (for such mixed marriages were not uncommon between the Hebrews and Moors those days),—but Rebecca firmly, but respectfully, declined the proposals of the Prince, saying that it was impossible she should unite herself with a man of a creed different to her own.

Although Isaac was, probably, not over well pleased at losing this chance of being father-in-law to a Royal Highness, yet as he passed among his people for a very strict character, and there were in his family several rabbis of great reputation and severity of conduct, the old gentleman was silenced by this objection of Rebecca's, and the young lady herself applauded by her relatives for her resolute behaviour. She took their congratulations in a very frigid manner, and said that it was her wish not to marry at all, but to devote herself to the practice of medicine altogether, and to helping the sick and needy of her people. Indeed, although she did not go to any public meetings, she was as benevolent a creature as the world ever saw : the poor blessed her wherever they knew her, and many benefited by her who guessed not whence her gentle bounty came.[1]

[1] Though I am writing but a Christmas farce, I hope the kind-hearted reader will excuse me for saying that I am thinking of the beautiful life and death of Adelaide the Queen.

But there are men in Jewry who admire beauty, and, as I have even heard, appreciate money too, and Rebecca had such a quantity of both that all the most desirable bachelors of the people were ready to bid for her. Ambassadors came from all quarters to propose for her. Her own uncle, the venerable Ben Solomons, with a beard as long as a Cashmere goat, and a reputation for learning and piety which still lives in his nation, quarrelled with his son Moses, the red-haired diamond merchant of Trebizond, and his son Simeon, the bald bill-broker of Bagdad, each putting in a claim for their cousin. Ben Minories came from London, and knelt at her feet; Ben Jochanan arrived from Paris, and thought to dazzle her with the latest waistcoats from the Palais Royal; and Ben Jonah brought her a present of Dutch herrings, and besought her to come back and be Mrs. Ben Jonah at the Hague.

Rebecca temporised as best she might. She thought her uncle was too old. She besought dear Moses and dear Simeon not to quarrel with each other, and offend their father by pressing their suit. Ben Minories, from London, she said, was too young, and Jochanan from Paris, she pointed out to Isaac of York, must be a spendthrift, or he would not wear those absurd waistcoats. As for Ben Jonah, she said she could not bear the notion of tobacco and Dutch herrings—she wished to stay with her papa, her dear papa. In fine, she invented a thousand excuses for delay, and it was plain that marriage was odious to her. The only man whom she received with anything like favour, was young Bevis Marks of London, with whom she was very familiar. But Bevis had come to her with a certain token that had been given to him by an English knight, who saved him from a faggot to which the ferocious Hospitaller Folko of Heydenbraten was about to condemn him. It was but a ring, with an emerald in it, that Bevis knew to be sham, and not worth a groat. Rebecca knew about the value of jewels too; but ah! she valued this one more than all the diamonds in Prester John's turban. She kissed it; she cried over it; she wore it in her bosom always; and when she knelt down at night and morning, she held it between her folded hands on her neck. . . . Young Bevis Marks went away finally no better off than the others; the rascal sold to the King of France a handsome ruby, the very size of the bit of glass in Rebecca's ring; but he always said he would rather have had her than ten thousand pounds, and very likely he would, for it was known she would at once have a plumb to her fortune.

These delays, however, could not continue for ever; and at a great family meeting held at Passover time, Rebecca was solemnly

ordered to choose a husband out of the gentlemen there present ;
her aunts pointing out the great kindness which had been shown
to her by her father, in permitting her to choose for herself.   One
aunt was of the Solomon faction, another aunt took Simeon's side,
a third most venerable old lady—the head of the family, and a
hundred and forty-four years of age—was ready to pronounce a
curse upon her, and cast her out, unless she married before the
month was over.   All the jewelled heads of all the old ladies in
council, all the beards of all the family wagged against her—it
must have been an awful sight to witness.

At last, then, Rebecca was forced to speak.   'Kinsmen!' she
said, turning pale, 'when the Prince Abou Abdil asked me in
marriage, I told you I would not wed but with one of my own
faith.'

'She has turned Turk,' screamed out the ladies.   'She wants
to be a princess, and has turned Turk,' roared the rabbis.

'Well, well,' said Isaac, in rather an appeased tone, 'let us
hear what the poor girl has got to say.   Do you want to marry
his Royal Highness, Rebecca ?   Say the word, yes or no.'

Another groan burst from the rabbis—they cried, shrieked,
chattered, gesticulated, furious to lose such a prize ; as were the
women, that she should reign over them, a second Esther.

'Silence,' cried out Isaac ; 'let the girl speak,—speak boldly,
Rebecca dear, there's a good girl.'

Rebecca was as pale as a stone.   She folded her arms on her
breast and felt the ring there.   She looked round all the assembly,
and then at Isaac.   'Father,' she said, in a thrilling low steady
voice, 'I am not of your religion—I am not of the Prince Boabdil's
religion—I—I am of *his* religion.'

'His ! whose ? in the name of Moses, girl,' cried Isaac.

Rebecca clasped her hands on her beating chest, and looked
round with dauntless eyes.   'Of his,' she said, 'who saved my
life and your honour, of my dear, dear champion's.   I never can
be his, but I will be no other's.   Give my money to my kinsmen ;
it is that they long for.   Take the dross, Simeon and Solomon,
Jonah and Jochanan, and divide it among you, and leave me.   I
will never be yours, I tell you, never.   Do you think, after knowing him and hearing him speak,—after watching him wounded on
his pillow, and glorious in battle ' (her eyes melted and kindled
again as she spoke these words), 'I can mate with such as *you ?*
Go.   Leave me to myself.   I am none of yours.   I love him, I
love him.   Fate divides us—long, long miles separate us ; and I
know we may never meet again.   But I love and bless him
always.   Yes, always.   My prayers are his ; my faith is his.

Yes, my faith is your faith, Wilfrid, Wilfrid! I have no kindred more,— I am a Christian!'. . .

At this last word there was such a row in the assembly, as my feeble pen would in vain endeavour to depict. Old Isaac staggered back in a fit, and nobody took the least notice of him. Groans, curses, yells of men, shrieks of women filled the room with such a furious jabbering, as might have appalled any heart less stout than Rebecca's; but that brave woman was prepared for all, expecting, and perhaps hoping, that death would be her instant lot. There was but one creature who pitied her, and that was her cousin and father's clerk, little Ben Davids, who was but thirteen, and had only just begun to carry a bag, and whose crying and boo-hooing, as she finished speaking, was drowned in the screams and maledictions of the elder Israelites. Ben Davids was madly in love with his cousin (as boys often are with ladies of twice their age), and he had presence of mind suddenly to knock over the large brazen lamp on the table, which illuminated the angry conclave, and whispering to Rebecca to go up to her own room and lock herself in, or they would kill her else, he took her hand and led her out.

From that day she disappeared from among her people. The poor and the wretched missed her, and asked for her in vain. Had any violence been done to her, the poorer Jews would have risen and put all Isaac's family to death; and besides, her old flame, Prince Boabdil, would have also been exceedingly wrathful. She was not killed then, but, so to speak, buried alive, and locked up in Isaac's back kitchen; an apartment into which scarcely any light entered, and where she was fed upon scanty portions of the most mouldy bread and water. Little Ben Davids was the only person who visited her, and her sole consolation was to talk to him about Ivanhoe, and how good and how gentle he was, how brave and how true; and how he slew the tremendous knight of the Templars, and how he married a lady whom Rebecca scarcely thought worthy of him, but with whom she prayed he might be happy; and of what colour his eyes were, and what were the arms on his shield, viz., a tree with the word 'Desdichado' written underneath, etc. etc. etc.; all which talk would not have interested little Davids, had it come from anybody else's mouth, but to which he never tired of listening as it fell from her sweet lips.

So, in fact, when old Isaac of York came to negotiate with Don Beltran de Cuchilla for the ransom of the Alfaqui's daughter of Xixona, our dearest Rebecca was no more dead than you and I; and it was in his rage and fury against Ivanhoe that Isaac told that cavalier the falsehood which caused the knight so much pain and such a prodigious deal of bloodshed to the Moors, and who knows, trivial as it may seem, whether it was not that very circumstance which caused the destruction in Spain of the Moorish power?

Although Isaac, we may be sure, never told his daughter that Ivanhoe had cast up again, yet Master Ben Davids did, who heard it from his employer; and he saved Rebecca's life by communicating the intelligence, for the poor thing would have infallibly perished but for this good news. She had now been in prison four years three months and twenty-four days, during which time she had partaken of nothing but bread and water (except such occasional tit-bits as Davids could bring her—and these were few indeed; for old Isaac was always a curmudgeon, and seldom had more than a pair of eggs for his own and Davids' dinner); and she was languishing away when the news came suddenly to revive her. Then, though in the darkness you could not see her cheeks, they began to bloom again: then her heart began to beat and her blood to flow, and she kissed the ring on her neck a thousand times a day at least; and her constant question was, 'Ben Davids! Ben Davids! when is He coming to besiege Valencia?' She knew he would come; and, indeed, the Christians were encamped before the town ere a month was over.

    *   *   *   *   *

And now, my dear boys and girls, I think I perceive behind that dark scene of the back kitchen (which is just a simple flat, painted stone-colour, that shifts in a minute) bright streaks of light flashing out, as though they were preparing a most brilliant, gorgeous, and altogether dazzling illumination, with effects never before attempted on any stage. Yes, the fairy in the pretty pink tights and spangled muslin is getting into the brilliant revolving chariot of the realms of bliss.—Yes, most of the fiddlers and trumpeters have gone round from the orchestra to join in the grand triumphal procession, where the whole strength of the company is already assembled, arrayed in costumes of Moorish and Christian chivalry, to celebrate the 'Terrible Escalade'—the 'Rescue of Virtuous Innocence'—the 'Grand Entry of the Christians into Valencia'—'Appearance of the Fairy Day-Star,' and 'Unexampled displays of pyrotechnic festivity.' Do you not, I say, perceive that we are come to the end of our history; and, after a quantity of rapid and terrific fighting, brilliant change of scenery, and songs, appropriate or otherwise, are bringing our hero and heroine together? Who wants a long scene at the last? Mammas are putting the girls' cloaks and boas on—papas have gone out to look for the carriage, and left the box-door swinging open, and letting in the cold air—if there *were* any stage-conversation, you could not hear it, for the scuffling of the people who are leaving the pit. See, the orange-women are preparing to retire. To-morrow their play-bills will be as so much waste-paper—so will some of our masterpieces, woe is me—but lo! here we come to Scene the last, and Valencia is besieged and captured by the Christians.

Who is the first on the wall, and who hurls down the green standard of the Prophet? Who chops off the head of the Emir Abou Whatdyecallem, just as the latter has cut over the cruel Don Beltran de Cuchilla y etc.? Who, attracted to the Jewish quarter by the shrieks of the inhabitants who are being slain by the Moorish soldiery, and by a little boy by the name of Ben Davids, who recognises the knight by his shield, finds Isaac of York *égorgé* on a threshold, and clasping a large back-kitchen key? Who but Ivanhoe—who but Wilfrid? 'An Ivanhoe to the rescue,' he bellows out; he has heard that news from little Ben Davids that makes him sing. And who is it that comes out of the house — trembling — panting—with her arms out—in a white dress—with her hair down—who is it but dear Rebecca! Look, they rush together, and Master Wamba is waving an immense banner over them, and knocks down a circumambient Jew with a ham, which he happens to have in his pocket. . . . As for Rebecca, now her head is laid upon Ivanhoe's heart: I shall not ask to hear what she is whispering, or describe further that scene of meeting, though I declare I am quite affected when I think of it. Indeed I have thought of it any time these five-and-twenty years —ever since, as a boy at school, I commenced the noble study of novels—ever since the day when, lying on sunny slopes of half-holidays, the fair chivalrous figures and beautiful shapes of knights and ladies were visible to me—ever since I grew to love Rebecca, that sweetest creature of the poet's fancy, and longed to see her righted.

That she and Ivanhoe were married follows of course; for Rowena's promise extorted from him was, that he would never wed a Jewess, and a better Christian than Rebecca now was never said her Catechism. Married I am sure they were, and adopted little Cedric; but I don't think they had any other children, or were subsequently very boisterously happy. Of some sort of happiness melancholy is a characteristic, and I think these were a solemn pair, and died rather early.

NOVELS BY EMINENT HANDS

PUNCH'S PRIZE NOVELISTS

PUNCH'S PRIZE NOVELISTS — so called because a TWENTY THOUSAND GUINEA PRIZE is to be awarded to the successful candidate—will embrace works by some of the most celebrated authors this country boasts of.

Their tales will appear in succession, and pretty continuously, in the pages of this Miscellany.

The publication will probably occupy about five-and-thirty years, or more or less, according to the reception with which the novels meet from our enlightened patrons—the generous British people.

All novels cannot be given entire, as a century would scarcely suffice, so numerous are our authors, so prolific and so eager has been the rush with stories, when our (confidential) announcement was sent into the literary world. But fair specimens of the authors' talents will be laid before the public, illustrated in our usual style of gorgeous splendour.

The first prize will be 20,000 guineas, viz., a lottery ticket to that amount, entitling the holder to the above sum or a palace at Vienna. The second prize will be the volume of *Punch* for the current half-year. The third a subscription to the British and Foreign Institute, etc., etc.

With a pride and gratification we cannot conceal, we at once introduce the public to GEORGE DE BARNWELL, by SIR E. L. B. L.BB LL. BBB. LLL., Bart.

We are not at liberty to reveal the gifted author's name, but the admirers of his works will no doubt recognise, in the splendid length of the words, the frequent employment of the Beautiful and the Ideal, the brilliant display of capitals, the profuse and profound classical learning, and, above all, in the announcement that this is to be the last of his works—one who has delighted us for many years.

GEORGE DE BARNWELL

In the Morning of Life the Truthful wooed the Beautiful, and their offspring was Love. Like his Divine parents, He is Eternal. He has his Mother's ravishing smile; his Father's steadfast eyes. He rises every day, fresh and glorious as the untired Sun-God. He is EROS, the ever young. Dark, dark were this world of ours hâd either Divinity left it—dark without the day-beams of the Latonian Charioteer, darker yet without the dædal Smile of the God of the Other Bow! Dost know him, Reader?

Old is he, EROS, the ever young! He and Time were children together. CHRONOS shall die, too; but Love is imperishable. Brightest of the Divinities, where hast thou not been sung? Other worships pass away; the idols for whom pyramids were raised lie in the desert crumbling and almost nameless; the Olympians are fled, their fanes no longer rise among the quivering olive-groves of Ilissus, or crown the emerald islets of the amethyst Ægean! These are gone, but thou remainest. There is still a garland for thy temple, a heifer for thy stone. A heifer? Ah, many a darker sacrifice. Other blood is shed at thy altars, Remorseless One, and the Poet-Priest who ministers at thy Shrine draws his auguries from the bleeding hearts of men!

While Love hath no end, Can the Bard ever cease singing? In Kingly and Heroic ages, 'twas of Kings and Heroes that the Poet spake. But in these, our times, the Artisan hath his voice as well as the Monarch. The People To-Day is King, and we chronicle his woes, as They of old did the sacrifice of the princely IPHIGENIA, or the fate of the crowned AGAMEMNON.

Is ODYSSEUS less august in his rags than in his purple? Fate, Passion, Mystery, the Victim, the Avenger, the Hate that arms, the Furies that tear, the Love that bleeds, are not these with us Still? are not these still the weapons of the Artist? the colours of his palette, the chords of his lyre? Listen! I tell thee a tale—not of Kings—but of Men—not of Thrones, but of Love, and Grief and Crime. Listen, and but once more. 'Tis for the last time (probably) these fingers shall sweep the strings.

E.L.B.L.B B.L L.B B B.L L L.

NOONDAY IN CHEPE

'Twas noonday in Chepe. High Tide in the mighty River City!—its banks well-nigh overflowing with the myriad-waved

Stream of Man! The toppling wains, bearing the produce of a thousand marts; the gilded equipage of the Millionary; the humbler, but yet larger, vehicle from the green metropolitan suburbs (the Hanging Gardens of our Babylon) in which every traveller might, for a modest remuneration, take a republican seat; the mercenary caroche, with its private freight; the brisk curricle of the letter-carrier, robed in royal scarlet; these and a thousand others were labouring and pressing onward and locked and bound and hustling together in the narrow channel of Chepe. The imprecations of the charioteers were terrible. From the noble's broidered hammer-cloth, or the driving-seat of the common coach, each driver assailed the other with floods of ribald satire. The pavid matron within the one vehicle (speeding to the Bank for her semestrial pittance) shrieked and trembled; the angry DIVES hastening to his offices (to add another thousand to his heap) thrust his head over the blazoned panels, and displayed an eloquence of objurgation which his very Menials could not equal; the dauntless street urchins, as they gaily threaded the Labyrinth of Life, enjoyed the perplexities and quarrels of the scene, and exacerbated the already furious combatants by their poignant infantile satire. And the Philosopher, as he regarded the hot strife and struggle of these Candidates in the race for Gold, thought with a sigh of the Truthful and the Beautiful, and walked on, melancholy and serene.

'Twas noon in Chepe. The ware-rooms were thronged. The flaunting windows of the mercers attracted many a purchaser: the glittering panes, behind which Birmingham had glazed its simulated silver, induced rustics to pause: although only noon, the savory odours of the Cook Shops tempted the ever-hungry citizen to the bun of Bath, or to the fragrant potage that mocks the turtle's flavour—the turtle! *O dapibus supremi grata testudo Jovis!* I am an Alderman when I think of thee! Well: it was noon in Chepe.

But were all battling for gain there? Among the many brilliant shops whose casements shone upon Chepe, there stood one a century back (about which period our tale opens) devoted to the sale of Colonial produce. A rudely carved image of a negro with a fantastic plume and apron of variegated feathers, decorated the lintel. The East and the West had sent their contributions to replenish the window.

The poor slave had toiled, died perhaps, to produce yon pyramid of swarthy sugar marked 'ONLY 6½d.'—That catty box, on which was the epigraph STRONG FAMILY CONGO ONLY 3s. 9d., was from the country of Confutzee—That heap of dark produce bore the legend 'TRY OUR REAL NUT'—'Twas Cocoa—and that nut the Cocoa-nut, whose milk has refreshed the traveller and perplexed the natural philosopher. The shop in question was, in a word, a Grocer's.

In the midst of the shop and its gorgeous contents sate one who, to judge from his appearance (though 'twas a difficult task, as in sooth, his back was turned), had just reached that happy period of life when the Boy is expanding into the Man. O Youth! Youth! Happy and Beautiful! O fresh and roseate dawn of life; when the dew yet lies on the flowers, ere they have been scorched and withered by Passion's fiery Sun! Immersed in thought or study, and indifferent to the din around him, sate the Boy. A careless guardian was he of the treasures confided to him. The crowd passed in Chepe he never marked it. The sun shone on Chepe he only asked that it should illumine the page he read. The knave might filch his treasures, he was heedless of the knave. The customer might enter; but his book was all in all to him.

And indeed a customer *was* there; a little hand was tapping on the counter with a pretty impatience; a pair of arch eyes were gazing at the boy, admiring, perhaps, his manly proportions through the homely and tightened garments he wore.

'Ahem! sir! I say, young man!' the customer exclaimed.

'*Ton d'apameibomenos prosephe*,' read on the Student, his voice choked with emotion. 'What language,' he said, 'How rich, how noble, how sonorous! *prosephe podas——*'

The customer burst out into a fit of laughter so shrill and cheery, that the young Student could not but turn round, and, blushing, for the first time remarked her. 'A pretty Grocer's boy you are,' she cried, 'with your applepiebomenos and your French and lingo. Am I to be kep waiting for hever?'

'Pardon, fair Maiden,' said he, with high-bred courtesy; ''Twas not French I read, 'twas the Godlike language of the blind old bard. In what can I be serviceable to ye, lady?' and to spring from his desk, to smooth his apron, to stand before her the obedient Shop Boy, the Poet no more, was the work of a moment.

'I might have prigged this box of figs,' the damsel said, good-naturedly, 'and you'd never have turned round.'

'They came from the country of HECTOR,' the boy said. 'Would you have currants, lady? These once bloomed in the island gardens of the blue Ægean. They are uncommon fine ones, and the figure is low; they're fourpence-halfpenny a pound. Would ye mayhap make trial of our teas? We do not advertise, as some folks do: but sell as low as any other house.'

'You're precious young to have all these good things,' the

girl exclaimed, not unwilling, seemingly, to prolong the conversation.   'If I was you, and stood behind the counter, I should be eating figs the whole day long.'

'Time was,' answered the lad, 'and not long since I thought so,

too, I thought I never should be tired of figs.   But my old uncle bade me take my fill, and now in sooth I am aweary of them.'

'I think you gentlemen are always so,' the coquette said.

'Nay, say not so, fair stranger!' the youth replied, his face kindling as he spoke and his eagle eyes flashing fire.   'Figs pall, but O! the Beautiful never does!   Figs rot, but O! the Truthful is eternal. I was born, lady, to grapple with the Lofty and the Ideal. My soul yearns for the Visionary. I stand behind the counter; it is true, but I ponder here upon the deeds of heroes, and muse over the thoughts of sages. What is grocery for one who has ambition? What sweetness hath Muscovado to him who hath tasted of Poesy? The Ideal, lady, I often think, is the true Real, and the Actual but a visionary hallucination. But pardon me; with what may I serve thee?'

'I came only for sixpenn'orth of tea-dust,' the girl said, with a faltering voice, 'but oh, I should like to hear you speak on for ever!'

Only for sixpenn'orth of tea-dust! Girl, thou camest for other things! Thou lovedst his voice? Syren! what was the witchery of thine own? He deftly made up the packet and placed it in the little hand. She paid for her small purchase and with a farewell glance of her lustrous eyes, she left him. She passed slowly through the portal, and in a moment more was lost in the crowd. It was noon in Chepe. And GEORGE DE BARNWELL was alone.

VOL. II

WE have selected the following episodical chapter in preference to any relating to the mere story of GEORGE BARNWELL, with which most readers are familiar.

Up to this passage (extracted from the beginning of Vol. ii.) the tale is briefly thus :—

That rogue of a MILLWOOD has come back every day to the grocer's shop in Chepe, wanting some sugar, or some nutmeg, or some figs, half-a-dozen times in the week.

She and GEORGE DE BARNWELL have vowed to each other an eternal attachment.

This flame acts violently upon GEORGE. His bosom swells with ambition. His genius breaks out prodigiously. He talks about the Good, the Beautiful, the Ideal, etc., in and out of all season, and is virtuous and eloquent almost beyond belief—in fact like DEVEREUX, or P. CLIFFORD, or E. ARAM, Esquires.

Inspired by MILLWOOD and LOVE, GEORGE robs the till, and mingles in the world which he is destined to ornament. He outdoes all the dandies, all the wits, all the scholars, and all the voluptuaries of the age—an indefinite period of time between QUEEN ANNE and GEORGE II.—dines with CURLL at St. John's

Gate, pinks COLONEL CHARTERIS in a duel behind Montague House, is initiated into the intrigues of the CHEVALIER ST. GEORGE, whom he entertains at his sumptuous pavilion at Hampstead, and likewise in disguise at the shop in Cheapside.

His uncle, the owner of the shop, a surly curmudgeon with very little taste for the True and the Beautiful, has retired from business to the pastoral village in Cambridgeshire from which the noble BARNWELLS came. GEORGE'S cousin ANNABEL is, of course, consumed with a secret passion for him.

Some trifling inaccuracies may be remarked in the ensuing brilliant little chapter ; but it must be remembered that the author wished to present an age at a glance ; and the dialogue is quite as fine and correct as that in *The Last of the Barons* or in *Eugene Aram*, or other works of our author, in which Sentiment and History, or the True and the Beautiful are united.

CHAPTER XXIV

BUTTON'S IN PALL MALL

THOSE who frequent the dismal and enormous Mansions of Silence which society has raised to Ennui in that Omphalos of town, Pall Mall, and which, because they knock you down with their dulness, are called Clubs no doubt ; those who yawn from a bay-window in St. James's Street, at a half-score of other dandies gaping from another bay-window over the way ; those who consult a dreary evening paper for news, or satisfy themselves with the jokes of the miserable *Punch*, by way of wit ; the men about town of the present day, in a word, can have but little idea of London some six or eight score years back. Thou pudding-sided old dandy of St. James's Street, with thy lackered boots, thy dyed whiskers, and thy suffocating waistband, what art thou to thy brilliant predecessor in the same quarter ? The Brougham from which thou descendest at the portal of the Carlton or the Travellers', is like everybody else's ; thy black coat has no more plaits, nor buttons, nor fancy in it than thy neighbours' ; thy hat was made on the very block on which LORD ADDLEPATE'S was cast, who has just entered the Club before thee. You and he yawn together out of the same omnibus-box every night ; you fancy yourselves men of pleasure ; you fancy yourselves men of fashion ; you fancy yourselves men of taste ; in fancy, in taste, in opinion, in philosophy, the newspaper legislates for you ; it is there you get your jokes, and your thoughts, and your facts and your wisdom—poor Pall Mall dullards. Stupid slaves of the Press, on that ground which you at present occupy, there were men of wit and pleasure and fashion, some five-and-twenty lustres ago.

We are at BUTTON'S—the well-known sign of the Turk's Head. The crowd of periwigged heads at the windows—the swearing chairmen round the steps (the blazoned and coronalled panels of whose vehicles denote the lofty rank of their owners)—the throng of embroidered beaux entering or departing and rendering the air fragrant with the odours of pulvillio and pomander, proclaim the celebrated resort of London's Wit and Fashion. It is the corner of Regent Street. Carlton House has not yet been taken down.

A stately gentleman in crimson velvet and gold is sipping chocolate at one of the tables in earnest converse with a friend whose suit is likewise embroidered, but stained by time, or wine mayhap, or wear. A little deformed gentleman in iron-grey is reading the *Morning Chronicle* newspaper by the fire, while a divine, with a broad brogue and a shovel hat and cassock is talking freely with a gentleman, whose star and riband, as well as the unmistakeable beauty of his Phidian countenance, proclaims him to be a member of Britain's aristocracy.

Two ragged youths, the one tall, gaunt, clumsy, and scrofulous ; the other with a wild, careless, beautiful look, evidently indicating Race, are gazing in at the window, not merely at the crowd in the celebrated Club, but at TIMOTHY, the waiter, who is removing a plate of that exquisite dish, the muffin (then newly invented) at the desire of some of the revellers within.

'I would, SAM,' said the wild youth to his companion, 'that I had some of my MOTHER MACCLESFIELD'S gold, to enable us to eat of those cates and mingle with yon springalds and beaux.'

'To vaunt a knowledge of the stoical philosophy,' said the youth addressed as SAM, 'might elicit a smile of incredulity upon the cheek of the parasite of pleasure ; but there are moments in life when History fortifies endurance ; and past study renders present deprivation more bearable. If our pecuniary resources be exiguous, let our resolution, DICK, supply the deficiencies of Fortune. The muffin we desire to-day would little benefit us to-morrow. Poor and hungry, as we are, are we less happy, DICK, than yon listless voluptuary who banquets on the food which you covet ? '

And the two lads turned away up Waterloo Place and past the Parthenon Club-House and disappeared to take a meal of

cow-heel at a neighbouring cook's shop. Their names were
SAMUEL JOHNSON and RICHARD SAVAGE.

Meanwhile the conversation at BUTTON'S was fast and
brilliant. 'By WOOD'S thirteens, and the divvle go wid 'em,'
cried the Church dignitary in the cassock. 'Is it in blue and
goold ye are this morning, SIR RICHARD, when you ought to be
in seebles?'

'Who's dead, DEAN?' said the nobleman, the dean's companion.

'Faix, mee LARD BOLINGBROKE, as sure as mee name's
JONATHAN SWIFT—and I'm not so sure of that neither, for who
knows his father's name?—there's been a mighty cruel murther
committed entirely. A child of DICK STEELE'S has been
barbarously slain, dthrawn, and quarthered, and it's JOE ADDISON
yondther has done it. Ye should have killed one of your own,
JOE, ye thief of the world.'

'I?' said the amazed and RIGHT HONOURABLE JOSEPH
ADDISON; 'I kill DICK'S child! I was God-father to the last.'

'And promised a cup and never sent it,' DICK ejaculated.
JOSEPH looked grave.

'The child I mean is SIR ROGER DE COVERLEY, KNIGHT AND
BARONET. What made ye kill him, ye savage Mohock? The
whole town is in tears about the good knight; all the ladies at
Church this afternoon were in mourning; all the booksellers are
wild; and LINTOT says not a third of the copies of the *Spectator*
are sold since the death of the brave old gentleman.' And the
DEAN OF ST. PATRICK'S pulled out the *Spectator* newspaper,
containing the well-known passage regarding SIR ROGER'S death.
'I bought it but now in Wellington Street,' he said; 'the news-
boys were howling all down the Strand.'

'What a miracle is Genius—Genius, the Divine and Beautiful,'
said a gentleman leaning against the same fireplace with the
deformed cavalier in iron-grey and addressing that individual who
was in fact MR. ALEXANDER POPE, 'what a marvellous gift is
this, and royal privilege of Art! To make the Ideal more
credible than the Actual : to enchain our hearts, to command our
hopes, our regrets, our tears, for a mere brain-born Emanation :
to invest with life the Incorporeal, and to glamour the cloudy
into substance—these are the lofty privileges of the Poet, if I
have read poesy aright ; and I am as familiar with the sounds
that rang from HOMER'S lyre, as with the strains which celebrate
the loss of BELINDA'S lovely locks, (MR. POPE blushed and
bowed, highly delighted)—'these, I say, sir, are the privileges of
the Poet—the Poietes—the Maker, he moves the world, and asks
no lever ; if he cannot charm death into life as ORPHEUS feigned

to do, he can create Beauty out of Naught, and defy Death by rendering Thought Eternal! Ho! JEMMY, another flask of Nantz.'

And the boy—for he who addressed the most brilliant com-

pany of wits in Europe was little more—emptied the contents of the brandy-flask in a silver flagon, and quaffed it gaily to the health of the company assembled. 'Twas the third he had taken during the sitting. Presently, and with a graceful salute to the Society, he quitted the coffee-house, and was seen cantering on a magnificent Arab past the National Gallery.

'Who is yon spark in blue and silver? He beats Joe Addison himself in drinking, and pious Joe is the greatest toper in the three kingdoms,' Dick Steele said good-naturedly.

'His paper in the *Spectator* beats thy best, Dick, thou sluggard,' the Right Honourable Mr. Addison exclaimed. 'He is the author of that famous No. 996 for which you have all been giving me the credit.'

'The rascal foiled me at capping verses,' Dean Swift said, 'and won a tenpenny piece of me, plague take him!'

'He has suggested an emendation in my *Homer*, which proves him a delicate scholar,' Mr. Pope exclaimed.

'He knows more of the French king than any man I have met with; and we must have an eye upon him,' said Lord Bolingbroke, then Secretary of State for Foreign Affairs, and beckoning a suspicious-looking person who was drinking at a side-table, whispered to him something.

Meantime who was he? where was he, this youth who had struck all the wits of London with admiration? His galloping charger had returned to the City; his splendid court-suit was doffed for the citizen's gabardine and grocer's humble apron.

George de Barnwell was in Chepe—in Chepe, at the knees of Martha Millwood.

VOL. III

THE CONDEMNED CELL

'*Quid me mollibus implicas lacertis,* my Ellinor? Nay,' George added, a faint smile illumining his wan but noble features, 'why speak to thee in the accents of the Roman poet, which thou comprehendest not? Bright One, there be other things in Life, in Nature, in this Inscrutable Labyrinth, this Heart on which thou leanest, which are equally unintelligible to thee! Yes, my pretty one, what is the Unintelligible but the Ideal; what is the Ideal but the Beautiful? what the Beautiful but the Eternal? And the Spirit of Man that would commune with these is like Him who wanders by the *thina poluphloisboio thalasses*, and shrinks awe-struck before that Azure Mystery.'

Emily's eyes filled with fresh gushing dew. 'Speak on, speak ever thus, my George,' she exclaimed. Barnwell's chains rattled as the confiding girl clung to him. Even Snoggin, the Turnkey, appointed to sit with the Prisoner, was affected by his noble and appropriate language, and also burst into tears. 'You weep, my SNOGGIN,' the Boy said, 'and why? Hath Life been so charming to me that I should wish to retain it? Hath Pleasure no after-Weariness? Ambition no Deception; Wealth no Care; and Glory no Mockery? Psha! I am sick of Success, palled of Pleasure, weary of Wine, and Wit—and—nay, start not, my ADELAIDE—and Woman. I fling away all these things as the Toys of Boyhood. Life is the Soul's Nursery. I am a Man and pine for the Illimitable! Mark you me! Has the Morrow any terrors for me, think ye? Did SOCRATES falter at his poison? Did SENECA blench in his bath? Did BRUTUS shirk the sword when his Great Stake was lost? Did even weak CLEOPATRA shrink from the Serpent's fatal nip? and why should I? My great Hazard hath been played, and I pay my forfeit. Lie sheathed in my heart, thou flashing Blade! Welcome to my Bosom, thou faithful Serpent! I hug thee, peace-bearing Image of the Eternal! Ha, the hemlock cup! Fill high, boy, for my soul is thirsty for the Infinite! Get ready the bath, friends; prepare me for the feast of To-morrow—bathe my limbs in odours and put ointment in my hair.'

'Has for a bath,' SNOGGIN interposed, 'they're not to be ad in this ward of the prison; but I dussay HEMMY will git you a little hoil for your air.'

The Prisoned One laughed loud and merrily. 'My guardian understands me not, pretty one—and thou? what sayst thou? from those dear lips methinks—*plura sunt oscula quam sententiæ* I kiss away thy tears, dove!—they will flow apace when I am gone, then they will dry, and presently these fair eyes will shine on another, as they have beamed on poor GEORGE BARNWELL. Yet wilt thou not all forget him, sweet one. He was an honest fellow, and had a kindly heart for all the world said——'

'That, that he had,' cried the gaoler and the girl in voices gurgling with emotion. And you who read! you, unconvicted Convict—you, murderer, though haply you have slain no one— you, Felon in *posse*, if not in *esse*—deal gently with one who has used the Opportunity that has failed thee—and believe that the Truthful and the Beautiful bloom sometimes in the dock and the convict's tawny Gabardine!

In the matter for which he suffered, GEORGE could never be brought to acknowledge that he was at all in the wrong. 'It may be an error of judgment,' he said to the Venerable Chaplain of the gaol, 'but it is no crime. Were it Crime, I should feel Remorse. Where there is no Remorse, Crime cannot exist. I am not sorry ; therefore, I am innocent.   Is the proposition a fair one ?'

The excellent Doctor admitted that it was not to be contested.

'And wherefore, Sir, should I have sorrow,' the Boy resumed, 'for ridding the world of a sordid worm ;[1] of a man whose very

[1] This is a gross plagiarism : the above sentiment is expressed much more eloquently in the ingenious romance of *Eugene Aram* :—'The burning desire I have known—the resplendent visions I have nursed—the sublime aspirings that have lifted me so often from sense and clay : these tell me that whether for good or ill, I am the thing of an immortality, and the creature of a God. . . . I have destroyed a man noxious to the world ; with the wealth by which he afflicted society, I have been the means of blessing many.'

soul was dross, and who never had a feeling for the Truthful and the Beautiful? When I stood before my uncle in the moonlight in the gardens of the ancestral halls of the DE BARNWELLS, I felt that I was the NEMESIS come to overthrow him. "Dog," I said to the trembling slave, "tell me where thy Gold is. Thou hast no use for it. I can spend it in relieving the Poverty on which thou tramplest; in aiding Science, which thou knowest not; in uplifting Art, to which thou art blind. Give Gold, and thou art free!" But he spake not, and I slew him.'

'I would not have this doctrine vulgarly promulgated,' said the admirable chaplain, 'for its general practice might chance to do harm. Thou, my son, the Refined, the Gentle, the Loving and Beloved, the Poet and Sage, urged by what I cannot but think a grievous error, hast appeared as Avenger. Think what would be the world's condition, were men without any Yearning after the Ideal to attempt to reorganise Society, to redistribute Property, to avenge Wrong.'

'A rabble of pigmies scaling Heaven,' said the noble though misguided young Prisoner. 'PROMETHEUS was a Giant, and he fell.'

'Yes, indeed, my brave youth!' the benevolent DR. FUZWIG exclaimed, clasping the Prisoner's marble and manacled hand; 'and the Tragedy of To-morrow will teach the World that Homicide is not to be permitted even to the most amiable Genius, and that the lover of the Ideal and Beautiful, as thou art, my son, must respect the Real likewise.'

'Look! here is supper!' cried BARNWELL gaily. 'This is the Real, Doctor; let us respect it and fall to.' He partook of the meal as joyously as if it had been one of his early festals; but the worthy chaplain could scarcely eat it for tears.

CODLINGSBY

By B. De Shrewsbury, Esq.

'The whole world is bound by one chain. In every city in the globe there is one quarter that certain travellers know and recognise from its likeness to its brother-district in all other places where are congregated the habitation of men. In Tehran, or Pekin, or Stamboul, or New York, or Timbuctoo, or London, there is a certain district where a certain man is not a stranger. Where the idols are fed with incense by the streams of Ching-wang-foo; where the minarets soar sparkling above the cypresses, their reflexions quivering in the lucid waters of the Golden Horn; where the yellow Tiber flows under broken bridges and over imperial glories; where the huts are squatted by the Niger, under the palm-trees; where the Northern Babel lies, with its warehouses and its bridges, its graceful factory-chimneys, and its clumsy fanes—hidden in fog and smoke by the dirtiest river in the world—in all the cities of mankind there is One Home whither men of one family may resort. Over the entire world spreads a vast brotherhood, suffering, silent, scattered, sympathising, waiting—an immense Free-Masonry. Once this world-spread band was an Arabian clan—a little nation alone and outlying amongst the mighty monarchies of ancient time, the Megatheria of history. The sails of their rare ships might be seen in the Egyptian waters; the camels of their caravans might thread the sands of Baalbec, or wind through the date-groves of Damascus; their flag was raised, not ingloriously, in many wars, against mighty odds; but 'twas a small people, and on one dark night the Lion of Judah went down before Vespasian's Eagles, and in flame, and death, and struggle, Jerusalem agonised and died. . . . Yes, the Jewish city is lost to Jewish men; but have they not taken the world in exchange?'

Mused thus Godfrey de Bouillon, Marquis of Codlingsby, as he debouched from Wych Street into the Strand. He had been to take a box for Armida at Madame Vestris's theatre. That little Armida was *folle* of Madame Vestris's theatre; and her little Brougham, and her little self, and her enormous eyes, and her prodigious opera-glass, and her miraculous bouquet, which cost Lord Codlingsby twenty guineas every evening at Nathan's in Covent Garden (the children of the gardeners of Sharon have still no rival for flowers), might be seen three nights in the week at least, in the narrow, charming, comfortable, little theatre.   GODFREY had the box.   He was strolling listlessly,

eastward, and the above thoughts passed through the young noble's mind as he came in sight of Holywell Street.

The occupants of the London Ghetto sat at their porches basking in the evening sunshine.   Children were playing on the

steps.   Fathers were smoking at the lintel.   Smiling faces looked
out from the various and darkling draperies with which the
warehouses were hung.   Ringlets glossy, and curly, and jetty
eyes black as night—midsummer night—when it lightens;
haughty noses bending like beaks of eagles—eager quivering
nostrils—lips curved like the bow of Love—every man or maiden,
every babe or matron in that English Jewry bore in his countenance one or more of these characteristics of his peerless Arab
race.

'How beautiful they are!' mused CODLINGSBY, as he surveyed
these placid groups calmly taking their pleasure in the sunset.

'D'you vant to look at a nishe coat?' a voice said, which
made him start; and then some one behind him began handling
a master-piece of STULTZ's with a familiarity which would have
made the Baron tremble.

'RAFAEL MENDOZA!' exclaimed GODFREY.

'The same, LORD CODLINGSBY,' the individual so apostrophised
replied.   'I told you we should meet again where you would
little expect me.   Will it please you to enter?   This is Friday,
and we close at sunset.   It rejoices my heart to welcome you
home.'   So saying, RAFAEL laid his hand on his breast and bowed,
an Oriental reverence.   All traces of the accent with which he first
addressed LORD CODLINGSBY had vanished; it was a disguise;
half the Hebrew's life is a disguise.   He shields himself in craft,
since the Norman boors persecuted him.

They passed under an awning of old clothes, tawdry fripperies,
greasy spangles, and battered masks, into a shop as black and
hideous as the entrance was foul.   'This your home, RAFAEL?'
said LORD CODLINGSBY.

'Why not?'   RAFAEL answered.   'I am tired of Schloss
Schinkenstein, the Rhine bores me after a while.   It is too hot
for Florence; besides they have not completed the picture-gallery,
and my palace smells of putty.   You wouldn't have a man, *mon
cher*, bury himself in his chateau in Normandy, out of the hunting
season.   The Rugantino Palace stupifies me.   Those Titians are
so gloomy.   I shall have my HOBBIMAS and TENIERS, I think,
from my house at the Hague, hung over them.'

'How many castles, palaces, houses, warehouses, shops, have
you, RAFAEL?'   LORD CODLINGSBY asked, laughing.

'This is one,' RAFAEL answered.   'Come in.'

M

The noise in the old town was terrific; Great Tom was booming sullenly over the uproar; the bell of Saint Mary's was clanging with alarm; St Giles's tocsin chimed furiously; howls, curses, flights of brickbats, stones shivering windows, groans of wounded men, cries of frightened females, cheers of either contending party as it charged the enemy from Carfax to Trumpington Street, proclaimed that the battle was at its height.

In Berlin they would have said it was a revolution, and the cuirassiers would have been charging, sabre in hand, amidst that infuriate mob. In France they would have brought down artillery and played on it with twenty-four pounders. In Cambridge nobody heeded the disturbance—it was a Town and Gown row.

The row arose at a boat-race. The Town boat (manned by eight stout bargees, with the redoubted RULLOCK for stroke) had bumped the Brazennose light oar, usually at the head of the river. High words arose regarding the dispute. After returning from Granchester, when the boats pulled back to Christchurch meadows, the disturbance between the Townsmen and the University youths— their invariable opponents—grew louder and more violent, until it broke out in open battle. Sparring and skirmishing took place along the pleasant fields that lead from the University gate down to the broad and shining waters of the Cam and under the walls of Baliol and Sidney Sussex. The DUKE OF BELLAMONT (then a dashing young sizar at Exeter) had a couple of rounds with BILLY BUTT, the bow oar of the Bargee boat. VAVASEUR OF BRAZENNOSE was engaged with a powerful butcher, a well-known champion of the Town party, when, the great University bells ringing to dinner, truce was called between the combatants and they retired to their several colleges for refection.

During the boat-race, a gentleman pulling in a canoe, and smoking a Nargilly, had attracted no ordinary attention. He rowed about a hundred yards ahead of the boats in the race, so that he could have a good view of that curious pastime. If the eight-oars neared him, with a few rapid strokes of his flashing paddles his boat shot a furlong ahead; then he would wait, surveying the race, and sending up volumes of odour from his cool Nargilly.

'Who is he?' asked the crowds who panted along the shore, encouraging, according to Cambridge wont, the efforts of the oarsmen in the race. Town and Gown alike asked who it was, who, with an ease so provoking in a barque so singular, with a form seemingly so slight, but a skill so prodigious, beat their best men. No answer could be given to the query, save that a gentleman in a dark travelling-chariot, preceded by six fourgons and a courier, had arrived the day before at the Hoop Inn, opposite Brazennose, and that the stranger of the canoe seemed to be the individual in question.

No wonder the boat, that all admired so, could compete with any that ever was wrought by Cambridge artificer or Putney workman. That boat—slim, shining, and shooting through the water like a pike after a small fish—was a caique from Tophana— it had distanced the Sultan's oarsmen, and the best crews of the Capitan Pasha in the Bosphorus; it was the workmanship of TOGRUL-BEG, Caikjee Bashee of his Highness. The Bashee had refused fifty thousand tomauns from COUNT BOUTENIEFF, the Russian Ambassador, for that little marvel. When his head was taken off, the Father of Believers presented the boat to RAFAEL MENDOZA.

It was RAFAEL MENDOZA that saved the Turkish Monarchy after the battle of Nezeeb. By sending three millions of piastres to the Seraskier; by bribing COLONEL DE ST. CORNICHON, the French envoy in the camp of the victorious IBRAHIM, the march of the Egyptian army was stopped—the menaced empire of the Ottomans was saved from ruin; the MARCHIONESS OF STOKEPOGIS, our Ambassador's lady, appeared in a suit of diamonds which out-blazed even the Romanoff jewels, and RAFAEL MENDOZA obtained the little caique. He never travelled without it. It was scarcely heavier than an arm-chair. BARONI, the courier, had carried it down to the Cam that morning, and RAFAEL had seen the singular sport which we have mentioned.

The dinner over, the young men rushed from their college, flushed, full-fed, and eager for battle. If the Gown was angry, the Town, too, was on the alert. From Iffley and Barnwell, from factory and mill, from wharf and warehouse, the Town poured out to meet their enemy, and the battle was soon general. From the Addenbrooke's hospital to the Blenheim turnpike, all Cambridge was in an uproar—the College gates closed—the shops barricaded—the shop-boys away in support of their brother townsmen—the battle raged, and the Gown had the worst of the fight.

A luncheon of many courses had been provided for RAFAEL MENDOZA at his inn, but he smiled at the clumsy efforts of the University cooks to entertain him, and a couple of dates and a glass of water formed his meal. In vain the discomfited landlord pressed him to partake of the slighted banquet. 'A breakfast! psha!' said he. 'My good man, I have nineteen cooks, at salaries rising from four hundred a year. I can have a dinner at any hour, but a Town and Gown row (a brickbat here flying through the window crashed the caraffe of water in MENDOZA'S hand)—a Town and Gown row is a novelty to me. The Town has the best of it, clearly, though ; the men outnumber the lads.

Ha, a good blow ! How that tall townsman went down befor yonder slim young fellow in the scarlet trencher-cap.'

'That is the LORD CODLINGSBY,' the landlord said.

'A light weight, but a pretty fighter,' MENDOZA remarked 'Well hit with your left, LORD CODLINGSBY, well parried LOR CODLINGSBY ; claret drawn, by Jupiter !'

'Ours is werry fine,' the landlord said. 'Will your highness have Chateau Margaux or Laffitte ?'

'He never can be going to match himself against that bargeman,' RAFAEL exclaimed, as an enormous boatman—no other than RULLOCK—indeed, the most famous bruiser of Cambridge, and before whose fists the gownsmen went down like ninepins, fought his way up to the spot where, with admirable spirit and resolution, LORD CODLINGSBY and one or two of his friends were making head against a number of the Town.

The young noble faced the huge champion with the gallantry of his race, but was no match for the enemy's strength, and weight, and sinew, and went down at every round. The brutal fellow had no mercy on the lad. The savage treatment chafed MENDOZA as he viewed the unequal combat from the inn-window. 'Hold your hand !' he cried to this GOLIATH ; 'don't you see he's but a boy ?'

'Down he goes again !' the bargeman cried, not heeding the interruption. 'Down he goes again ! I likes wapping a Lord !'

'Coward !' shouted MENDOZA, and to fling open the window amidst a shower of brickbats, to vault over the balcony, to slide down one of the pillars to the ground, was an instant's work.

At the next he stood before the enormous bargeman.

. . . . .

After the Coroner's inquest, MENDOZA gave ten thousand pounds to each of the bargeman's ten children, and it was thus his first acquaintance was formed with LORD CODLINGSBY.

But we are lingering on the threshold of the house in Holywell Street. Let us go in !

———

GODFREY and RAFAEL passed from the Street into the outer shop of the old mansion in Holywell Street. It was a masquerade warehouse, to all appearance. A dark-eyed damsel of the nation was standing at the dark and grimy counter, strewed with old feathers, old yellow boots, old stage mantles, painted masks, blind, and yet gazing at you with a look of sad death-like intelligence from the vacancy behind their sockets.

A medical student was trying one of the doublets of orange-tawney and silver, slashed with dirty light blue. He was going to a masquerade that night. He thought POLLY PATTENS would admire him in the dress—POLLY PATTENS, the fairest of maids-of-all-work—the Borough VENUS, adored by half the youth of GUY'S.

'You look like a Prince in it, MR. LINT,' pretty RACHAEL said, coaxing him with her beady black eyes.

'It is the cheese,' replied MR. LINT; 'it ain't the dress that don't suit, my rose of Sharon, it's the figure. Hullo, RAFAEL, is that you, my lad of sealing-wax! Come and intercede for me with this wild gazelle; she says I can't have it under fifteen bob for the night. And it's too much; cuss me if it's not too much, unless you'll take my little bill at two months, RAFAEL.'

'There's a sweet pretty brigand's dress you may have for half de monish,' RAFAEL replied; 'there's a splendid clown for eight bob; but for dat Spanish dress, selp ma MOSHESH, MDSHTER LINT, ve'd ask a guinea of any but you. Here's a gentlemansh just come to look at it. Look 'ear, MR. BROWNSH, did you ever shee a nisher ting dan dat?' So saying, RAFAEL turned to LORD CODLINGSBY with the utmost gravity and displayed to him the garment about which the young Medicus was haggling.

'Cheap at the money,' CODLINGSBY replied; 'if you won't make up your mind, sir, I should like to engage it myself.' But the thought that another should appear before POLLY PATTENS in that costume was too much for MR. LINT; he agreed to pay the fifteen shillings for the garment. And RAFAEL pocketing the money with perfect simplicity, said, 'Dis vay, MR. BROWNSH; dere's someting vill shoot you in the next shop.'

LORD CODLINGSBY followed him, wondering.

'You are surprised at our system,' said RAFAEL, marking the evident bewilderment of his friend. 'Confess you would call it meanness—my huxtering with yonder young fool. I call it simplicity. Why throw away a shilling without need? Our race never did. A shilling is four men's bread: shall I disdain to defile my fingers by holding them out relief in their necessity? It is you who are mean—you Normans—not we of the ancient race. You have your vulgar measurement for great things and small. You call a thousand pounds respectable and a shekel despicable. Psha, my CODLINGSBY! One is as the other. I trade in pennies and in millions. I am above or below neither.'

They were passing through a second shop, smelling strongly of cedar, and, in fact, piled up with bales of those pencils which the young Hebrews are in the habit of vending through the streets. 'I have sold bundles and bundles of these,' said RAFAEL. 'My little brother is now out with oranges in Piccadilly. I am bringing him up to be head of our house at Amsterdam. We all do it. I had myself to see ROTHSCHILD in Eaton Place this morning, about the Irish loan, of which I have taken three millions; and as I wanted to walk, I carried the bag.

'You should have seen the astonishment of LAUDA LATYMER, the ARCHBISHOP OF CROYDON'S daughter, as she was passing to St. Bennet's, Knightsbridge, and as she fancied she recognised in the man who was crying old clothes the gentleman with whom

she had talked at the COUNT DE SAINT AULAIRE'S the night before.' Something like a blush flushed over the pale features of MENDOZA as he mentioned the LADY LAUDA'S name. 'Come on,' said he. They passed through various warehouses—the orange room, the sealing-wax room, the six-bladed-knife depart-

ment, and finally came to an old baize door. RAFAEL opened
the baize door by some secret contrivance, and they were in a
black passage with a curtain at the end.

He clapped his hands, the curtain at the end of the passage
drew back, and a flood of golden light streamed on the Hebrew
and his visitor.

CHAPTER XXIV

THEY entered a moderate-sized apartment—indeed, Holywell
Street is not above a hundred yards long, and this chamber was
not more than half that length—and fitted up with the simple
taste of its owner.

The carpet was of white velvet—(laid over several webs of
Aubusson, Ispahan, and Axminster, so that your foot gave no
more sound as it trod upon the yielding plain than the shadow
did which followed you)—of white velvet, painted with flowers,
arabesques, and classic figures, by SIR WILLIAM ROSS, J. M.
TURNER, R.A., MRS. MEE, and PAUL DELAROCHE. The edges
were wrought with seed-pearls and fringed with Valenciennes lace
and bullion. The walls were hung with cloth of silver, embroidered with gold figures, over which were worked pomegranates,
polyanthuses, and passion-flowers, in ruby, amethyst, and smaragd.
The drops of dew which the artificer had sprinkled on the flowers
were diamonds. The hangings were over-hung by pictures yet
more costly. GIORGIONE the gorgeous, TITIAN the golden,
RUBENS the ruddy and pulpy (the PAN of Painting), some of
MURILLO's beautified shepherdesses, who smile on you out of
darkness like a star ; a few score first-class LEONARDOS and fifty
of the master-pieces of the patron of JULIUS and LEO, the
Imperial genius of URBINO covered the walls of the little chamber.
Divans of carved amber covered with ermine went round the
room, and in the midst was a fountain, pattering and babbling
with jets of double-distilled otto of roses.

'Pipes, GOLIATH!' RAFAEL said gaily to a little negro with a
silver collar (he spoke to him in his native tongue of Dongola) ;
'and welcome to our snuggery, my CODLINGSBY. We are quieter
here than in the front of the house, and I wanted to show you a
picture. I'm proud of my picture. That LEONARDO came from
Genoa, and was a gift to our father from my cousin, MARSHAL
MANASSEH ; that MURILLO was pawned to my uncle by MARIE
ANTOINETTE before the flight to Varennes—the poor lady could

not redeem the pledge, you know, and the picture remains with us. As for the RAFAEL, I suppose you are aware that he was one of our people. But what are you gazing at? Oh! my sister —I forgot—MIRIAM! this is the LORD CODLINGSBY.'

She had been seated at an ivory piano-forte on a mother-of-pearl music-stool trying a sonata of HERZ. She rose when thus apostrophised. MIRIAM DE MENDOZA rose and greeted the stranger.

The Talmud relates that ADAM had two wives—ZILLAH the dark beauty; EVA the fair one. The ringlets of ZILLAH were black; those of EVA were golden. The eyes of ZILLAH were night; those of EVA were morning. CODLINGSBY was fair—of the fair Saxon race of HENGIST and HORSA—they called him MISS CODLINGSBY at school: but how much fairer was MIRIAM the Hebrew!

Her hair had that deep glowing tinge in it which has been the delight of all painters, and which, therefore, the vulgar sneer at. It was of burning auburn. Meandering over her fairest shoulders in twenty thousand minute ringlets, it hung to her waist and below it. A light blue velvet fillet clasped with a diamond aigrette, (valued at two hundred thousand tomauns, and bought from LIEUTENANT VICOVICH who had received it from DOST MAHOMED) with a simple bird of paradise formed her head-gear. A sea-green cymar with short sleeves, displayed her exquisitely moulded arms to perfection, and was fastened by a girdle of emeralds over a yellow satin frock. Pink gauze trowsers spangled with silver, and slippers of the same colour as the band which clasped her ringlets (but so covered with pearls that the original hue of the charming little papoosh disappeared entirely) completed her costume. She had three necklaces on, each of which would have dowered a Princess—her fingers glistened with rings to their rosy tips, and priceless bracelets, bangles, and armlets wound round an arm that was whiter than the ivory grand piano on which it leaned.

As MIRIAM DE MENDOZA greeted the stranger, turning upon him the solemn welcome of her eyes, CODLINGSBY swooned almost in the brightness of her beauty. It was well she spoke; the sweet kind voice restored him to consciousness. Muttering a few words of incoherent recognition, he sank upon a sandal-wood settee, as GOLIATH, the little slave, brought aromatic coffee in cups of opal and alabaster spittoons, and pipes of the fragrant Gibelly.

'My lord's pipe is out,' said MIRIAM with a smile, remarking the bewilderment of her guest—who in truth forgot to smoke—

and taking up a thousand pound note from a bundle on the piano, she lighted it at the taper and proceeded to reillume the extinguished chibouk of LORD CODLINGSBY.

———

When MIRIAM, returning to the mother-of-pearl music-stool, at a signal from her brother touched the silver and enamelled keys of the ivory piano, and began to sing, LORD CODLINGSBY felt as if he were listening at the gates of Paradise, or were hearing JENNY LIND.

'LIND is a name of the Hebrew race; so is MENDELSOHN, the Son of Almonds; so is ROSENTHAL, the Valley of the Roses; so is LOWE or LEWIS or LYONS or LION—the beautiful and the brave alike give cognizances to the ancient people—you Saxons call yourselves BROWN, or SMITH, or RODGERS,' RAFAEL observed to his friend; and drawing the instrument from his pocket, he accompanied his sister, in the most ravishing manner, on a little gold and jewelled harp of the kind peculiar to his nation.

All the airs which the Hebrew maid selected were written by composers of her race; it was either a hymn by ROSSINI, a polacca by BRAHAM, a delicious romance by SLOMAN, or a melody by WEBER, that, thrilling on the strings of the instrument, wakened a harmony on the fibres of the heart, but she sang no other than the songs of her nation.

'Beautiful one! sing ever, sing always,' CODLINGSBY thought. 'I could sit at thy feet as under a green palm-tree, and fancy that Paradise-birds were singing in the boughs.'

RAFAEL read his thoughts. 'We have Saxon blood too in our veins,' he said. 'You smile, but it is even so. An ancestress of ours made a *mésalliance* in the reign of your KING JOHN. Her name was REBECCA, daughter of ISAAC OF YORK, and she married in Spain, whither she had fled to the Court of KING BOABDIL, SIR WILFRID OF IVANHOE, then a widower by the demise of his first lady ROWENA. The match was deemed a cruel insult amongst our people; but WILFRID conformed, and was a Rabbi of some note at the synagogue at Cordova. We are descended from him lineally. It is the only blot upon the escutcheon of the MENDOZAS.'

As they sate talking together, the music finished and MIRIAM having retired (though her song and her beauty were still present to the soul of the stranger) at a signal from MENDOZA, various messengers from the outer apartments came in to transact business with him.

First it was MR. AMINADAB, who kissed his foot, and brought papers to sign. 'How is the house in Grosvenor Square, AMINADAB; and is your son tired of his yacht yet?' MENDOZA asked. 'That is my twenty-fourth cashier,' said RAFAEL to CODLINGSBY, when the obsequious clerk went away. 'He is fond of display, and all my people may have what money they like.'

Entered presently the LORD BAREACRES, on the affair of his mortgage. The LORD BAREACRES, strutting into the apartment with a haughty air, shrank back, nevertheless, with surprise on beholding the magnificence around him. 'Little Mordecai,' said RAFAEL to a little orange-boy who came in at the heels of the noble, 'take this gentleman out and let him have ten thousand pounds. I can't do more for you, my lord, than this—I'm busy. Good-bye!' and RAFAEL waved his hand to the peer and fell to smoking his Nargilly.

A man with a square face, cat-like eyes, and a yellow moustache, came next. He had an hour-glass of a waist, and walked uneasily upon his high-heeled boots. 'Tell your master that he shall have two millions more, but not another shilling,' RAFAEL said. 'That story about the five-and-twenty millions of ready money at Cronstadt is all bosh. They won't believe it in Europe. You understand me, COUNT GROGOMOFFSKI?'

'But his Imperial Majesty said four millions, and I shall get the knout unless——'

'Go and speak to MR. SHADRACH, in room Z 94, the fourth Court,' said MENDOZA good-naturedly. 'Leave me at peace, Count; don't you see it is Friday and almost sunset?' The Calmuck envoy retired cringing, and left an odour of musk and candle-grease behind him.

An orange-man, an emissary from LOLA MONTES; a dealer in piping bulfinches; and a Cardinal in disguise, with a proposal for a new loan for the Pope, were heard by turns, and each, after a rapid colloquy in his own language, was dismissed by RAFAEL.

'The QUEEN must come back from Aranjuez, or that king must be disposed of,' RAFAEL exclaimed, as a yellow-faced ambassador from Spain, GENERAL THE DUKE OF OLLA PODRIDA, left him. 'Which shall it be, my CODLINGSBY?' CODLINGSBY was about laughingly to answer, for indeed he was amazed to find all the affairs of the world represented here, and Holywell Street the centre of Europe, when three knocks of a peculiar nature were heard, and MENDOZA, starting up, said, 'Ha! there are only four men in the world who know that signal.' At once, and with a reverence quite distinct from his former *nonchalant* manner, he advanced towards the new-comer.

He was an old man—an old man evidently too, of the Hebrew race—the light of his eyes was unfathomable—about his mouth

there played an inscrutable smile. He had a cotton umbrella, and old trowsers, and old boots, and an old wig, curling at the top like a rotten old pear.

He sate down as if tired, in the first seat at hand, as RAFAEL made him the lowliest reverence.

'I am tired,' says he; 'I have come in fifteen hours. I am

ill at Neuilly,' he added with a grin. 'Get me some *eau sucrée* and tell me the news, PRINCE DE MENDOZA. These bread rows ; this unpopularity of GUIZOT ; this odious Spanish conspiracy against my darling MONTPENSIER and daughter ; this ferocity of PALMERSTON against COLETTI, made me quite ill. Give me your opinion, my dear duke. But ha ! whom have we here ?'

The august individual who had spoken, had used the Hebrew language to address MENDOZA, and the LORD CODLINGSBY might easily have pleaded ignorance of that tongue. But he had been at Cambridge, where all the youth acquire it perfectly.

'*Sire*,' said he, 'I will not disguise from you that I know the ancient tongue in which you speak. There are probably secrets between MENDOZA and your MAJ——'

'Hush !' said RAFAEL, leading him from the room. '*Au revoir*, dear CODLINGSBY. His Majesty is one of *us*,' he whispered at the door ; 'so is the Pope of Rome ; so is . . .'—a whisper concealed the rest.

'Gracious powers ! is it so ?' said CODLINGSBY musing. He entered into Holywell Street. The sun was sinking.

'It is time,' said he, 'to go and fetch ARMIDA to the Olympic.'

LORDS AND LIVERIES

By the authoress of 'Dukes and Dejeuners,' 'Hearts and Diamonds,' 'Marchionesses and Milliners,' etc. etc.

'ORBLEU! What a lovely creature that was in the Fitz-battleaxe box to-night,' said one of a group of young dandies, who were leaning over the velvet-cushioned balconies of the Coventry Club, smoking their full-flavoured Cubas (from Hudson's) after the opera.

Everybody stared at such an exclamation of enthusiasm from the lips of the young Earl of Bagnigge, who was never heard to admire anything except a *coulis de dindonneau à la St. Méné-hould,* or a *suprême de cochon en torticolis à la Piffarde;* such as Champollion, the chef of the Travellers, only knows how to dress, or the *bouquet* of a flask of Médoc, of Carbonell's best quality; or a *goutte* of Marasquin, from the cellars of Briggs and Hobson.

Alured de Pentonville, eighteenth Earl of Bagnigge, Viscount Paon of Islington, Baron Pancras, Kingscross, and a Baronet, was, like too many of our young men of *ton,* utterly *blasé,* although only in his twenty-fourth year. Blest, luckily, with a mother of excellent principles, (who had imbued his young mind with that Morality which is so superior to all the vain pomps of the world!) it had not been always the young Earl's lot to wear the coronet for which he now in sooth cared so little. His father, a Captain of Britain's navy, struck down by the side of the gallant Collingswood in the Bay of Fundy, left little but his sword and spotless name to his young, lovely, and inconsolable widow, who passed the first years of her mourning in educating her child in an elegant though small cottage in one of the romantic

marine villages of beautiful Devonshire. Her child! What a
gush of consolation filled the widow's heart as she pressed him
to it! how faithfully did she instil into his young bosom those
principles which had been the pole-star of the existence of his
gallant father.

In this secluded retreat, rank and wealth almost boundless
found the widow and her boy. The seventeenth Earl—gallant
and ardent, and in the prime of youth,—went forth one day from
the Eternal City to a steeple-chase in the Campagna. A mutilated
corpse was brought back to his hotel in the Piazza de Spagna.
Death, alas! is no respecter of the Nobility. That shattered
form was all that remained of the fiery, the haughty—the wild,
but the generous Altamont de Pentonville! Such, such is
fate!

The admirable Emily de Pentonville trembled with all a
mother's solicitude at the distinctions and honours which thus
suddenly descended on her boy. She engaged an excellent
clergyman of the Church of England to superintend his studies;
to accompany him on foreign travel when the proper season
arrived; to ward from him those dangers which dissipation always
throws in the way of the noble, the idle, and the wealthy. But
the Reverend Cyril Delaval died of the measles at Naples;
and henceforth the young Earl of Bagnigge was without a
guardian.

What was the consequence? That, at three-and-twenty he
was a cynic and an epicure. He had drained the cup of pleasure
until it had palled in his unnerved hand. He had looked at the
Pyramids without awe, at the Alps without reverence. He was
as unmoved by the sandy solitudes of the desert as by the placid
depths of Mediterranea's sea of blue. Bitter, bitter tears did
Emily de Pentonville weep, when, on Alured's return from
the Continent, she beheld the awful change that dissipation had
wrought in her beautiful, her blue-eyed, her perverted, her still-
beloved boy!

'Corpo di bacco,' he said, pitching the end of his cigar on to
the red nose of the Countess of Delawaddymore's coachman,
who, having deposited her fat ladyship at No. 236, Piccadilly,
was driving the carriage to the stables, before commencing his
evening at the Fortune of War Public-house. 'What a lovely
creature that was! What eyes! what hair! Who knows her?
Do you, *mon cher Prince?*'

'*E bellissima, certamente,*' said the Duca di Montepulciano,
and stroked down his jetty moustache.

'*Ein gar schönes Mädchen,*' said the Hereditary Grand

DUKE OF EULENSCHRECKENSTEIN, and turned up his carroty
one.

'*Elle n'est pas mal, ma foi !*' said the PRINCE DE BORODINO,
with a scowl on his darkling brows. '*Mon Dieu, que ces cigarres
sont mauvais !*' he added, as he too cast away his Cuba.

'Try one of my Pickwicks,' said FRANKLIN FOX, with a sneer,
offering his gold *etui* to the young Frenchman, 'they are some of
PONTET's best, Prince. What, do you bear malice? Come, let
us be friends,' said the gay and careless young patrician; but a
scowl on the part of the Frenchman was the only reply.

'Want to know who she is? BORODINO knows who she is,
BAGNIGGE,' the wag went on.

Everybody crowded round MONSIEUR DE BORODINO thus
apostrophised. The MARQUIS OF ALICOMPAYNE, young DE BOOTS
of the Life Guards, TOM PROTOCOL of the Foreign Office; the
gay young peers FARINTOSH, POLDOODY, and the rest; and BAG-
NIGGE, for a wonder, not less eager than any one present.

'No, he will tell you nothing about her. Don't you see he
has gone off in a fury!' FRANKLIN FOX continued. 'He has
his reasons, *ce cher Prince;* he will tell you nothing, but I will.
You know that I am *au mieux* with the dear old Duchess.'

'They say FRANK and she are engaged after the Duke's death,'
cried POLDOODY.

'I always thought FWANK was the Duke's illicit gweat-gwand-
son,' drawled out DE BOOTS.

'I heard that he doctored her Blenheim, and used to bring
her wigs from Paris,' cried that malicious TOM PROTOCOL, whose
mots are known in every diplomatic *salon* from Petersburgh to
Palermo.

'Burn her wigs, and hang her poodle,' said BAGNIGGE. 'Tell
us about this girl, FRANKLIN FOX.'

'In the first place, she has five hundred thousand acres, in a
ring fence, in Norfolk; a County in Scotland; a Castle in Wales,
a Villa at Richmond, a corner-house in Belgrave Square, and
eighty thousand a-year in the Three per Cents.'

'*Après,*' said BAGNIGGE still yawning.

'Secondly, BORODINO *lui fait la cour*. They are cousins, her
mother was an Armagnac of the emigration; the old Marshal,
his father, married another sister. I believe he was footman in
the family, before NAPOLEON princified him.'

'No, no, he was second coachman,'—TOM PROTOCOL good-
naturedly interposed—'cavalry officer, FRANK, not an infantry
man.'

'Faith, you should have seen his fury (the young one's, I

mean) when he found me in the Duchess's room this evening,
tête-à-tête with the heiress, who deigned to accept a *bouquet* from
this hand.'

'It cost me three guineas,' poor FRANK said, with a shrug and
a sigh, 'and that Covent Garden scoundrel gives no credit; 'but
she took the flowers;—eh, BAGNIGGE?'

'And flung them to ALBONI,' the Peer replied, with a haughty
sneer. And poor little FRANKLIN FOX was compelled to own
that she had.

The *maître-d'hôtel* announced that supper was served. It
was remarked that even the *coulis de dindonneau* made no impression on BAGNIGGE that night.

———

The sensation produced by the *début* of AMETHYST PIMLICO at the Court of the Sovereign, and in the salons of the *beau-monde*, was such as has seldom been created by the appearance of any other beauty. The men were raving with love, and the women with jealousy. Her eyes, her beauty, her wit, her grace, her *ton*, caused a perfect *fureur* of admiration or envy.

Introduced by the DUCHESS OF FITZBATTLEAXE, along with her Grace's daughters, the Ladies GWENDOLINE and GWINEVER PORTCULLIS, the heiress's regal beauty quite flung her cousins' simple charms into the shade, and blazed with a splendour which caused all 'minor lights' to twinkle faintly. Before a day the *beau-monde*, before a week even the vulgarians of the rest of the town, rang with the fame of her beauty ; and while the dandies and the beauties were raving about her or tearing her to pieces in May Fair, even MRS. DOBBS (who had been to the pit of the 'Hoperer' in a green turban and a crumpled yellow satin) talked about the great *hairess* to her D. in Bloomsbury Square.

Crowds went to SQUAB and LYNCH'S, in Long Acre, to examine the carriages building for her, so faultless, so splendid, so quiet, so odiously unostentatious and provokingly simple ! Besides the ancestral services of *argenterie* and *vaisselle plate*, contained in a hundred and seventy-six plate chests at MESSRS. CHILDS, RUMBLE and BRIGGS prepared a gold service, and GARRAWAY, of the Haymarket, a service of the BENVENUTO CELLINI pattern, which were the admiration of all London. Before a month it is a fact that the wretched haberdashers in the city exhibited blue stocks, called 'Heiress-killers, very chaste, two-and-six ;' long before that, the *monde* had rushed to MADAME CRINOLINE'S, or sent couriers to MADAME MARABOU, at Paris, so as to have copies of her dresses ; but, as the Mantuan bard observes, 'Non cuivis contigit,'—every foot cannot accommodate itself to the *chaussure* of CINDERELLA.

With all this splendour, this worship, this beauty ; with these cheers following her, and these crowds at her feet, was AMETHYST happy ? Ah, no ! It is not under the necklace the most brilliant that BRIGGS and RUMBLE can supply ; it is not in LYNCH'S best cushioned chariot that the heart is most at ease. '*Que je me ruinerai*,' says FRONSAC in a letter to BOSSUET, '*si je savais ou acheter le bonheur.*'

With all her riches, with all her splendour, AMETHYST was wretched—wretched, because lonely ; wretched, because her loving heart had nothing to cling to. Her splendid mansion was a convent ; no male person ever entered it, except FRANKLIN FOX, (who counted for nothing), and the Duchess's family, her kinsman old LORD HUMPINGTON, his friend old SIR JOHN FOGEY, and her cousin, the odious, odious BORODINO.

The PRINCE DE BORODINO declared openly that AMETHYST was engaged to him. *Criblé de dettes*, it is no wonder that he should choose such an opportunity to *refaire sa fortune*. He gave out that he would kill any man who should cast an eye on the heiress, and the monster kept his word. MAJOR GRIGG, of the Life Guards, had already fallen by his hand at Ostend. The O'TOOLE, who had met her on the Rhine, had received a ball in his shoulder at Coblentz, and did not care to resume so dangerous a courtship. BORODINO could snuff a *bougie* at a hundred and fifty yards. He could beat BERTRAND or ALEXANDER DUMAS himself with the small sword; he was the dragon that watched this *pomme d'or*, and very few persons were now inclined to face a champion *si redoutable*.

Over a *Salmi d'escargot* at the Coventry, the dandies whom we introduced in our last volume were assembled there talking of the heiress, and her story was told by FRANKLIN FOX to LORD BAGNIGGE, who for a wonder was interested in the tale. BORODINO's pretensions were discussed, and the way in which the fair AMETHYST was confined. FITZBATTLEAXE House in Belgrave Square is — as everybody knows — the next mansion to that occupied by AMETHYST. A communication was made between the two houses. She never went out except accompanied by the Duchess's guard, which it was impossible to overcome.

'Impossible! Nothing's impossible,' said LORD BAGNIGGE.

'I bet you what you like you don't get in,' said the young MARQUIS OF MARTINGALE.

'I bet you a thousand ponies I stop a week in the heiress's house before the season's over,' LORD BAGNIGGE replied with a yawn; and the bet was registered with shouts of applause.

But it seemed as if the Fates had determined against LORD BAGNIGGE, for the very next day, riding in the Park, his horse fell with him; he was carried home to his house with a fractured limb and a dislocated shoulder, and the doctor's bulletins pronounced him to be in the most dangerous state.

MARTINGALE was a married man, and there was no danger of *his* riding by the FITZBATTLEAXE carriage. A fortnight after the above events, his Lordship was prancing by her Grace's great family coach, and chattering with LADY GWINEVER about the strange wager.

'Do you know what a pony is, LADY GWINEVER?' he asked. Her Ladyship said yes; she had a cream-coloured one at Castle

Barbican; and stared when LORD MARTINGALE announced that
he should soon have a thousand ponies; worth five-and-twenty
pounds each, which were all now kept at COUTTS'S. Then he
explained the circumstances of the bet with BAGNIGGE. Parlia-

ment was to adjourn in ten days; the season would be over
BAGNIGGE was lying ill *chez lui;* and the five-and-twenty thousand
were irrecoverably his.   And he vowed he would buy LORD
BINNACLE'S yacht—crew, captain, guns, and all.

On returning home that night from LADY POLKIMORE'S
MARTINGALE found among the many *billets* upon the gold *plateau*

n his *anti-chambre*, the following brief one, which made him
start :—

'DEAR MARTINGALE,—Don't be too sure of BINNACLE's yacht.
There are still ten days before the season is over ; and my ponies
may lie at COUTTS's for some time to come.—Yours,

'BAGNIGGE.'

'*P.S.* I write with my left hand ; for my right is still
splintered up from that confounded fall.'

The tall footman, number four, who had come in the place of
JOHN, cashiered (for want of proper *mollets*, and because his hair
did not take powder well) had given great satisfaction to the
under-butler, who reported well of him to his chief, who had
mentioned his name with praise to the house-steward. He was
so good-looking and well-spoken a young man, that the ladies in
the housekeeper's room deigned to notice him more than once ;
nor was his popularity diminished on account of a quarrel in
which he engaged with MONSIEUR ANATOLE, the enormous
Walloon *chasseur*, who was one day found embracing MISS
FLOUNCY, who waited on AMETHYST's own maid. The very
instant MISS FLOUNCY saw MR. JEAMES entering the Servants'
Hall, where MONSIEUR ANATOLE was engaged in ' aggravating '
her, MISS FLOUNCY screamed—at the next moment the Belgian
giant lay sprawling upon the carpet—and JEAMES, standing over
him, assumed so terrible a look, that the *chasseur* declined any
further combat. The victory was made known to the house-
steward himself, who, being a little partial to MISS FLOUNCY
herself, complimented JEAMES on his valour, and poured out a
glass of Madeira in his own room.

Who was JEAMES ? He had come recommended by the
BAGNIGGE people. He had lived, he said, in that family
two years. ' But where there was no ladies,' he said, ' a gentleman's hand was spiled for service,' and JEAMES's was a very
delicate hand ; MISS FLOUNCY admired it very much, and of
course he did not defile it by menial service ; he had in a young
man who called him ' Sir,' and did all the coarse work ; and
JEAMES read the morning paper to the ladies ; not spellingly
and with hesitation, as many gentlemen do, but easily and
elegantly, speaking off the longest words without a moment's

difficulty. He could speak French, too, MISS FLOUNCY found, who was studying it under MADEMOISELLE GRANDE, *fille-de-chambre de confiance;* for when she said to him, '*Polly voo Fransy,* MUNSEER JEAMES?' he replied readily, '*We, Mademaselle, j'ai passay boco de tong a Parry. Commong voo potty voo?*' How MISS FLOUNCY admired him as he stood before

her, the day after he had saved MISS AMETHYST, when the horses had run away with her in the Park!

Poor FLOUNCY, poor FLOUNCY! JEAMES had been but a week in AMETHYST's service, and already the gentle heart of the washing-girl was irrecoverably gone! Poor FLOUNCY! poor FLOUNCY! he thought not of thee.

It happened thus. MISS AMETHYST being engaged to drive with her cousin the Prince in his phaeton, her own carriage was sent into the Park simply with her companion, who had charge of her little Fido, the dearest little spaniel in the world. JEAMES and FREDERICK were behind the carriage with their long sticks and neat dark liveries; the horses were worth a thousand guineas each, the coachman a late Lieutenant Colonel of cavalry; the whole ring did not boast a more elegant turn-out.

The Prince drove his curricle, and had charge of his *belle cousine*. It may have been the red fezzes in the carriage of the Turkish ambassador which frightened the Prince's greys, or MRS. CHAMPIGNON's new yellow liveries, which were flaunting in the Park, or hideous LADY GORGON's preternatural ugliness, who passed in a low pony-carriage at the time, or the Prince's own want of skill, finally; but certain it is that the horses took fright, dashed wildly along the mile, scattered equipages, *pietons*, dandies' cabs, and Snobs' *pheaytons*. AMETHYST was screaming; and the Prince, deadly pale, had lost all presence of mind; as the curricle came rushing by the spot where MISS AMETHYST's carriage stood.

'I'm blest,' FREDERICK exclaimed to his companion, 'if it ain't the Prince a-drivin' our Missis! They'll be in the Serpingtine, or dashed to pieces, if they don't mind;' and the runaway steeds at this instant came upon them as a whirlwind.

But if those steeds ran at whirlwind pace, JEAMES was swifter. To jump from behind, to bound after the rocking, reeling curricle, to jump into it, aided by the long stick which he carried and used as a leaping-pole, and to seize the reins out of the hands of the miserable BORODINO, who shrieked piteously, as the dauntless valet leapt on his toes and into his seat, was the work of an instant. In a few minutes the mad, swaying rush of the horses was reduced to a swift but steady gallop; presently a canter, then a trot; until finally they pulled up smoking and trembling, but quite quiet, by the side of AMETHYST's carriage, which came up at a rapid pace.

'Give me the reins, *malappris! tu m'ecrasses les cors, manant!*' yelled the frantic nobleman, writhing underneath the intrepid charioteer.

'*Tant pis pour toi, nigaud,*' was the reply. The lovely AMETHYST of course had fainted; but she recovered as she was placed in her carriage, and rewarded her preserver with a celestial smile.

The rage, the fury, the maledictions of BORODINO, as he saw the latter—a liveried menial—stoop gracefully forward and kiss AMETHYST's hand, may be imagined rather than described. But JEAMES heeded not his curses. Having placed his adored mistress in the carriage, he calmly resumed his station behind.

Passion or danger seemed to have no impression upon that pale marble face.

BORODINO went home furious; nor was his rage diminished, when, on coming to dinner that day, a *recherché* banquet served in the *Frangipane* best style, and requesting a supply of a *purée a la bisque aux ecrevisses*, the clumsy attendant who served him let fall the assiette of *vermeille ciselé*, with its scalding contents, over the Prince's chin, his Mechlin *jabot*, and the grand *cordon* of the Legion of Honour which he wore.

'*Infâme*,' howled BORODINO, '*tu l'as fait exprès !*'

'*Oui, je l'ai fait exprès*,' said the man, with the most perfect Parisian accent. It was JEAMES.

Such insolence of course could not be passed unnoticed even after the morning's service, and he was *chasséd* on the spot. He had been but a week in the house.

The next month the newspapers contained a paragraph which may possibly elucidate the above mystery, and to the following effect :—

'*Singular Wager*.—One night, at the end of last season, the young and eccentric EARL OF B—GN—GGE laid a wager of twenty-five thousand pounds with a broken sporting patrician, the dashing MARQUIS OF M—RT—NG—LE, that he would pass a week under the roof of a celebrated and lovely young heiress, who lives not a hundred miles from B—LGR—VE SQU—RE. The bet having been made, the Earl pretended an illness, and having taken lessons from one of his lordship's own foot-men (MR. JAMES PLUSH, whose name he also borrowed) in "*the mysteries of the profession*" actually succeeded in making an entry into MISS P—ML—CO's mansion, where he stopped one week exactly ; having time to win his bet, and to save the life of the lady, whom we hear he is about to lead to the altar. He disarmed the PRINCE OF BORODINO in a duel fought on Calais sands—and, it is said, appeared at the C—— club wearing his *plush costume* under a cloak, and displaying it as a proof that he had won his wager.'

Such indeed, were the circumstances. The young couple have not more than nine hundred thousand a year, but they live cheer-fully, and manage to do good ; and EMILY DE PENTONVILLE, who adores her daughter-in-law, and her little grand-children, is blest in seeing her darling son *enfin un homme rangé*.

BARBAZURE

By G. P. R. Jeames, Esq, etc.

It was upon one of those balmy evenings of November which are only known in the valleys of Languedoc and among the mountains

of Alsace, that two cavaliers might have been perceived by the naked eye threading one of the rocky and romantic gorges that skirt the mountain-land between the Marne and the Garonne. The rosy tints of the declining luminary were gilding the peaks and crags which lined the path, through which the horsemen wound slowly; and as those eternal battlements with which Nature had hemmed in the ravine which our travellers trod,

blushed with the last tints of the fading sunlight, the valley
below was grey and darkling, and the hard and devious course
was sombre in twilight. A few goats, hardly visible among the
peaks, were cropping the scanty herbage here and there. The
pipes of shepherds, calling in their flocks as they trooped home-
wards to their mountain villages, sent up plaintive echoes which
moaned through those rocky and lonely steeps ; the stars began
to glimmer in the purple heavens, spread serenely overhead ; and
the faint crescent of the moon, which had peered for some time
scarce visible in the azure, gleamed out more brilliantly at every
moment, until it blazed as if in triumph at the sun's retreat.
'Tis a fair land that of France, a gentle, a green, and a beautiful ;
the home of arts and arms, of chivalry and romance, and (however sadly stained by the excesses of modern times) 'twas the
unbought grace of nations once, and the seat of ancient renown
and disciplined valour.

And of all that fair land of France, whose beauty is so bright,
and bravery so famous, there is no spot greener or fairer than
that one over which our travellers wended, and which stretches
between the good towns of Vendemiaire and Nivose. 'Tis
common now to a hundred thousand voyagers : the English
tourist, with his chariot and his HARVEY'S Sauce, and his
imperials ; the bustling *commis-voyageur* on the roof of the
rumbling diligence ; the rapid *malle-poste* thundering over the
chaussée at twelve miles an hour—pass the ground hourly and
daily now : 'twas lonely and unfrequented at the end of that
seventeenth century with which our story commences.

Along the darkening mountain paths the two gentlemen (for
such their outward bearing proclaimed them) caracolled together.
The one, seemingly the younger of the twain, wore a flaunting
feather in his barrat-cap, and managed a prancing Andalusian
palfrey that bounded and curvetted gaily. A surcoat of peach-
coloured samite and a purfled doublet of vair bespoke him noble,
as did his brilliant eye, his exquisitely chiselled nose, and his
curling chestnut ringlets.

Youth was on his brow ; his eyes were dark and dewy, like
spring violets ; and spring-roses bloomed upon his cheek—roses,
alas ! that bloom and die with life's spring ! Now bounding over
a rock, now playfully whisking off with his riding-rod a flowret
in his path, PHILIBERT DE COQUELICOT rode by his darker
companion.

His comrade was mounted upon a *destrière* of the true Norman
breed, that had first champed grass on the green pastures of
Acquitaine. Thence through Berry, Picardy, and the Limousin,

halting at many a city and commune, holding joust and tourney in many a castle and manor of Navarre, Poitou, and St. Germain l'Auxerrois, the warrior and his charger reached the lonely spot where now we find them.

The warrior who bestrode the noble beast was in sooth worthy of the steed which bore him. Both were caparisoned in the fullest trappings of feudal war. The arblast, the mangonel, the demiculverin, and the cuissart of the period, glittered upon the neck and chest of the war-steed; while the rider, with chamfron and catapult, with ban and arrière-ban, morion and tumbril, battle-axe and rifflard, and the other appurtenances of ancient chivalry, rode stately on his steel-clad charger, himself a tower of steel. This mighty horseman was carried by his steed as lightly as the young springald by his Andalusian hackney.

''Twas well done of thee, PHILIBERT,' said he of the proof-armour, 'to ride forth so far to welcome thy cousin and companion in arms.'

'Companion in battledore and shuttlecock, ROMANÉ DE CLOS-VOUGEOT!' replied the young Cavalier. 'When I was yet a page, thou wert a belted knight; and thou wert away to the Crusade ere ever my beard grew.'

'I stood by RICHARD of England at the gates of Ascalon, and drew the spear from sainted KING LOUIS in the tents of Damietta,' the individual addressed as ROMANÉ replied. 'Well-a-day! since thy beard grew, boy (and marry 'tis yet a thin one), I have broken a lance with SOLYMAN at Rhodes, and smoked a chibouque with SALADIN at Acre. But enough of this. Tell me of home—of our native valley—of my hearth, and my lady mother, and my good chaplain—tell me of *her*, PHILIBERT,' said the knight, executing a demivolte, in order to hide his emotion.

PHILIBERT seemed uneasy, and to strive as though he would parry the question. 'The Castle stands on the rock,' he said, 'and the swallows still build in the battlements. The good chaplain still chants his vespers at morn, and snuffles his matins at even-song. The lady-mother still distributeth tracts, and knitteth Berlin linsey-woolsey. The tenants pay no better, and the lawyers dun as sorely, kinsman mine,' he added with an arch look.

'But FATIMA, FATIMA, how fares she?' ROMANÉ continued. 'Since Lammas was a twelvemonth, I hear nought of her; my letters are unanswered. The postman hath traversed our camp every day, and never brought me a billet. How is FATIMA, PHILIBERT DE COQUELICOT?'

'She is—well,' PHILIBERT replied; 'her sister ANNE is the fairest of the twain, though.'

'Her sister ANNE was a baby when I embarked for Egypt.
A plague on sister ANNE! Speak of FATIMA, PHILIBERT—my
blue-eyed FATIMA!'

'I say she is—well,' answered his comrade, gloomily.

'Is she dead? Is she ill? Hath she the measles? Nay,
hath she had small-pox, and lost her beauty? Speak! speak,
boy!' cried the knight, wrought to agony.

'Her cheek is as red as her mother's, though the old Countess
paints hers every day. Her foot is as light as a sparrow's, and
her voice as sweet as a minstrel's dulcimer; but give me nathless
the LADY ANNE,' cried PHILIBERT, 'give me the peerless LADY
ANNE! As soon as ever I have won spurs, I will ride all
Christendom through, and proclaim her the Queen of Beauty.
Ho, LADY ANNE! LADY ANNE!' and so saying—but evidently
wishing to disguise some emotion, or conceal some tale his friend
could ill brook to hear—the reckless *damoiseau* galloped wildly
forward.

But swift as was his courser's pace, that of his companion's
enormous charger was swifter. 'Boy,' said the elder, 'thou hast
ill tidings. I knew it by thy glance. Speak: shall he who hath
bearded grim Death in a thousand fields shame to face truth from
a friend? Speak, in the name of Heaven and good SAINT
BOTIBOL, ROMANÉ DE CLOS-VOUGEOT will bear your tidings like
a man.'

'FATIMA is well,' answered PHILIBERT once again; 'she hath
had no measles: she lives and is still fair.'

'Fair, aye, peerless fair; but what more, PHILIBERT? Not
false? By SAINT BOTIBOL, say not false,' groaned the elder
warrior.

'A month syne,' PHILIBERT replied, 'she married the BARON
DE BARBAZURE.'

With that scream which is so terrible in a strong man in
agony, the brave knight ROMANÉ DE CLOS-VOUGEOT sank back at
these words, and fell from his charger to the ground, a lifeless
mass of steel.

IKE many another fabric of feudal war and splendour, the once vast and magnificent Castle of Barbazure is now a moss-grown ruin. The traveller of the present day, who wanders by the banks of the silvery Loire, and climbs the steep on which the magnificent edifice stood, can scarcely trace, among the shattered masses of ivy-coloured masonry which lie among the lonely crags, even the skeleton of the proud and majestic palace stronghold of the Barons of Barbazure.

In the days of our tale its turrets and pinnacles rose as stately, and seemed (to the pride of sinful man!) as strong as the eternal rocks on which they stood. The three mullets on a gules wavy reversed, surmounted by the sinople couchant Or, the well-known cognizance of the house, blazed in gorgeous heraldry on a hundred banners, surmounting as many towers. The long lines of battlemented walls spread down the mountain to the Loire, and were defended by thousands of steel-clad serving-men. Four hundred knights and six times as many archers fought round the banner of BARBAZURE at Bouvines, Malplaquet, and Azincour. For his services at Fontenoy against the English, the heroic CHARLES MARTEL appointed the fourteenth Baron Hereditary Grand Boot-jack of the kingdom of France: and for wealth, for splendour, and for skill and fame in war, RAOUL the twenty-eighth Baron, was in no wise inferior to his noble ancestors.

That the BARON RAOUL levied toll upon the river, and mail upon the shore; that he now and then ransomed a burgher, plundered a neighbour, or drew the fangs of a Jew; that he burned an enemy's castle with the wife and children within;— these were points for which the country knew and respected the stout Baron. When he returned from victory, he was sure to endow the Church with a part of his spoil, so that when he went

forth to battle he was always accompanied by her blessing.   Thus
lived the BARON RAOUL, the pride of the country in which he
dwelt, an ornament to the Court, the Church, and his neighbours.

But in the midst of all his power and splendour there was a
domestic grief which deeply afflicted the princely BARBAZURE.
His lovely ladies died one after the other.   No sooner was he
married than he was a widower ; in the course of eighteen years
no less than nine bereavements had befallen the chieftain.   So
true it is, that if fortune is a parasite, grief is a republican, and
visits the hall of the great and wealthy as it doth the humbler
tenements of the poor.

.   .   .

'Leave off deploring thy faithless, gad-about lover,' said the
Lady of Chacabacque to her daughter the lovely FATIMA, 'and
think how the noble BARBAZURE loves thee ! · Of all the damsels
at the ball last night, he had eyes for thee and thy cousin
only.'

'I am sure my cousin hath no good looks to be proud of,' the
admirable FATIMA exclaimed, bridling up.   'Not that I care for
my LORD OF BARBAZURE's looks.   My heart, dearest mother, is
with him who is far away !'

'He danced with thee four galliards, nine quadrilles, and
twenty-three corantoes, I think, child,' the mother said, eluding
her daughter's remark.

'Twenty-five,' said lovely FATIMA, casting her beautiful eyes
to the ground.   'Heigho ! but ROMANÉ danced them very
well.'

'He had not the court air,' the mother suggested.

'I don't wish to deny the beauty of the LORD OF BARBAZURE's
dancing, Mamma,' FATIMA replied.   'For a short, lusty man, 'tis
wondrous how active he is ; and in dignity the King's Grace
himself could not surpass him.'

'You were the noblest couple in the room, love,' the lady
cried.

'That pea-green doublet, slashed with orange-tawney, those
ostrich plumes, blue, red and yellow, those parti-coloured hose and
pink shoon became the noble Baron wondrous well,' FATIMA
acknowledged.   'It must be confessed that, though middle-aged,
he hath all the agility of youth.   But alas ! Madam ! The noble
Baron hath had nine wives already.'

'And your cousin would give her eyes to become the tenth,'
the mother replied.

'My cousin give her eyes !' FATIMA exclaimed.   'It's not

much, I'm sure, for she squints abominably;' and thus the ladies prattled, as they rode home at night after the great ball at the house of the BARON OF BARBAZURE.

The gentle reader, who has overheard their talk, will understand the doubts which pervaded the mind of the lovely FATIMA, and the well-nurtured English maiden will participate in the divided feelings which rent her bosom. 'Tis true, that on his departure for the holy wars, ROMANÉ and FATIMA were plighted to each other; but the folly of long engagements is proverbial: and though for many months the faithful and affectionate girl had looked in vain for news from him, her admirable parents had long spoken with repugnance of a match which must bring inevitable poverty to both parties. They had suffered, 'tis true, the engagement to subsist, hostile as they ever were to it; but when on the death of the ninth lady of BARBAZURE, the noble Baron remarked FATIMA at the funeral, and rode home with her after the ceremony, her prudent parents saw how much wiser, better, happier, for their child it would be to have for life a partner like the Baron, than to wait the doubtful return of the penniless wanderer to whom she was plighted.

Ah! how beautiful and pure a being! how regardless of self! how true to duty! how obedient to parental command, is that earthly angel, a well-bred woman of genteel family! Instead of indulging in splenetic refusals or vain regrets for her absent lover, the exemplary FATIMA, at once signified to her excellent parents her willingness to obey their orders; though she had sorrows (and she declared them to be tremendous) the admirable being disguised them so well, that none knew they oppressed her. She said she would try to forget former ties, and (so strong in her mind was *duty* above every other feeling; so strong may it be in every British maiden!) the lovely girl kept her promise.

'My former engagements,' she said, packing up ROMANÉ'S letters and presents, (which, as the good knight was mortal poor were in sooth of no great price)—'my former engagements I look upon as childish follies; my affections are fixed where my dear parents graft them—on the noble, the princely, the polite BARBAZURE. 'Tis true he is not comely in feature, but the chaste and well-bred female knows how to despise the fleeting charms of form. 'Tis true he is old; but can woman be better employed than in tending her aged and sickly companion? That he has been married is likewise certain—but ah, my mother! who knows not that he must be a good and tender husband, who, nine times wedded, owns that he cannot be happy without another partner?'

It was with these admirable sentiments, the lovely FATIMA proposed obedience to her parents' will, and consented to receive the magnificent marriage gift presented to her by her gallant bridegroom.

The old COUNTESS OF CHACABACQUE had made a score of vain attempts to see her hapless daughter. Ever, when she came, the porters grinned at her savagely through the grating of the portcullis of the vast embattled gate of the Castle of Barbazure, and rudely bade her begone. 'THE LADY OF BARBAZURE sees nobody but her confessor, and keeps her chamber,' was the invariable reply of the dogged functionaries to the entreaties of the agonised mother. And at length, so furious was he at her perpetual calls at his gate, that the angry LORD OF BARBAZURE himself, who chanced to be at the postern, armed a cross-bow, and let fly an arblast at the crupper of the lady's palfrey, whereon she fled finally, screaming, and in terror. 'I will aim at the rider next time!' howled the ferocious Baron, 'and not at the horse!' And those who knew his savage nature and his unrivalled skill as a bowman, knew that he would neither break his knightly promise nor miss his aim.

Since the fatal day when the Grand Duke of Burgundy gave his famous passage of arms at Nantes, and all the nobles of France were present at the joustings, it was remarked that the BARBAZURE'S heart was changed towards his gentle and virtuous lady.

For the three first days of that famous festival, the redoubted BARON OF BARBAZURE had kept the field against all the knights who entered. His lance bore everything down before it. The most famous champions of Europe, assembled at those joustings, had dropped one by one, before this tremendous warrior. The prize of the tourney was destined to be his, and he was to be proclaimed bravest of the brave, as his lady was fairest of the fair.

On the third day, however, as the sun was declining over the Vosges, and the shadows were lengthening over the plain where the warrior had obtained such triumphs;—after having overcome two hundred and thirteen knights of different nations, including the fiery DUNOIS, the intrepid WALTER MANNY, the spotless BAYARD, and the undaunted DUGUESCLIN, as the conqueror sate still erect on his charger, and the multitude doubted whether ever another champion could be found to face him, three blasts of a trumpet were heard, faint at first, but at every moment ringing more clearly, until a knight in pink armour rode into the lists with his visor down, and riding a tremendous dun charger, which he managed to the admiration of all present.

The heralds asked him his name and quality.

'Call me,' said he, in a hollow voice, "the Jilted Knight." What was it made the LADY OF BARBAZURE tremble at his accents?

The knight refused to tell his name and qualities; but the companion who rode with him, the young and noble PHILIBERT DE COQUELICOT, who was known and respected universally through the neighbourhood, gave a warranty for the birth and noble degree of the Jilted Knight,—and RAOUL DE BARBAZURE, yelling hoarsely for a two hundred and fourteenth lance, shook the huge weapon in the air as though it were a reed, and prepared to encounter the intruder.

According to the wont of chivalry, and to keep the point of the spear from harm, the top of the unknown knight's lance was shielded with a bung, which the warrior removed; and galloping up to BARBAZURE'S pavilion, over which his shield hung, touched that noble cognizance with the sharpened steel.   A thrill of excitement ran through the assembly at this daring challenge to a *combat à l'outrance*. 'Hast thou confessed, Sir Knight?' roared the BARBAZURE; 'take thy ground, and look to thyself; for by Heaven thy last hour is come!' Poor youth, poor youth! sighed the spectators; he has called down his own fate. The next minute the signal was given, and as the simoom across the desert, the cataract down the rock, the shell from the howitzer, each warrior rushed from his goal. . . .

'Thou wilt not slay so good a champion!' said the Grand Duke, as at the end of that terrific combat the knight in rose armour stood over his prostrate foe, whose helmet had rolled off when he was at length unhorsed, and whose blood-shot eyes glared unutterable hate and ferocity on his conqueror.

'Take thy life,' said he who had styled himself the Jilted Knight; 'thou hast taken all that was dear to mine;' and the sun setting, and no other warrior appearing to do battle against him, he was proclaimed the conqueror, and rode up to the duchess's balcony to receive the gold chain which was the reward of the victor. He raised his visor as the smiling princess guerdoned him—raised it, and gave *one* sad look towards the LADY FATIMA at her side!

'ROMANÉ DE CLOS - VOUGEOT!' shrieked she, and fainted. The BARON OF BARBAZURE heard the name as he writhed on the ground with his wound, and by his slighted honour, by his broken ribs, by his roused fury, he swore revenge; and the LADY FATIMA, who had come to the tourney as a Queen, returned to her castle as a prisoner.

(As it is impossible to give in the limits of our periodical the whole of this remarkable novel, let it suffice to say briefly here, that in about a volume and a half, in which the descriptions of scenery, the account of the agonies of the Baroness kept on bread and water in her dungeon, and the general tone of morality, are all excellently worked out, the BARON DE BARBAZURE resolves upon putting his wife to death by the hands of the public executioner.)

.   .   .   .   .

Two minutes before the clock struck noon, the savage Baron was on the platform to inspect the preparations for the frightful ceremony of mid-day.

The block was laid forth—the hideous minister of vengeance, masked and in black, with the flaming glaive in his hand, was ready. The Baron tried the edge of the blade with his finger, and asked the dreadful swordsman if his hand was sure? A nod was the reply of the man of blood. The weeping garrison and domestics shuddered and shrank from him. There was not one there but loved and pitied the gentle lady.

Pale, pale as a stone, she was brought from her dungeon. To all her lord's savage interrogatories, her reply had been, 'I am innocent.' To his threats of death, her answer was, 'You are my lord; my life is in your hands, to take or to give.' How few are the wives, in our day, who show such angelic meekness! It touched all hearts around her, save that of the implacable BARBAZURE. Even the LADY BLANCHE (FATIMA'S cousin) whom he had promised to marry upon his faithless wife's demise, besought for her kinswoman's life, and a divorce, but BARBAZURE had vowed her death.

'Is there no pity, sir?' asked the chaplain who had attended her. 'No pity,' echoed the weeping serving-maid. 'Did I not aye say I would die for my lord?' said the gentle lady, and placed herself at the block.

SIR RAOUL DE BARBAZURE seized up the long ringlets of her raven hair. 'Now!' shouted he to the executioner, with a stamp of his foot, 'Now strike!'

The man (who knew his trade) advanced at once, and poised himself to deliver his blow : and, making his flashing sword sing in the air, with one irresistible, rapid stroke, it sheared clean off the head of—the furious, the blood-thirsty, the implacable Baron DE BARBAZURE !

Thus he fell a victim to his own jealousy ; and the agitation of the LADY FATIMA may be imagined when the executioner, flinging off his mask, knelt gracefully at her feet, and revealed to her the well-known features of ROMANÉ DE CLOS-VOUGEOT.

PHIL FOGARTY—A TALE OF THE FIGHTING ONETY-ONETH

By Harry Rollicker

THE gabion was ours.   After two hours' fighting we were in possession of the first embrasure, and made ourselves as comfortable as circumstances would admit.   JACK DELAMERE, TOM DELANEY, JERRY BLAKE, the Doctor, and myself, sate down under a pontoon, and our servants laid out a hasty supper on a tumbril.   Though CAMBACÉRÈS had escaped me so provokingly after I cut him down, his spoils were mine, a cold fowl and a Bologna sausage were found in the Marshal's holsters; and in the haversack of a French private who lay a corpse on the glacis, we found a loaf of bread, his three days' ration.   Instead of salt we had gunpowder; and you may be sure, wherever the Doctor was, a flask of good brandy was behind him in his instrument-case.   We sate down and made a soldier's supper.   The Doctor pulled a few of the delicious fruit from the lemon-trees growing near (and round which the Carabiniers and the 24th Leger had made a desperate rally), and punch was brewed in JACK DELAMERE's helmet.

'Faith, it never had so much wit in it before,' said the Doctor, as he ladled out the drink.   We all roared with laughter, except the guardsman, who was as savage as a Turk at a christening.

'*Buvez-en*,' said old SAWBONES to our French prisoner; '*ça vous fera du bien, mon vieux coq !*' and the Colonel, whose wound had been just dressed, eagerly grasped at the proffered cup, and drained it with a health to the donors.

How strange are the chances of war!   But half-an-hour before he and I were engaged in mortal combat, and our prisoner was all but my conqueror.   Grappling with CAMBACÉRÈS, whom I had knocked from his horse, and was about to despatch, I felt a lunge behind, which luckily was parried by my sabretasche, a herculean grasp was at the next instant at my throat—I was on the ground —my prisoner had escaped, and a gigantic warrior in the uniform of a colonel of the regiment of Artois glaring over me with pointed sword.

'*Rends-toi, coquin !*' said he.

'*Allez au Diable !*' says I, 'a FOGARTY never surrenders.'

I thought of my poor mother and my sisters, at the old house in Killaloo—I felt the tip of his blade between my teeth—I breathed a prayer and shut my eyes—when the tables were turned

—the butt-end of LANTY CLANCY'S musket knocked the sword up and broke the arm that held it.

'*Thonamoundiaoul nabochlish*,' said the French officer, with a curse in the purest Irish. It was lucky that I stopped laughing time enough to bid LANTY hold his hand, for the honest fellow would else have brained my gallant adversary. We were the better friends for our combat, as what gallant hearts are not?

The breach was to be stormed at sunset, and like true soldiers we sate down to make the most of our time. The rogue of a Doctor took the liver-wing for his share—we gave the other to our guest, a prisoner; those scoundrels JACK DELAMERE and TOM DELANEY took the legs—and, faith, poor I was put off with the Pope's nose, and a bit of the back.

'How d'ye like his Holiness's *fayture?*' said JERRY BLAKE.

'Anyhow you'll have a *merry thought*,' cried the incorrigible Doctor, and all the party shrieked at the witticism.

'*De mortuis nil nisi bonum*,' said Jack, holding up the drumstick clean.

'Faith, there's not enough of it to make us *chicken-hearted*, anyhow,' said I; 'come, boys, let's have a song.'

'Here goes,' said TOM DELANEY, and sang the following lyric, of his own composition :—

> 'Dear JACK, this white mug that with GUINNESS I fill,
> And drink to the health of sweet NAN of the Hill,
> Was once TOMMY TOSSPOT's, as jovial a sot,
> As e'er drew a spiggot, or drained a full pot—
> In drinking all round 'twas his joy to surpass,
> And with all merry tipplers he drank off his glass.

> 'One morning in summer, while seated so snug,
> In the porch of his garden, discussing his jug,
> Stern Death, on a sudden, to TOM did appear,
> And said, "Honest THOMAS, come take your last bier;"
> We kneaded his clay in the shape of this can,
> From which let us drink to the health of my NAN.'

'Psha!' said the Doctor, 'I've heard that song before; here's a new one for you, boys!' and SAWBONES began, in a rich Corkagian voice :—

> 'You've all heard of LARRY O'TOOLE,
> Of the beautiful town of Drumgoole;
> He had but one eye,
> To ogle ye by—
> O, murther, but that was a jew'l!
> A fool
> He made of de girls, dis O'TOOLE.

'Twas he was the boy didn't fail,
That tuck down pataties and mail ;
    He never would shrink,
    From any sthrong dthrink,
Was it whisky or Drogheda ale ;
      I'm bail
This LARRY would swallow a pail.

O, many a night, at the bowl,
With LARRY I've sot cheek by jowl ;
    He's gone to his rest,
    Where there's dthrink of the best,
And so let us give his old sowl
      A howl,
For 'twas he made the noggin to rowl.'

I observed the French Colonel's eye glisten as he heard these well-known accents of his country ; but we were too well-bred to pretend to remark his emotion.

The sun was setting behind the mountains as our songs were finished, and each began to look out with some anxiety for the preconcerted signal, the rocket from SIR HUSSEY VIVIAN'S quarters, which was to announce the recommencement of hostilities. It came just as the moon rose in her silver splendour, and ere the rocket-stick fell quivering to earth at the feet of GENERAL PICTON and Sir LOWRY COLE, who were at their posts at the head of the storming parties, nine hundred and ninety-nine guns in position opened their fire from our batteries, which were answered by a tremendous cannonade from the fort.

'Who's going to dance ?' said the Doctor, 'the ball's begun. Ha ! there goes poor JACK DELAMERE'S head off ! The ball chose a soft one, anyhow. Come here, TIM, till I mend your leg. Your wife need only knit half as many stockings next year, Doolan, my boy. Faix ! there goes a big one had well-nigh stopped my talking ; bedad ! it has snuffed the feather off my cocked hat !'

In this way, with eighty-four pounders roaring over us like hail, the undaunted little Doctor pursued his jokes and his duty. That he had a feeling heart, all who served with him knew, and none more so than PHILIP FOGARTY, the humble writer of this tale of war.

Our embrasure was luckily bomb-proof, and the detachment of the gallant Onety-oneth under my orders suffered comparatively little. 'Be cool, boys,' I said ; 'it will be hot enough work for

you ere long.' The honest fellows answered with an Irish cheer.
I saw that it affected our prisoner.

'Countryman,' said I, 'I know you; but an Irishman was
never a traitor.'

'*Taisez-vous!*' said he, putting his finger to his lip. '*C'est la
fortune de la guerre:* if ever you come to Paris, ask for the
MARQUIS D' O'MAHONY, and I may render you the hospitality
which your tyrannous laws prevent me from exercising in the
ancestral halls of my own race.'

I shook him warmly by the hand as a tear bedimmed his eye.
It was, then, the celebrated Colonel of the Irish Brigade, created a
Marquis by NAPOLEON on the field of Austerlitz!

'Marquis,' said I, 'the country which disowns you is proud of
you; but—ha! here, if I mistake not, comes our signal to advance.'
And in fact CAPTAIN VANDELEUR, riding up through the shower
of shot, asked for the commander of the detachment, and bade me
hold myself in readiness to move as soon as the flank companies
of the Ninety-ninth, and Sixty-sixth, and the Grenadier Brigade of
the German Legion began to advance up the echelon. The devoted
band soon arrived: JACK BOWSER heading the Ninety-ninth,

(when was he away and a storming party to the fore?), and the gallant POTZTAUSEND with his Hanoverian veterans.

The second rocket flew up.

'Forward, Onety-oneth,' cried I, in a voice of thunder. 'Killaloo boys, follow your Captain!' and with a shrill hurray, that sounded above the tremendous fire from the fort, we sprung up the steep; BOWSER, with the brave Ninety-ninth, and the bold POTZTAUSEND, keeping well up with us. We passed the demilune, we cleared the culverin, bayoneting the artillerymen at their guns; we advanced across the two tremendous demilunes which flank the counterscarp, and prepared for the final spring upon the citadel. SOULT I could see quite pale on the wall; and the scoundrel CAMBACÉRÈS, who had been so nearly my prisoner that day, trembled as he cheered his men. 'On boys, on!' I hoarsely exclaimed. 'Hurroo,' said the fighting Onety-oneth.

But there was a movement among the enemy. An officer, glittering with orders, and another in a grey coat and a cocked hat, came to the wall, and I recognised the EMPEROR NAPOLEON and the famous JOACHIM MURAT.

'We are hardly pressed, methinks,' NAPOLEON said sternly. 'I must exercise my old trade as an artilleryman;' and MURAT loaded, and the EMPEROR pointed the only hundred-and-twenty-four pounder that had not been silenced by our fire.

'Hurray, Killaloo boys!' shouted I. The next moment a sensation of numbness and death seized me, and I lay like a corpse upon the rampart.

'HUSH!' said a voice, which I recognised to be that of the MARQUIS D' O'MAHONY. 'Heaven be praised, reason has returned to you. For six weeks those are the only sane words I have heard from you.'

'Faix, and 'tis thrue for you, Colonel dear,' cried another voice, with which I was even more familiar; 'twas that of my honest and gallant LANTY CLANCY, who was blubbering at my bedside, overjoyed at his master's recovery.

'O musha! MASTHER PHIL. Agrah! but this will be the great day intirely, when I send off the news, which I would, barrin' I can't write, to the lady, your mother,

and your sisters, at Castle Fogarty ; and 'tis his Riv'rence FATHER
LUKE will jump for joy thin, when he reads the letthur ! Six weeks
ravin' and roarin' as bould as a lion, and as mad as MICK MALONY's
pig, that mistuck MICK's wig for a cabbage, and died of atin' it !'

'And have I then lost my senses ?' I exclaimed feebly.

'Sure, didn't ye call me your beautiful DONNA ANNA only
yesterday, and catch hould of me whiskers as if they were the
Signora's jet black ringlets ?' LANTY cried.

At this moment, and blushing deeply, the most beautiful young
creature I ever set my eyes upon, rose from a chair at the foot of
the bed, and sailed out of the room.

'Confusion ! you blundering rogue,' I cried, 'who is that
lovely lady whom you frightened away by your impertinence ?
DONNA ANNA ? Where am I ?'

'You are in good hands, PHILIP,' said the Colonel, 'you are at
my house in the Place Vendôme, at Paris, of which I am the
Military Governor. You and LANTY were knocked down by the
wind of the cannon-ball at Burgos. Do not be ashamed : 'twas
the EMPEROR pointed the gun ;' and the Colonel took off his hat
as he mentioned the name darling to France. 'When our troops
returned from the sally in which your gallant storming-party was
driven back, you were found on the glacis, and I had you brought
into the city. Your reason had left you, however, when you
returned to life ; but, unwilling to desert the son of my old friend,
PHILIP FOGARTY, who saved my life in '98, I brought you in my
carriage to Paris.'

'And many's the time you tried to jump out of the windy,
MASTHER PHIL,' said CLANCY.

'Brought you to Paris,' resumed the Colonel smiling, 'where,
by the *soins* of my friends BROUSSAIS, ESQUIROL, and BARON
LARREY, you have been restored to health, thank Heaven !'

'And that lovely angel who quitted the apartment ?' I cried.

'That lovely angel is the LADY BLANCHE SARSFIELD, my
ward, a descendant of the gallant LUCAN, and who may be, when
she chooses, MADAME LA MARÉCHALE DE CAMBACÉRÈS, DUCHESS
OF ILLYRIA.'

'Why did you deliver the ruffian when he was in my grasp ?'
I cried.

'Why did LANTY deliver you when in mine ?' the Colonel
replied. *C'est la fortune de la guerre, mon garçon ;* but calm
yourself, and take this potion which BLANCHE has prepared for you.'

I drank the *tisane* eagerly when I heard whose fair hands had
compounded it, and its effects were speedily beneficial to me, for
I sank into a cool and refreshing slumber.

From that day I began to mend rapidly, with all the elasticity of youth's happy time. BLANCHE—the enchanting BLANCHE—ministered henceforth to me, for I would take no medicine but from her lily hand. And what were the effects? Faith, ere a month was past, the patient was over head and ears in love with the doctor; and as for BARON LARREY, and BROUSSAIS, and ESQUIROL, they were sent to the right-about. In a short time I was in a situation to do justice to the *gigot aux navets*, the *bœuf aux cornichons*, and the other delicious *entremets* of the Marquis's board, with an appetite that astonished some of the Frenchmen who frequented it.

'Wait till he's quite well, Miss,' said LARRY, who waited always behind me. 'Faith! when he's in health, I'd back him to ate a cow, barrin' the horns and teel.' I sent a decanter at the rogue's head, by way of answer to his impertinence.

Although the disgusting CAMBACÉRÈS did his best to have my parole withdrawn from me, and to cause me to be sent to the English depôt of prisoners at Verdun, the Marquis's interest with the EMPEROR prevailed, and I was allowed to remain at Paris, the happiest of prisoners at the Colonel's hotel at the Place Vendôme. I here had the opportunity (an opportunity not lost, I flatter myself, on a young fellow with the accomplishments of PHILIP FOGARTY, ESQ.) of mixing with the *élite* of French society, and meeting with many of the great, the beautiful, and the brave. TALLEYRAND was a frequent guest of the Marquis's. His *bon-mots* used to keep the table in a roar. NEY frequently took his chop with us; MURAT, when in town, constantly dropt in for a cup of tea and friendly round game. Alas! who would have thought those two gallant heads would be so soon laid low! My wife has a pair of earrings which the latter, who always wore them, presented to her—but we are advancing matters. Anybody could see, '*avec un demi-œil*' as the PRINCE OF BENEVENTO remarked, how affairs went between me and BLANCHE; but though she loathed him for his cruelties and the odiousness of his person, the brutal CAMBACÉRÈS still pursued his designs upon her.

I recollect it was on ST. PATRICK'S Day. My lovely friend had procured, from the gardens of the EMPRESS JOSEPHINE, at Malmaison (whom we loved a thousand times more than her Austrian successor, a sandy-haired woman, between ourselves, with an odious squint), a quantity of shamrock, to garnish the hotel, and all the Irish in Paris were invited to the national festival.

I and PRINCE TALLEYRAND danced a double hornpipe with PAULINE BONAPARTE and MADAME DE STAEL; MARSHAL SOULT went down a couple of sets with MADAME RECAMIER; and

Robespierre's widow—an excellent gentle creature, quite unlike her husband—stood up with the Austrian Ambassador. Besides, the famous artists Baron Gros, David and Nicholas Poussin, and Canova, who was in town making a statue of the Emperor, for Leo X., and in a word all the celebrities of Paris— as my gifted countrywoman, the Wild Irish Girl, calls them—were assembled in the Marquis's elegant receiving-rooms.

At last a great outcry was raised for *La Gigue Irlandaise!* *La Gigue Irlandaise!* a dance which had made a *fureur* amongst the Parisians ever since the lovely Blanche Sarsfield had danced it. She stepped forward and took me for a partner, and amidst the bravos of the crowd, in which stood Ney, Murat, Lannes, the Prince of Wagram, and the Austrian Ambassador, we showed to the *beau monde* of the French capital, I flatter myself, a not unfavourable specimen of the dance of our country.

As I was cutting the double-shuffle, and toe-and-heeling it in the ‘rail’ style, Blanche danced up to me, smiling, and said, ‘Be on your guard; I see Cambacérès talking to Fouché, the Duke of Otranto, about us—and when Otranto turns his eyes upon a man, they bode him no good.’

‘Cambacérès is jealous,’ said I. ‘I have it,’ says she; ‘I’ll make him dance a turn with me.’ So presently, as the music was going like mad all this time, I pretended fatigue from my late wounds, and sate down. The lovely Blanche went up smiling, and brought out Cambacérès as a second partner.

The Marshal is a lusty man, who makes desperate efforts to give himself a waist, and the effect of the exercise upon him was speedily visible. He puffed and snorted like a walrus, drops trickled down his purple face, while my lovely mischief of a Blanche went on dancing at treble quick, till she fairly danced him down.

‘Who’ll take the flure with me?’ said the charming girl, animated by the sport.

‘Faix, den, ’tis I, Lanty Clancy!’ cried my rascal, who had been mad with excitement at the scene; and, stepping in with a whoop and a hurroo, he began to dance with such a rapidity, as made all present stare.

As the couple were footing it, there was the noise as of a cavalcade rapidly traversing the Place Vendôme, and stopping at the Marquis's door. A crowd appeared to mount the stair; the great doors of the reception-room were flung open, and two pages announced their Majesties the Emperor and the Empress. So engaged were Lanty and Blanche, that they never heard the tumult occasioned by the august approach.

It was indeed the Emperor, who returning from the Theatre
Français, and seeing the Marquis's windows lighted up, proposed
to the Empress to drop in on the party.   He made signs to the
musicians to continue ; and the conqueror of Marengo and Friedland watched with interest the simple evolutions of two happy

Irish people.   Even the Empress smiled ; and, seeing this, all the
courtiers, including NAPLES and TALLEYRAND, were delighted.
  'Is not this a great day for Ireland?' said the Marquis, with a
tear trickling down his noble face.   'O Ireland !   O my country !
But no more of that.   Go up, Phil, you divvle, and offer her
Majesty the choice of punch or negus.'

AMONG the young fellows with whom I was most intimate in Paris, was EUGÈNE BEAUHARNAIS, the son of the ill-used and unhappy JOSEPHINE by her former marriage with a French gentleman of good family. Having a smack of the old blood in him, EUGÈNE'S manners were much more refined than those of the new-fangled dignitaries of the EMPEROR'S Court; where (for my knife and fork was regularly laid at the Tuileries) I have seen my poor friend MURAT repeatedly mistake a fork for a toothpick, and the gallant MASSENA devour peas by means of his knife, in a way more innocent than graceful. TALLEYRAND, EUGÈNE, and I, used often to laugh at these eccentricities of our brave friends, who certainly did not shine in the drawing-room, however brilliant they were in the field of battle. The EMPEROR always asked me to take wine with him, and was full of kindness and attention. 'I like EUGÈNE' (he would say to me, pinching my ear confidentially, as his way was,) —'I like EUGÈNE to keep company with such young fellows as you; you have manners; you have principles; my rogues from the camp have none. And I like you, PHILIP my boy,' he added, 'for being so attentive to my poor wife—the EMPRESS JOSEPHINE, I mean.' All these honours made my friends at the Marquis's very proud, and my enemies at Court *crever* with envy. Among these, the atrocious CAMBACÉRÈS was not the least active and envenomed.

The cause of the many attentions which were paid to me, and which, like a vain coxcomb, I had chosen to attribute to my own personal amiability, soon was apparent. Having formed a good opinion of my gallantry from my conduct in various actions and forlorn hopes during the war, the EMPEROR was most anxious to attach me to his service. The Grand Cross of St. Louis, the title of Count, the command of a crack cavalry regiment, the 14me Chevaux Marins, were the bribes that were actually offered to me; and, must I say it! BLANCHE, the lovely, the perfidious BLANCHE, was one of the agents employed to tempt me to commit this act of treason.

'Object to enter a foreign service!' she said, in reply to my refusal. 'It is you, PHILIP, who are in a foreign service. The Irish nation is in exile, and in the territories of its French allies.

Irish traitors are not here ; they march alone under the accursed flag of the Saxon, whom the great NAPOLEON would have swept from the face of the earth, but for the fatal valour of Irish mercenaries ! Accept this offer, and my heart, my hand, my all are yours. Refuse it, PHILIP, and we part.'

'To wed the abominable CAMBACÉRÈS !' I cried, stung with rage. 'To wear a duchess's coronet, BLANCHE ! Ha, ha ! Mushrooms, instead of strawberry-leaves, should decorate the brows of the upstart French nobility. I shall withdraw my parole. I demand to be sent to prison—to be exchanged—to die —anything rather than be a traitor, and the tool of a traitress !' Taking up my hat, I left the room in a fury ; and flinging open the door, tumbled over CAMBACÉRÈS, who was listening at the keyhole, and must have overheard every word of our conversation.

We tumbled over each other, as BLANCHE was shrieking with laughter at our mutual discomfiture. Her scorn only made me more mad ; and, having spurs on, I began digging them into CAMBACÉRÈS' fat sides as we rolled on the carpet, until the Marshal howled with rage and anger.

'This insult must be avenged with blood !' roared the DUKE OF ILLYRIA.

'I have already drawn it,' says I, 'with my spurs.'

'*Malheur et malédiction !*' roared the Marshal.

'Hadn't you better settle your wig ?' says I, offering it to him on the tip of my cane, 'and we'll arrange time and place when you have put your jasey in order.' I shall never forget the look of revenge which he cast at me, as I was thus turning him into ridicule before his mistress.

'LADY BLANCHE,' I continued bitterly, 'as you look to share the Duke's coronet, hadn't you better see to his wig ?' and so saying, I cocked my hat, and walked out of the Marquis's place, whistling 'Garryowen.'

I knew my man would not be long in following me, and waited for him in the Place Vendôme, where I luckily met EUGÈNE too, who was looking at the picture-shop in the corner. I explained to him my affair in a twinkling. He at once agreed to go with me to the ground, and commended me, rather than otherwise, for refusing the offer which had been made to me. 'I knew it would be so,' he said kindly ; 'I told my father you wouldn't. A man with the blood of the FOGARTIES, PHIL, my boy, doesn't wheel about like these fellows of yesterday.' So, when CAMBACÉRÈS came out, which he did presently, with a more furious air than before, I handed him at once over to EUGÈNE, who begged him to name a friend, and an early hour for the meeting to take place.

'Can you make it before eleven, PHIL?' said BEAUHARNAIS. 'The EMPEROR reviews the troops in the Bois de Boulogne at that hour, and we might fight there handy before the review.'

'Done!' said I. 'I want, of all things, to see the newly arrived Saxon cavalry manœuvre;' on which CAMBACÉRÈS giving me a look, as much as to say, 'See sights! Watch cavalry manœuvres! Make your soul, and take measure for a coffin, my boy!' walked away, naming our mutual acquaintance, MARSHAL NEY, to EUGÈNE, as his second in the business.

I had purchased from MURAT a very fine Irish horse, *Bugaboo* out of *Smithereens*, by *Fadladeen*, which ran into the French ranks at Salamanca, with poor JACK CLONAKILTY, of the 13th, dead on the top of him. Bugaboo was much too ugly an animal for the KING of NAPLES, who, though a showy horseman, was a bad rider across country; and I got the horse for a song. A wickeder and uglier brute never wore pig-skin; and I never put my leg over such a timber-jumper in my life. I rode the horse down to the Bois de Boulogne on the morning that the affair with CAMBACÉRÈS was to come off, and LANTY held him as I went in, 'sure to win,' as they say in the ring.

CAMBACÉRÈS was known to be the best shot in the French army; but I, who am a pretty good hand at a snipe, thought a man was bigger, and that I could wing him if I had a mind. As soon as NEY gave the word, we both fired; I felt a whizz past my left ear, and putting up my hand there, found a large piece of my whiskers gone; whereas at the same moment, and shrieking a horrible malediction, my adversary reeled and fell.

'*Mon Dieu, il est mort!*' cried NEY.

'*Pas du tout,*' said BEAUHARNAIS. '*Ecoute; il jure toujours.*'

And such, indeed, was the fact: the supposed dead man lay on the ground cursing most frightfully. We went up to him: he was blind with the loss of blood, and my ball had carried off the bridge of his nose. He recovered; but he was always called the Prince of Ponterotto in the French army, afterwards. The surgeon in attendance having taken charge of this unfortunate warrior, we rode off to the review, where NEY and EUGÈNE were on duty at the head of their respective divisions; and where, by the way, CAMBACÉRÈS, as the French say, '*se faisait désirer.*'

It was arranged that CAMBACÉRÈS' division of six battalions and nine-and-twenty squadrons should execute a *ricochet* movement, supported by artillery in the intervals, and converging by different *epauléments* on the light infantry, that formed, as usual, the centre of the line. It was by this famous manœuvre that at Arcola, at Montenotte, at Friedland, and subsequently at Mazagran,

SUWAROFF, PRINCE CHARLES, and GENERAL CASTANOS were defeated with such victorious slaughter : but it is a movement which, I need not tell every military man, requires the greatest delicacy of execution, and which, if it fails, plunges an army into confusion.

'Where is the DUKE OF ILLYRIA?' NAPOLEON asked. 'At the head of his division, no doubt,' said MURAT : at which EUGÈNE, giving me an arch look, put his hand to his nose, and caused me almost to fall off my horse with laughter. NAPOLEON looked sternly at me ; but at this moment the troops getting in motion, the celebrated manœuvre began, and His Majesty's attention was taken off from my impudence.

MILHAUD'S Dragoons, their bands playing *Vive Henri Quatre*, their cuirasses gleaming in the sunshine, moved upon their own centre from the left flank in the most brilliant order, while the Carabineers of FOY, and the Grenadiers of the Guard under DROUET D'ERLON, executed a carambolade on the right, with the precision which became those veteran troops ; but the Chasseurs of the young guard, marching by twos instead of threes, bore consequently upon the Bavarian Uhlans (an ill-disciplined and ill-affected body), and these, falling back in disorder, became entangled with the artillery and the left centre of the line, and in one instant thirty thousand men were in inextricable confusion.

'Clubbed, by Jabers !' roared out LANTY CLANCY. 'I wish we could show 'em the Fighting Onety-Oneth, Captain, darling.'

'Silence, fellow !' I exclaimed. I never saw the face of a man express passion so vividly as now did the livid countenance of NAPOLEON. He tore off GENERAL MILHAUD'S epaulettes, which he flung into FOY's face. He glared about him wildly, like a demon, and shouted hoarsely for the DUKE OF ILLYRIA. 'He is wounded, Sire,' said GENERAL FOY, wiping a tear from his eye, which was blackened by the force of the blow ; 'he was wounded an hour since in a duel, Sire, by a young English prisoner, MONSIEUR DE FOGARTY.'

'Wounded ! a Marshal of France wounded ! Where is the Englishman ? Bring him out, and let a file of grenadiers——'

'Sire !' interposed EUGÈNE.

'Let him be shot !' shrieked the EMPEROR, shaking his spy-glass at me with the fury of a fiend.

This was too much. 'Here goes !' said I, and rode slap at him.

There was a shriek of terror from the whole of the French army, and I should think at least forty thousand guns were levelled at me in an instant. But as the muskets were not

P

loaded, and the cannon had only wadding in them, these facts, I presume, saved the life of PHIL FOGARTY from this discharge.

Knowing my horse, I put him at the EMPEROR's head, and *Bugaboo* went at it like a shot. He was riding his famous white Arab, and turned quite pale as I came up and went over the horse and the EMPEROR, scarcely brushing the cockade which he wore.

'Bravo!' said MURAT, bursting into enthusiasm at the leap.

'Cut him down!' said SIÉYÈS, once an Abbé, but now a gigantic Cuirassier; and he made a pass at me with his sword. But he little knew an Irishman on an Irish horse. *Bugaboo* cleared SIÉYÈS, and fetched the monster a slap with his near hind hoof which sent him reeling from his saddle—and away I went, with an army of a hundred-and-seventy-three thousand eight hundred men at my heels.

CRINOLINE

BY JE—MES PL—SH, ESQ.

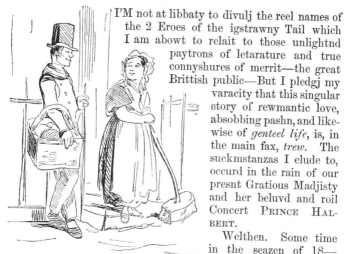

I'M not at libbaty to divulj the reel names of the 2 Eroes of the igstrawny Tail which I am abowt to relait to those unlightnd paytrons of letarature and true connyshures of merrit—the great Brittish public—But I pledgj my varacity that this singular story of rewmantic love, absobbing pashn, and likewise of *genteel life*, is, in the main fax, *trew*. The suckmstanzas I elude to, occurd in the rain of our presnt Gratious Madjisty and her beluvd and roil Concert PRINCE HAL-BERT.

Welthen. Some time in the seazen of 18— (mor I dar not rewheel) there arrived in this metropulus, per seknd class of the London and Dover Railway, an ellygant young foring gentleman, whom I shall danomminate MUNSEER JOOLS DE CHACABAC.

Having read through the *Vicker of Wackfield* in the same oridgnal English tung, in which this very harticle I write is wrote too, and halways been remarkyble, both at collidge and in the estamminy, for his aytred and orror of perfidgus Halbion, MUNSEER JOOLS was considered by the prapriretors of the newspaper in which he wrote, at Parris, the very man to come to this country, igsamin its manners and customs, cast an i upon the politticle and finanshle stat of the Hempire, and igspose the mackynations of the infymus PALMERSTON, and the ebomminable SIR PILL—both enemies of France, as is every other Britten of that great, gloarus, libberal, and peasable country. In one word, JOOLS DE CHACABAC was a penny-a-liner.

'I will go and see with my own I's,' he said, 'that infimus hiland of which the innabitants are shopkeepers, gorged with roast beef and treason. I will go and see the murderers of the Hirish, the pisoners of the Chynese, the villains who put the Hemperor to death in Saintyleany, the artful dodges who wish to smother Europe with their cotton, and can't sleep or rest heasy for henvy and hatred of the great inwinsable French nation. I will igsammin, face to face, these hotty insularies; I will penny-trate into the secrets of their Jessywhittickle cabinet, and beard PALMERSTON in his denn.' When he jumpt on shor at Foaxton (after having been tremenguously sick in the four-cabbing), he exclaimed, '*Enfin je te tiens, Ile maudite! je te crache à la figure, veille Angleterre! Je te foule à mes pieds au nom du monde outragé,*' and so proseaded to inwade the metropulus.

As he wisht to micks with the very chicest sosiaty, and git the best of infamation about this country, MUNSEER JOOLS of coarse went and lodgd in Lester Square—Lester Squarr, as he calls it—which, as he was infommed in the printed suckular presented to him by a very greasy but polite comishner at the Custumus Stares, was in the scenter of the town, contiggus to the Ouses of Parlyment, the prinsple Theayters, the Parx, St. Jams Pallice, and the Corts of Lor. 'I can surwhey them all at one cut of the eye,' JOOLS thought; 'the Sovring, the infamus Ministers plotting the destruction of my immortial country; the business and pleasure of these pusproud Londoners and aristoxy; I can look round and see all.' So he took a three-pair back in a French hotel, the Hôtel de l'Ail, kep by MONSIEUR GIGOTOT, Cranbourne Street, Lester Squarr, London.

In this Otell there's a billiard-room on the first floor, and a tabbledoat at eighteenpence peredd at 5 o'clock; and the landlord, who kem into JOOLS's room smoakin a segar, told the young gent that the house was friquented by all the British nobillaty, who reglar took their dinners there. 'They can't ebide their own *quiseen*,' he said. 'You'll see what a dinner we'll serve you to-day.' JOOLS wrote off to his paper—

'The members of the haughty and luxurious English aristo-cracy, like all the rest of the world, are obliged to fly to France for the indulgence of their luxuries. The nobles of England, quitting their homes, their wives, *miladies* and *mistriss*, so fair but so cold, dine universally at the tavern. That from which I write is frequented by PEEL and PALMERSTON. I *frémis* to think that I may meet them at the board to day.'

Singular to say, PEEL and PALMERSTON didn't dine at the Hôtel de l'Ail on that evening. 'It's quite igstronnary they don't come,' said MUNSEER DE L'AIL.

'Peraps they're ingaged at some boxing match, or some *combaw de cock,'* MUNSEER JOOLS sejested ; and the landlord egreed that was very likely.

Instedd of English there was, however, plenty of foring sociaty, of every nation under the sun.   Most of the noblemen were great hamatures of hale and porter.   The tablecloth was marked over with brown suckles, made by the pewter pots on that and the privious days.

'It is the usage here,' wrote JOOLS to his newspaper, 'among the Anglais of the *fashonne* to absorb immense quantities of ale and porter during their meals.   These stupefying, but cheap, and not unpalatable liquors are served in shining pewter vessels.   A mug of foaming *hafanaf* (so a certain sort of beer is called) was placed by the side of most of the *convives.*   I was disappointed of seeing SIR PEEL : he was engaged to a combat of cocks which occurs at Windsor.'

Not one word of English was spoke during this dinner, excep when the gentlemen said ' Garsong de *l'afanaf,'* but JOOLS was very much pleased to meet the *eleet* of the foringers in town, and ask their opinions about the reel state of thinx.   Was it likely that the Bishops were to be turned out of the Chambre des Communes ?   Was it true that LOR PALMERSTON had boxéd with LOR BROGHAMM in the House of Lords, until they were separ-ayted by the LOR MAIRE ?   Who was the LOR MAIRE ?   Wasn't he Premier Minister ? and wasn't the ARCHEVÉQUE DE CANTOR-BÉRY a Quaker ?   He got answers to these questions from the various gents round about during the dinner—which, he remarked, was very much like a French dinner, only dirtier.   And he wrote off all the infamation he got to his newspaper.

'The Lord Maire, LORD LANSDOWNE, is Premier Ministre. His Grace has his dwelling in the City.   The Archbishop of Cantabery is not turned Quaker, as some people stated.   Quakers may not marry nor sit in the Chamber of Peers.   The minor Bishops have seats in the House of Commons, where they are attacked by the bitter pleasantries of LORD BROUGHAM.   A boxer is in the House ; he taught PALMERSTON the science of the pugilate, who conferred upon him the seat,' etc. etc.

His writing hover, JOOLS came down and ad a gaym at pool with two Poles, a Bulgian, and 2 of his own countrymen.   This being done amidst more hafanaf, without which nothink is done in England, and as there was no French play that night, he and the two French gents walked round and round Lester Squar smoking segaws in the faces of other French gents who were smoaking 2.   And they talked about the granjer of France and the perfidgusness of England, and looked at the aluminated pictur of

MADAME WHARTON as *Haryadne*, till bed-time.   But befor he slep, he finished his letter you may be sure, and called it his ' Fust Imprestiuns of Anglyterre.'

'Mind and wake me early,' he said to Boots, the ony British

subject in the Hôtel de l'Ail, and who therefore didn't understand him.   'I wish to be at Smithfield at 6 hours to *see the men sell their wives.*'

And the young roag fell asleep, thinking what sort of a one he'd buy.

This was the way JOOLS passed his days, and got infamation

about Hengland and the Henglish — walking round, and round
Lester Squarr all day, and every day with the same company,
occasionally dewussified by an Oprer Chorus-singer or a Jew or
two, and every afternoon in the Quaddrant admiring the genteal
sosiaty there. MUNSEER JOOLS was not over well funnisht with
pocket-money, and so his pleasure was of the gratis sort cheafly.

Well, one day as he and a friend was taking their turn among
the aristoxy, under the Quadrant—they were struck all of a heap
by seeing—— But, stop, who *was* JOOLS's friend? Here you
have pictures of both—but the Istory of JOOLS's friend must be
kep for another innings.

NOT fur from that knowble and
cheerfle Squear which MUN-
SEER JOOLS DE CHACABAC
had selacted for his eboad in
London—not fur, I say,
from Lester Squarr, is a
rainje of bildings called
Pipping's Row, leading to
Blue Lion Court, leading to
St. Martin's Lane. You
know Pipping's Buildings
by its greatest ornament,
an am and beefouce (where
JOOLS has often stood ad-
miring the degstaraty of the
carver a-cuttin the varous
jints), and by the little
fishmungur's, where you
remark the mouldy lob-
sters, the fly-blown pickle-
sammon, the playbills, and
the gingybear bottles in the
window—above all, by the Constantinople Divan, kep by the
MISSES MORDEKY, and well known to every lover of 'a prime
sigaw and an exlent cup of red Moky Coffy for 6d.'

The Constantinople Divan is greatly used by the foring gents of
Lester Squar. I never ad the good fortn to pass down Pipping's
Buildings without seeing a haf-a-duzen of 'em on the threshole of
the extablishment, giving the street an oppertunity of testing the

odar of the MISSES MORDEKY'S prime Avannas. Two or three mor may be visable inside, settn on the counter or the chestis, indulging in their fav'rit whead, the rich and spisy Pickwhick, the ripe Manilly, or the flagrant and arheumatic Qby.

'These Divanns are, as is very well known, the knightly resott of the young Henglish nobillaty. It is ear a young Pier, after an arjus day at the House of Commons, solazes himself with a glas of gin-and-water (the national beveridge), with cheerful conversation on the ewents of the day, or with an armless gaym of baggytell in the back-parlor.'

So wrote at least our friend JOOLS to his newspaper, the *Horriflam;* and of this back-parlor and baggytell bord, of this counter, of this Constantinople Divan, he became almost as reglar a frequenter as the plaster of Parish Turk who sits smoking a hookey between the two blue coffee cups in the winder.

I have oftin, smokin my own shroot in silents in a corner of the Diwann, listened to JOOLS and his friends inwaying aginst Hingland, and boastin of their own immortial country. How they did go on about WELLINTUN, and what an arty contamp they ad for him!—how they used to prove that France was the Light, the Scenter-pint, the Igsample and Hadmiration of the whole world. And though I scarcely take a French paper nowadays (I lived in early days as groom in a French famly three years, and therefore knows the languidg), though, I say, you can't take up JOOLS's paper, the *Orriflam,* without readin that a minister has committed bribery and perjury, or that a littery man has committed perjury and murder, or that a Duke has stabbed his wife in fifty places, or some story equally horrable ; yet for all that it's admiral to see how the French gents will swagger,—how they will be the scenters of civilisation—how they will be the Igsamples of Europ, and nothink shall prevent 'em—knowing they will have it, I say I listen, smokin my pip in silence. But to our tail.

Reglar every evening there came to the Constantanople a young gent etired in the igth of fashn ; and indeed presenting by the cleanlyness of his appearants and linning (which was generally a pink or blew shurt, with a cricketer or a dansuse pattern) rayther a contrast to the dinjy and wistkcard sosiaty of the Diwann. As for wiskars, this young mann had none beyond a little yellow tought to his chin, which you woodn notas, only he was always pulling at it. His statue was diminnative, but his coschume supubb, for he had the tippiest Jane boots, the ivoryheadest canes, the most gawjus scarlick Jonville ties, and the most Scotch-plaidest trowseys, of any customer of that establishment. He was univusaly called Milord.

'*Qui est ce jeune seigneur ?* Who is this young hurl, who comes knightly to the Constantanople, who is so proddigl of his gold, (for indeed the young gent would frequinly propoase gininwater to the company), and who drinks so much gin?' asked Munseer Chacabac of a friend from the Hôtel de l'Ail.

'His name is Lord Yardham,' answered that friend. 'He never comes here but at night—and why?'

'Y?' igsclaimed Jools, istonisht.

'Why? because he is engaygd all day—and do you know where he is engaygd all day?'

'Where?' asked Jools.

'At the Foring Office—*now* do you beginn to understand?' —Jools trembled.

'He speaks of his uncle, the head of that office.—Who is the head of that offis?—Palmerston.'

'The nephew of Palmerston!' said Jools, almost in a fit.

'Lor Yardham pretends not to speak French,' the other went on. 'He pretends he can only say *wee* and *commong porty voo.* Shallow humbug!—I have marked him during our conversations. When we have spoken of the glory of France among the nations, I have seen his eye kindle, and his perfidious lip curl with rage. When they have discussed before him, the Imprudents! the affairs of Europe, and Raggybritchovich has shown us the next Circassian Campaign, or Sapousne has laid bare the plan of the Calabrian patriots for the next insurrection, I have marked this stranger—this Lor Yardham. He smokes, 'tis to conceal his countenance; he drinks gin, 'tis to hide his face in the goblet.— And be sure, he carries every word of our conversation to the perfidious Palmerston, his uncle.'

'I will beard him in his den,' thought Jools. 'I will meet him *corps-à-corps*—the tyrant of Europe shall suffer through his nephew, and I will shoot him as dead as Dujarrier.'

When Lor Yardham came to the Constantinople that night, Jools i'd him savidgely from edd to foot, while Lord Yardham replied the same. It wasn't much for either to do—neyther being more than 4 foot ten hi—Jools was a grannydear in his company of the Nashnal Gard, and was as brayv as a lion.

'*Ah, l'Angleterre, l'Angleterre, tu nous dois une revanche,*' said Jooles, crossing his arms and grinding his teeth at Lord Yardham.

'Wee,' said Lord Yardham; 'wee.'

'*Delenda est Carthago!*' howled out Jools.

'*O, wee,*' said the Erl of Yardham, and at the same momint his glas of ginawater coming in, he took a drink, saying, '*A voter santy, Munseer*': and then he offered it like a man of fashn to Jools.

A light broak on Jools's mind as he igsepted the refreshmint. 'Sapoase,' he said, 'instead of slaughtering this nephew of the infamous Palmerston, I extract his secrets from him; suppose I pump him—suppose I unveil his schemes and send them to my paper? *La France* may hear the name of Jools de Chacabac, and the star of honour may glitter on my bosom.'

So, axepting Lord Yardham's cortasy, he returned it by ordering another glass of gin at his own expense, and they both drank it on the counter, where Jools talked of the affaers of Europ all night. To everything he said, the Earl of Yardham answered '*Wee, wee;*' except at the end of the evening, when he squeeged his & and said '*Bong swore.*'

'There's nothing like goin amongst 'em to equire the reel pronounciation,' his Lordship said, as he let himself into his lodgings with his latch-key. 'That was a very eloquent young gent at the Constantinople, and I'll patronise him.'

'*Ah, perfide, je te démasquerai !*' JOOLS remarked to himself as he went to bed in his Hôtel de l'Ail. And they met the next night, and from that heavning the young men were continyonally together.

Well, one day as they were walking in the Quadrant, JOOLS talking, and LORD YARDHAM saying 'Wee, wee,' they were struck all of a heap by seeing—— But my paper is igshosted, and I must dixcribe what they sor in the nex number.

CHAPTER III

THE CASTLE OF THE ISLAND OF FOGO

THE travler who pesews his dalitefle coarse through the fair rellum of Franse, (as a great romantic landskippist and neamsack of mind would say) never chaumed his i's with a site more lovely, or vu'd a pallis more magniffiznt than that which was the buthpiace of the Eroing of this Trew Tale. Phansy a country through whose werdant planes the selvery Garonne wines, like—like a benevvolent sarpent. In its plasid busum antient cassles, picturask willidges, and waving woods are reflected. Purple hills, crownd with inteak ruings; rivvilets babbling through gentle greenwoods; wight farm ouses, hevvy with hoveranging vines, and from which the appy and peaseful okupier can cast his glans over goolden waving cornfealds, and M.Herald meddows in which the lazy cattle are graysinn; while the sheppard, tending his snoughy flox, wiles away the leisure mominx on his loot—these hoffer but a phaint pictur of the rurial felissaty in the midst of widge CRINOLINE and HESTERIA DE VIDDLERS were bawn.

Their Par, the MARCUS DE VIDDLERS, Shavilear of the Legend

of Honor and of the Lion of Bulgum, the Golden Flease, Grand Cross of the Eflant and Castle, and of the Catinbagpipes of Hostria, Grand Chamberleng of the Crownd, and Major-Genaril of Hoss-Mareens, &c., &c., &c.,—is the twenty-foth or fith Marquis that has bawn the Tittle; is disended lenyally from KING PIPPING, and has almost as antient a paddygree as any which the Ollywell Street frends·of the Member of Buckinumsheer can supply.

His Marchyniss, the lovely & ecomplisht EMILY DE ST. CORNICHON, quitted this mortial spear very soon after she had presented her Lord with the two little dawling Cherrybins above dixcribed, in whomb, after the loss of that angle his wife, the disconslit widderer found his only jy on huth. In all his emusemints they ecampanied him; their edjacation was his sole bisniss; he atcheaved it with the assistance of the ugliest and most lernid masters, and the most hidjus and egsimplary governices which money could procure. R, how must his peturnle art have bet, as these Budds, which he had nurrisht, bust into buty, and twined in blooming flagrance round his pirentile Busm!

The villidges all round his hancestral Alls blessed the Marcus and his lovely hoffsprig. Not one villidge in their naybrood but was edawned by their elygint benifisms, and where the inhabitnts weren't rendered appy. It was a pattern pheasantry. All the old men in the district were wertuous and tockative, ad red stockins, and i-eeled drab shoes, and beautiful snowy air. All the old women had peaked ats, and crookid cains, and chince gowns tucked into the pockits of their quiltid petticoats; they sat in pictarask porches, pretendin to spinn, while the lads and lassis of the villidges danst under the hellums. O, 'tis a noble sight to whitniss that of an appy pheasantry! Not one of those rustic wassals of the Ouse of WIDDLERS, but ad his hair curled and his shirt sleaves tied up with pink ribbing as he led to the macy dance some appy country gal, with a black velvit boddice, and a redd or yaller petticoat, a hormylu cross on her neck, and a silver harrow in her air!

When the Marcus and ther young ladies came to the villidge it would have done the i's of the flanthropist good to see how all reseaved 'em! The little children scattered calico flowers on their path, the snowy-aired old men with red faces and rinkles took off their brown-paper ats to slewt the noble Marcus. Young and old led them to a woodn bank painted to look like a bower of roses, and when they were sett down danst ballys before them. O 'twas a noble site to see the Marcus too, smilin ellygint with fethers in his edd and all his stars on, and the young Marchynisses with their ploomes, and trains, and little coronicks!

They lived in a tremenjus splendor at home in their pyturnle alls, and had no end of pallises, willers, and town and country resadences, but their fayvorit resadence was called the Castle of the Island of Fogo.

Add I the penn of the hawther of a Codlingsby himself, I coodnt dixcribe the gawjusness of their aboad.   They add twenty-

four footmen in livery, besides a boy in codroys for the knives and shoes.   They had nine meels aday—Shampayne and pineapples were served to each of the young ladies in bed before they got up. Was it Prawns, Sherry-cobblers, lobster-salids, or maids of honour, they had but to ring the bell and call for what they chose.   They had two new dresses every day—one to ride out in the open carriage, and another to appear in the gardens of the Castle of the

Island of Fogo, which were illuminated every night like Voxhall. The young noblemen of France were there ready to dance with them, and festif suppers concluded the jawyus night.

Thus they lived in ellygant ratirement until Misfortune bust upon this appy fammaly. Etached to his Princes and abommanating the ojous LEWYPHLIP, the Marcus was conspiring for the benefick of the helder branch of the BOREBONES—and what was the consquince?—One night a fleat presented itself round the Castle of the Island of Fogo—and skewering only a couple of chests of jewils, the Marcus and the two young ladies in disgyise, fled from that island of bliss. And whither fled they?—To England!—England the ome of the brave, the refuge of the world, where the pore slave never setts his foot, but he is free!

Such was the ramantic tail which was told to 2 friends of ours by the MARCUS DE VIDDLERS himself, whose daughters, walking with their page from Ungerford Market (where they had been to purchis a paper of srimps for the umble supper of their noble father), YARDHAM and his equaintnce, MUNSEER JOOLS, had remarked and admired.

But how had those two young Erows become equainted with the noble Marcus?—That is a mistry we must elucydate in a futur vollam.

THE STARS AND STRIPES

BY THE AUTHOR OF 'THE LAST OF THE MULLIGANS,' 'PILOT,' ETC.

THE KING OF FRANCE was walking on the terrace of Versailles; the fairest, not only of Queens, but of women, hung fondly on the Royal arm; while the children of France were indulging in their infantile hilarity in the alleys of the magnificent garden of LE NOTRE (from which NIBLO'S garden has been copied, in our own Empire city of New York), and playing at leap-frog with their uncle, the COUNT OF PROVENCE; gaudy courtiers, emblazoned with orders, glittered in the groves, and murmured frivolous talk in the ears of high-bred beauty.

'MARIE, my beloved,' said the ruler of France, taking out his watch, ''tis time that the Minister of America should be here.'

'Your Majesty should know the time,' replied MARIE ANTOINETTE, archly, and in an Austrian accent; 'is not my Royal LOUIS the first watchmaker in his empire?'

The King cast a pleased glance at his repeater, and kissed

with courtly grace the fair hand of her who had made him the compliment.

'My Lord Bishop of Autun,' said he to Monsieur de Talleyrand Périgord, who followed the royal pair, in his quality of Arch-Chamberlain of the Empire, 'I pray you look through the gardens, and tell His Excellency Doctor Franklin that the King waits.' The Bishop ran off, with more than youthful agility, to seek the United States Minister. 'These Republicans,' he added, confidentially, and with something of a supercilious look, 'are but rude courtiers, methinks.'

'Nay,' interposed the lovely Antoinette, 'rude courtiers, Sire, they may be; but the world boasts not of more accomplished gentlemen. I have seen no grandee of Versailles that has the noble bearing of this American Envoy and his suite. They have the refinement of the Old World, with all the simple elegance of the New. Though they have perfect dignity of manner, they have an engaging modesty which I have never seen equalled by the best of the proud English nobles with whom they wage war. I am told they speak their very language with a grace which the haughty Islanders who oppress them never attained. They are independent, yet never insolent; elegant, yet always respectful; and brave, but not in the least boastful.'

'What! savages and all, Marie?' exclaimed Louis, laughing and chucking the lovely Queen playfully under the Royal chin. 'But here comes Doctor Franklin, and your friend the Cacique with him.' In fact, as the monarch spoke, the Minister of the United States made his appearance, followed by a gigantic warrior in the garb of his native woods.

Knowing his place as Minister of a sovereign State (yielding even then in dignity to none, as it surpasses all now in dignity, in valour, in honesty, in strength, and civilisation), the Doctor nodded to the Queen of France, but kept his hat on as he faced the French monarch, and did not cease whittling the cane he carried in his hand.

'I was waiting for you, Sir,' the king said peevishly, in spite of the alarmed pressure which the Queen gave his royal arm.

'The business of the Republic, Sire, must take precedence even of your Majesty's wishes,' replied Dr. Franklin. 'When I was a poor printer's boy, and ran errands, no lad could be more punctual than poor Ben Franklin; but all other things must yield to the service of the United States of North America. I have done. What would you, Sire?' and the intrepid Republican eyed the monarch with a serene and easy dignity which made the descendant of St. Louis feel ill at ease.

'I wished to—to say farewell to TATUA before his departure,' said LOUIS XVI., looking rather awkward. 'Approach TATUA.' And the gigantic Indian strode up, and stood undaunted before the first magistrate of the French nation; again the feeble monarch quailed before the terrible simplicity of the glance of the denizen of the primæval forests.

The redoubted Chief of the Nose-ring Indians was decorated in his war-paint, and in his top-knot was a peacock's feather, which had been given him out of the head-dress of the beautiful PRINCESS OF LAMBALLE. His nose, from which hung the ornament from which his ferocious tribe took its designation, was painted a light-blue, a circle of green and orange was drawn round each eye, while serpentine stripes of black, white, and vermilion alternately were smeared on his forehead, and descended over his cheek-bones to his chin. His manly chest was similarly tattooed and painted, and round his brawny neck and arms hung innumerable bracelets and necklaces of human teeth, extracted (one only from each skull) from the jaws of those who had fallen by the terrible tomahawk at his girdle. His moccasins, and his blanket, which was draped on his arm, and fell in picturesque folds to his feet, were fringed with tufts of hair— the black, the grey, the auburn, the golden ringlet of beauty, the red lock from the forehead of the Scottish or the Northern soldier, the snowy tress of extreme old age, the flaxen down of infancy—all were there, dreadful reminiscences of the chief's triumphs in war. The warrior leaned on his enormous rifle, and faced the King.

'And it was with that carabine that you shot WOLFE in '57?' said LOUIS, eyeing the warrior and his weapon. ''Tis a clumsy lock, and methinks I could mend it,' he added mentally.

'The Chief of the French pale-faces speaks truth,' TATUA said. 'TATUA was a boy when he went first on the war-path with MONTCALM.'

'And shot a WOLFE at the first fire!' said the King.

'The English are braves, though their faces are white,' replied the Indian. 'TATUA shot the raging WOLFE of the English, but the other wolves caused the foxes to go to earth.' A smile played round DR. FRANKLIN'S lips, as he whittled his cane with more vigour than ever.

'I believe, your Excellency, TATUA has done good service elsewhere than at Quebec,' the King said, appealing to the American Envoy; 'at Bunker's Hill, at Brandywine, at York Island? Now that LAFAYETTE and my brave Frenchmen are among you, your Excellency need have no fear but that the war

will finish quickly—yes, yes, it will finish quickly. They will
teach you discipline, and the way to conquer.'

'KING LOUIS OF FRANCE,' said the Envoy, clapping his hat
down over his head, and putting his arms akimbo, 'we have

learned that from the British, to whom we are superior in everything: and I'd have your Majesty to know, that in the art of
whipping the world, we have no need of any French lessons. If
your reglars jines GENERAL WASHINGTON, 'tis to larn from *him*
how Britishers are licked, for I'm blest if yu know the way yet.'

TATUA said, 'Ugh,' and gave a rattle with the butt of his

Q

carabine, which made the timid monarch start; the eyes of the lovely ANTOINETTE flashed fire, but it played round the head of the dauntless American Envoy harmless as the lightning which he knew how to conjure away.

The King fumbled in his pocket, and pulled out a Cross of the Order of the Bath. 'Your Excellency wears no honour,' the monarch said; 'but TATUA, who is not a subject, only an ally of the United States, may. Noble TATUA, I appoint you Knight Companion of my noble Order of the Bath. Wear this cross upon your breast in memory of LOUIS OF FRANCE;' and the King held out the decoration to the Chief.

Up to that moment the Chief's countenance had been impassible. No look either of admiration or dislike had appeared upon that grim and war-painted visage. But now, as LOUIS spoke, TATUA's face assumed a glance of ineffable scorn, as, bending his head, he took the bauble.

'I will give it to one of my squaws,' he said. 'The papooses in my lodge will play with it. Come, Medicine, TATUA will go and drink fire-water;' and, shouldering his carabine, he turned his broad back without ceremony upon the monarch and his train, and disappeared down one of the walks of the garden. FRANKLIN found him when his own interview with the French Chief Magistrate was over, being attracted to the spot where the Chief was, by the crack of his well-known rifle. He was laughing in his quiet way. He had shot the Colonel of the Swiss Guards through his cockade.

Three days afterwards, as the gallant frigate, the *Repudiator*, was sailing out of Brest Harbour, the gigantic form of an Indian might be seen standing on the binnacle in conversation with COMMODORE BOWIE, the commander of the noble ship. It was TATUA, the Chief of the Nose-rings.

EATHERLEGS and TOM COX-
SWAIN did not accompany
TATUA when he went to the
Parisian metropolis on a visit
to the father of the French
pale-faces. Neither the Legs
nor the Sailor cared for the
gaiety and the crowd of cities;
the stout mariner's home was
in the puttock-shrouds of the
old *Repudiator.* The stern
and simple trapper loved the
sound of the waters better
than the jargon of the French
of the old country. 'I can
follow the talk of a Pawnee,'
he said, 'or wag my jaw, if so
be necessity bids me to speak,
by a Sioux's council-fire; and
I can patter Canadian French
with the hunters who come
for peltries to Nachitoches or
Thichimuchimachy; but from the tongue of a French-woman, with
white flour on her head, and war-paint on her face, the Lord
deliver poor NATTY PUMPO.'

'Amen and amen!' said TOM COXSWAIN. 'There was a
woman in our aft-scuppers when I went a-whalin in the little
Grampus—and Lord love you, PUMPO, you poor land-swab, she
was as pretty a craft as ever dowsed a tarpauling—there was a
woman on board the *Grampus*, who before we'd struck our first
fish, or biled our first blubber, set the whole crew in a mutiny. I
mind me of her now, NATTY—her eye was sich a piercer that you
could see to steer by it in a Newfoundland fog; her nose stood out
like the *Grampus's* jib-boom, and her woice, Lord love you, her
woice sings in my ears even now:—it set the Captain a-quarrelin
with the Mate, who was hanged in Boston harbour for harpoonin
of his officer in Baffin's Bay;—it set me and BOB BUNTING a-
pouring broadsides into each other's old timbers, whereas me and
BOB was worth all the women that ever shipped a hawser. It
cost me three years' pay as I'd stowed away for the old mother,
and might have cost me ever so much more, only bad luck to me,
she went and married a little tailor out of Nantucket; and I've

hated women and tailors ever since!' As he spoke, the hardy tar dashed a drop of brine from his tawny cheek, and once more betook himself to splice the taffrail.

Though the brave frigate lay off Havre de Grace, she was not idle. The gallant BOWIE and his intrepid crew made repeated descents upon the enemy's seaboard. The coasts of Rutland and merry Leicestershire have still many a legend of fear to tell; and the children of the British fishermen tremble even now when they speak of the terrible *Repudiator*. She was the first of the mighty American war-ships that have taught the domineering Briton to respect the valour of the Republic.

The novelist ever and anon finds himself forced to adopt the sterner tone of the historian, when describing deeds connected with his country's triumphs. It is well known that during the two months in which she lay off Havre, the *Repudiator* had brought more prizes into that port than had ever before been seen in the astonished French waters. Her actions with the *Dettingen* and the *Elector* frigates form part of our country's history; their defence—it may be said without prejudice to national vanity—was worthy of Britons and of the audacious foe they had to encounter; and it must be owned, that but for a happy fortune which presided on that day over the destinies of our country, the chance of the combat might have been in favour of the British vessels. It was not until the *Elector* blew up, at a quarter-past 3 P.M., by a lucky shot which fell into her caboose, and communicated with the powder-magazine, that COMMODORE BOWIE was enabled to lay himself on board the *Dettingen*, which he carried sword in hand. Even when the American boarders had made their lodgment on the *Dettingen's* binnacle, it is possible that the battle would still have gone against us. The British were still seven to one; their carronades, loaded with marline-spikes, swept the gun-deck, of which we had possession, and decimated our little force; when a rifle-ball from the shrouds of the *Repudiator* shot CAPTAIN MUMFORD under the star of the Guelphic Order, which he wore, and the Americans, with a shout, rushed up the companion to the quarter-deck, upon the astonished foe. Pike and cutlass did the rest of the bloody work. RUMFORD, the gigantic first lieutenant of the *Dettingen*, was cut down by COMMODORE BOWIE's own sword, as they engaged hand to hand; and it was TOM COXSWAIN who tore down the British flag, after having slain the Englishman at the wheel. Peace be to the souls of the brave! The combat was honourable alike to the victor and the vanquished; and it never can be said that an American warrior depreciated a gallant foe. The bitterness of defeat was enough to the haughty islanders who had to suffer. The people of Herne Bay were lining the shore, near which the combat took place, and cruel must have been the pang to them when they saw the Stars and Stripes rise over the old flag of the Union, and the *Dettingen* fall down the river in tow of the republican frigate.

Another action BOWIE contemplated ; the boldest and most daring perhaps ever imagined by seaman. It is this which has been so wrongly described by European annalists, and of which the British until now have maintained the most jealous secrecy.

Portsmouth Harbour was badly defended. Our intelligence in that town and arsenal gave us precise knowledge of the disposition of the troops, the forts, and the ships there ; and it was determined to strike a blow which should shake the British power in its centre.

That a frigate of the size of the *Repudiator* should enter the harbour unnoticed, or could escape its guns unscathed, passed the notions of even American temerity. But upon the memorable 26th of June, 1782, the *Repudiator* sailed out of Havre Roads in a thick fog, under cover of which she entered and cast anchor in Bonchurch Bay, in the Isle of Wight. To surprise the Martello Tower and take the feeble garrison thereunder, was the work of TOM COXSWAIN and a few of his bluejackets. The surprised garrison laid down their arms before him.

It was midnight before the boats of the ship, commanded by LIEUTENANT BUNKER, pulled off from Bonchurch with muffled oars, and in another hour were off the Common Hard of Portsmouth, having passed the challenge of the *Thetis* and the *Amphion* frigates, and the *Polyanthus* brig.

There had been on that day great feasting and merriment on board the Flag-ship lying in the harbour. A banquet had been given in honour of the birthday of one of the princes of the royal line of the GUELPHS—the reader knows the propensity of Britons when liquor is in plenty. All on board that royal ship were more or less overcome. The Flag-ship was plunged in a death-like and drunken sleep. The very officer of the watch was intoxicated ; he could not see the *Repudiator's* boats as they shot swiftly through the waters ; nor had he time to challenge her seamen as they swarmed up the huge sides of the ship.

At the next moment TOM COXSWAIN stood at the wheel of the *Royal George*—the Briton who had guarded, a corpse at his feet. The hatches were down. The ship was in possession of the *Repudiator's* crew. They were busy in her rigging, bending her sails to carry her out of the harbour. The well-known heave of the men at the windlass, woke up KEMPENFELT in his state-cabin.   We know, or rather do not know the result ; for who can tell by whom the lower-deck ports of the brave ship were opened, and how the haughty prisoners below sunk the ship and its conquerors rather than yield her as a prize to the Republic !

Only TOM COXSWAIN escaped of victors and vanquished.   His tale was told to his Captain and to Congress ; but WASHINGTON forbade its publication ; and it was but lately that the faithful seaman told it to me, his grandson, on his hundred and fifteenth birthday.

A PLAN FOR A PRIZE NOVEL

In a Letter from the eminent Dramatist BROWN to the eminent Novelist SNOOKS

Café des Aveugles.

'My dear Snooks,

'I am on the look-out here for materials for original comedies such as those lately produced at your theatre; and in the course of my studies, I have found something, my dear Snooks, which I think will suit your book. You are bringing, I see, your admirable novel, *The Mysteries of May Fair*, to an end—(by the way, the scene, in the 200th Number, between the Duke, his Grandmother, and the Jesuit Butler, is one of the most harrowing and exciting I ever read)—and, of course, you must turn your real genius to some other channel; and we may expect that your pen shall not be idle.

'The original plan I have to propose to you, then, is taken from the French; just like the original dramas above mentioned; and, indeed, I found it in the law report of the *National* newspaper, and a French literary gentleman, M. Emanuel Gonzales, has the credit of the invention. He and an Advertisement Agent fell out about a question of money, the affair was brought before the Courts, and the little plot so got wind. But there is no reason why you should not take the plot and act on it yourself. You are a known man; the public relishes your works; anything bearing the name of Snooks is eagerly read by the masses; and though Messrs. Hookey, of Holywell Street, pay you handsomely, I make no doubt you would like to be rewarded at a still higher figure.

'Unless he writes with a purpose, you know, a novelist in our days is good for nothing. This one writes with a Socialist purpose; that with a Conservative purpose: this author or authoress with the most delicate skill insinuates Catholicism into you, and you find yourself all but a Papist in the third volume : another doctors you with Low Church remedies to work inwardly upon you, and which you swallow down unsuspiciously, as children do calomel in jelly. Fiction advocates all sorts of truths and causes—doesn't the delightful bard of the Minories find MOSES in everything? M. GONZALES'S plan, and the one which I recommend to my dear SNOOKS, simply was to write an advertisement novel. Look over the *Times* or the *Directory*, walk down Regent Street or Fleet Street any day—see what houses advertise most, and put yourself into communication with their proprietors. With your rings, your chains, your studs, and the tip on your chin, I don't know any greater swell than BOB SNOOKS. Walk into the shops, I say, ask for the principal, and introduce yourself, saying—"I am the great SNOOKS; I am the author of the *Mysteries of May Fair ;* my weekly sale is 281,000 ; I am about to produce a new work called *The Palace of Pimlico, or the Curse of the Court,* describing and lashing fearlessly the vices of the aristocracy—this book will have the sale of at least 530,000 ; it will be on every table ; in the boudoir of the pampered Duke, as in the chamber of the honest artisan. The myriads of foreigners who are coming to London, and are anxious to know about our national manners, will purchase my book, and carry it to their distant homes. So, MR. TAYLOR, or MR. HABERDASHER, or MR. JEWELLER—how much will you stand if I recommend you in my forthcoming novel?" You may make a noble income in this way, SNOOKS.

'For instance, suppose it is an upholsterer. What more easy, what more delightful, than the description of upholstery? As thus :—

'LADY EMILY was reclining on one of DOWN AND EIDER'S voluptuous ottomans, the only couch on which Belgravian beauty now reposes, when LORD BATHERSHINS entered, stepping noiselessly over one of TOMKINS'S elastic Axminster carpets. "Good heavens, my lord!" she said—and the lovely creature fainted. The earl rushed to the mantel-piece, where he saw a flacon of OTTO'S eau-de-Cologne, and, etc.

'Or say it's a cheap furniture-shop, and it may be brought in just as easily. As thus :—

'"We are poor, ELIZA," said HARRY HARDHAND, looking affectionately at his wife, "but we have enough, love, have we not, for our humble wants? The rich and luxurious may go to DILLOW'S or GOBIGGIN'S, but we can get our rooms comfortably furnished at TIMMONSON'S for £20." And putting on her bonnet, and hanging affectionately on her husband, the stoker's pretty bride tripped gaily to the well-known mart, where TIMMONSON, with his usual affability, was ready to receive them.

'Then you might have a touch at the wine merchant and purveyor. "Where do you get this delicious claret, or *pâté de foie gras*, or what you please?" said COUNT BLAGOWSKI to the gay young SIR HORACE SWELLMORE. The voluptuous Bart. answered—at So-and-So's, or So-and-So's. The answer is obvious. You may furnish your cellar or your larder in this way. Begad, SNOOKS! I lick my lips at the very idea!

'Then, as to tailors, milliners, bootmakers, etc., how easy to get a word for them! AMRAMSON, the tailor, waited upon LORD PADDINGTON with an assortment of his unrivalled waistcoats, or clad in that simple but aristocratic style, of which SCHNEIDER *alone* has the secret. PARVY NEWCOME really looked like a gentleman, and though corpulent and crooked, SCHNEIDER had managed to give him, etc. Don't you see what a stroke of business you might do in this way?

'The shoemaker. LADY FANNY flew, rather than danced, across the ball-room; only a *Sylphide*, or TAGLIONI, or a lady *chausséed* by CHEVILLET of Bond Street, could move in that fairy way; and——

'The hairdresser. "COUNT BARBAROSSA is seventy years of age," said the Earl. "I remember him at the Congress of Vienna, and he has not a single grey hair." WIGGINS laughed. "My good LORD BALDOCK," said the old wag, "I saw BARBAROSSA'S hair coming out of DUCROISSANT'S shop, and under his valet's arm—ho! ho! ho!"—and the two *bon-vivans* chuckled as the Count passed by, talking with, etc. etc.

'The gunmaker. The antagonists faced each other; and undismayed before his gigantic enemy KILCONNEL raised his pistol. It was one of CLICKER'S manufacture, and SIR MARMADUKE knew he could trust the maker and the weapon. "One, two, three," cried O'TOOL, and the two pistols went off at that instant, and uttering a terrific curse, the Life Guardsman, etc.—a sentence of this nature from your pen, my dear SNOOKS, would, I should think, bring a case of pistols and a double-barrelled gun to your lodgings, and, though heaven forbid you should use such weapons, you might sell them, you know, and we could make merry with the proceeds.

'If my hint is of any use to you, it is quite at your service, dear SNOOKS; and should anything come of it, I hope you will remember your friend.'

NOTES OF A JOURNEY

FROM

CORNHILL TO GRAND CAIRO

BY WAY OF

LISBON, ATHENS, CONSTANTINOPLE, AND JERUSALEM

PERFORMED IN THE STEAMERS OF THE PENINSULAR
AND ORIENTAL COMPANY

TO

CAPTAIN SAMUEL LEWIS,

OF THE

PENINSULAR AND ORIENTAL STEAM NAVIGATION COMPANY'S SERVICE

My DEAR LEWIS,—After a voyage, during which the captain of the ship has displayed uncommon courage, seamanship, affability, or other good qualities, grateful passengers often present him with a token of their esteem, in the shape of teapots, tankards, trays, etc., of precious metal. Among authors, however, bullion is a much rarer commodity than paper, whereof I beg you to accept a little in the shape of this small volume. It contains a few notes of a voyage which your skill and kindness rendered doubly pleasant; and of which I don't think there is any recollection more agreeable, than that it was the occasion of making your friendship.

If the noble Company in whose service you command (and whose fleet alone makes them a third-rate maritime power in Europe) should appoint a few admirals in their navy, I hope to hear that your flag is hoisted on board one of the grandest of their steamers. But, I trust, even there you will not forget the *Iberia*, and that delightful Mediterranean cruise we had in her in the Autumn of 1844.

Most faithfully yours,

My dear LEWIS,

W. M. THACKERAY.

LONDON,
December 24, 1845.

PREFACE

On the 24th of July 1844, the writer of this little book went to dine at the —— Club, quite unconscious of the wonderful events which Fate had in store for him.

Mr. William was there, giving a farewell dinner to his friend, Mr. James (now Sir James). These two asked Mr. Titmarsh to join company with them, and the conversation naturally fell upon the tour Mr. James was about to take. The Peninsular and Oriental Company had arranged an excursion in the Mediterranean, by which, in the space of a couple of months, as many men and cities were to be seen as Ulysses surveyed and noted in ten years. Malta, Athens, Smyrna, Constantinople, Jerusalem, Cairo were to be visited and everybody was to be back in London by Lord Mayor's Day.

The idea of beholding these famous places inflamed Mr. Titmarsh's mind; and the charms of such a journey were eloquently impressed upon him by Mr. James. 'Come,' said that kind and hospitable gentleman, 'and make one of my family party; in all your life you will never probably have a chance again to see so much in so short a time. Consider—it is as easy as a journey to Paris or to Baden.' Mr. Titmarsh considered all these things; but also the difficulties of the situation : he had but six-and-thirty hours to get ready for so portentous a journey—he had engagements at home—finally, could he afford it ? In spite of these objections, however, with every glass of claret the enthusiasm somehow rose, and the difficulties vanished.

But when Mr. James, to crown all, said he had no doubt that his friends, the Directors of the Peninsular and Oriental Company, would make Mr. Titmarsh the present of a berth for the voyage, all objections ceased on his part : to break his outstanding engagements—to write letters to his amazed family, stating that they were not to expect him at dinner on Saturday fortnight, as he would be at Jerusalem on that day—to purchase eighteen shirts and lay in a sea-stock of Russia ducks,—was the work of four-and-twenty hours ; and on the 26th of July, the *Lady Mary Wood* was sailing from Southampton with the 'subject of the present memoir,' quite astonished to find himself one of the passengers on board.

These important statements are made partly to convince some incredulous friends—who insist still that the writer never went abroad at all, and wrote the following pages, out of pure fancy, in retirement at Putney ; but mainly, to give him an opportunity of thanking the Directors of the Company in question for a delightful excursion.

It was one so easy, so charming, and I think profitable—it leaves such a store of pleasant recollections for after days—and creates so many new sources of interest (a newspaper letter from Beyrout, or Malta, or Algiers has twice the interest now that it had formerly),—that I can't but recommend all persons who have time and means to make a similar journey—vacation idlers to extend their travels and pursue it : above all, young, well-educated men entering life, to take this course, we will say, after that at college ; and, having their book-learning fresh in their minds, see the living people and their cities, and the actual aspect of Nature, along the famous shores of the Mediterranean.

A JOURNEY FROM CORNHILL TO CAIRO

CHAPTER I

VIGO

THE sun brought all the sick people out of their berths this morning, and the indescribable moans and noises which had been issuing from behind the fine painted doors on each side of the cabin happily ceased. Long before sunrise, I had the good fortune to discover that it was no longer necessary to maintain the horizontal posture, and, the very instant this truth was apparent, came on deck, at two o'clock in the morning, to see a noble full moon sinking westward, and millions of the most brilliant stars shining overhead. The night was so serenely pure, that you saw them in magnificent airy perspective: the blue sky around and over them, and other more distant orbs sparkling above, till they glittered away faintly into the immeasurable distance. The ship went rolling over a heavy, sweltering, calm sea. The breeze was a warm and soft one; quite different to the rigid air we had left behind us, two days since, off the Isle of Wight. The bell kept tolling its half-hours, and the mate explained the mystery of watch and dog-watch.

The sight of that noble scene cured all the woes and discomfitures of sea-sickness at once, and if there were any need to communicate such secrets to the public, one might tell of much more good that the pleasant morning-watch effected; but there are a set of emotions about which a man had best be shy of talking lightly,—and the feelings excited by contemplating this vast, magnificent, harmonious Nature are among these. The view of it inspires a delight and ecstasy which is not only hard to describe, but which has something secret in it that a man should not utter loudly. Hope, memory, humility, tender yearnings towards dear friends, and inexpressible love and reverence towards the Power which created the infinite universe blazing above eternally, and the vast ocean shining and rolling around—fill the heart with a solemn, humble happiness, that a person dwelling in a city has rarely occasion to enjoy. They are coming away from London parties at this time : the dear little eyes are closed in sleep under mother's wing. How far off city cares and pleasures appear to be ! how small and mean they seem, dwindling out of sight before this magnificent brightness of Nature ! But the best thoughts only grow and strengthen under it. Heaven shines above, and the humbled spirit looks up reverently towards that boundless aspect of wisdom and beauty. You are at home, and with all at rest there, however far away they may be ; and through the distance the heart broods over them, bright and wakeful like yonder peaceful stars overhead.

The day was as fine and calm as the night ; at seven bells, suddenly a bell began to toll very much like that of a country church, and on going on deck we found an awning raised, a desk with a flag flung over it close to the compass, and the ship's company and passengers assembled there to hear the captain read the Service in a manly respectful voice. This, too, was a novel and touching sight to me. Peaked ridges of purple mountains rose to the left of the ship,—Finisterre and the coast of Gallicia. The sky above was cloudless and shining ; the vast dark ocean smiled peacefully round about, and the ship went rolling over it, as the people within were praising the Maker of all.

In honour of the day, it was announced that the passengers would be regaled with champagne at dinner ; and accordingly that exhilarating liquor was served out in decent profusion, the company drinking the captain's health with the customary orations of compliment and acknowledgment. This feast was scarcely ended, when we found ourselves rounding the headland into Vigo Bay, passing a grim and tall island of rocky mountains which lies in the centre of the bay.

Whether it is that the sight of land is always welcome to weary mariners, after the perils and annoyances of a voyage of three days, or whether the place is in itself extraordinarily beautiful, need not be argued ; but I have seldom seen anything more charming than the amphitheatre of noble hills into which the ship now came—all the features of the landscape being lighted up with a wonderful clearness of air, which rarely adorns a view in our country. The sun had not yet set, but over the town and lofty rocky castle of Vigo a great ghost of a moon was faintly visible, which blazed out brighter and brighter as the superior luminary retired behind the purple mountains of the headland to rest. Before the general background of waving heights which encompassed the bay, rose a second semicircle of undulating hills, as cheerful and green as the mountains behind them were grey and solemn. Farms and gardens, convent towers, white villages and churches, and buildings that no doubt were hermitages once, upon the sharp peaks of the hills, shone brightly in the sun. The sight was delightfully cheerful, animated, and pleasing.

Presently the captain roared out the magic words, 'Stop her!' and the obedient vessel came to a standstill, at some three hundred yards from the little town, with its white houses clambering up a rock, defended by the superior mountain whereon the castle stands. Numbers of people, arrayed in various brilliant colours of red, were standing on the sand close by the tumbling, shining, purple waves: and there we beheld, for the first time, the royal red and yellow standard of Spain floating on its own ground, under the guardian-ship of a light blue sentinel, whose musket glittered in the sun. Numerous boats were seen, incontinently, to put off from the little shore.

And now our attention was withdrawn from the land to a sight of great splendour on board. This was Lieutenant Bundy, the

guardian of her Majesty's mails, who issued from his cabin in his long swallow-tailed coat, with anchor buttons; his sabre clattering between his legs; a magnificent shirt-collar, of several inches in height, rising round his good-humoured sallow face; and above it a cocked hat, that shone so, I thought it was made of polished tin (it may have been that or oilskin), handsomely laced with black worsted, and ornamented with a shining gold cord. A little squat boat, rowed by three ragged gallegos, came bouncing up to the ship. Into this Mr. Bundy and her Majesty's royal mail embarked with much majesty; and in the twinkling of an eye, the royal standard of England, about the size of a pocket-handkerchief,—and at the bows of the boat, the man-of-war's pennant, being a strip of bunting considerably under the value of a farthing,—streamed out.

'They know that flag, sir,' said the good-natured old tar, quite solemnly, in the evening afterwards: 'they respect it, sir.' The authority of her Majesty's lieutenant on board the steamer is stated to be so tremendous, that he may order it to stop, to move, to go larboard, starboard, or what you will; and the captain dare only disobey him, *suo periculo.*

It was agreed that a party of us should land for half-an-hour, and taste real Spanish chocolate on Spanish ground. We followed Lieutenant Bundy, but humbly in the providor's boat; that officer going on shore to purchase fresh eggs, milk for tea (in place of the slimy substitute of whipped yolk of egg, which we had been using for our morning and evening meals), and, if possible, oysters, for which it is said the rocks of Vigo are famous.

It was low tide, and the boat could not get up to the dry shore. Hence it was necessary to take advantage of the offers of sundry gallegos, who rushed barelegged into the water, to land on their shoulders. The approved method seems to be, to sit upon one shoulder only, holding on by the porter's whiskers; and though some of our party were of the tallest and fattest men whereof our race is composed, and their living sedans exceedingly meagre and small, yet all were landed without accident upon the juicy sand, and forthwith surrounded by a host of mendicants, screaming—'I say, sir! penny, sir! I say, English! tam your ays! penny!' in all voices, from extreme youth to the most lousy and venerable old age. When it is said that these beggars were as ragged as those of Ireland, and still more voluble, the Irish traveller will be able to form an opinion of their capabilities.

Through this crowd we passed up some steep rocky steps, through a little low gate, where, in a little guard-house and barrack, a few dirty little sentinels were keeping a dirty little guard; and by low-roofed, whitewashed houses, with balconies, and women in them,—the very same women, with the very same head-clothes, and yellow fans and eyes, at once sly and solemn, which Murillo painted,—by a neat church into which we took a peep, and, finally, into the Plaza del Constitucion, or *grand place* of the town, which may be about as big as that pleasing square, Pump Court, Temple. We were taken to an inn, of which I forget the name, and were shown from one chamber and story to another, till we arrived at that apartment where the real Spanish chocolate was finally to be served out. All these rooms were as clean as scrubbing and whitewash could make them; with simple French prints (with Spanish titles) on the walls; a few rickety half-finished articles of furniture; and, finally, an air of extremely respectable poverty. A jolly, black-eyed, yellow-shawled Dulcinea conducted us through the apartment, and provided us with the desired refreshment.

Sounds of clarions drew our eyes to the Place of the Constitution; and, indeed, I had forgotten to say, that that majestic square was filled with military, with exceedingly small firelocks, the men ludicrously young and diminutive for the most part, in a uniform at once cheap and tawdry,—like those supplied to the warriors at Astley's, or from still humbler theatrical wardrobes: indeed, the whole scene was just like that of a little theatre; the houses curiously small, with arcades and balconies, out of which looked women apparently a great deal too big for the chambers they inhabited; the warriors were in ginghams, cottons, and tinsel; the officers had huge epaulets of sham silver lace drooping over their bosoms, and looked as if they were attired at a very small expense. Only the general—the captain-general (Pooch, they told us, was his name: I know not how 'tis written in Spanish)—was well got up, with a smart hat, a real feather, huge stars glittering on his portly chest, and tights and boots of the first order. Presently, after a good deal of trumpeting, the little men marched off the place, Pooch and his staff coming into the very inn in which we were awaiting our chocolate.

Then we had an opportunity of seeing some of the civilians of the town. Three or four ladies passed, with fan and mantle; to them came three or four dandies, dressed smartly in the French fashion, with strong Jewish physiognomies. There was one, a solemn lean fellow in black, with his collars extremely turned over, and holding before him a long ivory-tipped ebony cane, who tripped along the little place with a solemn smirk, which gave one an indescribable feeling of the truth of *Gil Blas*, and of those delightful bachelors and licentiates who have appeared to us all in our dreams.

In fact we were but half-an-hour in this little queer Spanish town; and it appears like a dream, too, or a little show got up to amuse us. Boom! the gun fired at the end of the funny little entertainment. The women and the balconies, the beggars and the walking Murillos, Pooch and the little soldiers in tinsel, disappeared, and were shut up in their box again. Once more we were carried on the beggars' shoulders out of the shore, and we found ourselves again in the great stalwart roast-beef world; the stout British

steamer bearing out of the bay, whose purple waters had grown
more purple.   The sun had set by this time, and the moon above
was twice as big and bright as our degenerate moons are.

The providor had already returned with his fresh stores, and
Bundy's tin hat was popped into its case, and he walking the deck
of the packet denuded of tails.   As we went out of the bay, occurred
a little incident with which the great incidents of the day may be
said to wind up.   We saw before us a little vessel, tumbling and
plunging about in the dark waters of the bay, with a bright light
beaming from the mast.   It made for us at about a couple of miles
from the town, and came close up, flouncing and bobbing in the very
jaws of the paddle, which looked as if it would have seized and
twirled round that little boat and its light, and destroyed them for
ever and ever.   All the passengers, of course, came crowding to the
ship's side to look at the bold little boat.

'I SAY!' howled a man; 'I say!—a word!—I say!
Passagero! Passagero! Passage-e-ero!'   We were two hundred
yards ahead by this time.

'Go on,' says the captain.

'You may stop if you like,' says Lieutenant Bundy, exerting
his tremendous responsibility.   It is evident that the lieutenant has
a soft heart, and felt for the poor devil in the boat who was howling
so piteously 'Passagero!'

But the captain was resolute.   His duty was *not* to take the
man up.   He was evidently an irregular customer—some one
trying to escape, possibly.

The lieutenant turned away, but did not make any further hints.
The captain was right; but we all felt somehow disappointed, and
looked back wistfully at the little boat, jumping up and down far
astern now; the poor little light shining in vain, and the poor
wretch within screaming out in the most heart-rending accents a
last faint, desperate—'I say! Passagero-o!'

We all went down to tea rather melancholy; but the new milk,
in the place of that abominable whipped-egg, revived us again; and
so ended the great events on board the *Lady Mary Wood* steamer,
on the 25th August 1844.

CHAPTER II

LISBON—CADIZ

A GREAT misfortune which befals a man who has but a single day to stay in a town, is that fatal duty which superstition entails upon him of visiting the chief lions of the city in which he may happen to be. You must go through the ceremony, however much you may sigh to avoid it; and however much you know that the lions in one capital roar very much like the lions in another; that the churches are more or less large and splendid; the palaces pretty spacious, all the world over; and that there is scarcely a capital city in this Europe but has its pompous bronze statue or two of some periwigged, hook nosed emperor, in a Roman habit, waving his bronze baton on his broad-flanked brazen charger. We only saw these state old lions in Lisbon, whose roar has long since ceased to frighten one. First we went to the church of St. Roch, to see a famous piece of mosaic work there. It is a famous work of art, and was bought by I don't know what king, for I don't know how much money. All this information may be perfectly relied on, though the fact is we did not see the mosaic work; the sacristan, who guards it, was yet in bed; and it was veiled from our eyes in a side chapel by great dirty damask curtains, which could not be removed, except when the sacristan's toilette was done, and at the price of a dollar. So we were spared this mosaic exhibition; and I think I always feel relieved when such an event occurs. I feel I have done my duty in coming to see the enormous animal—if he is not at home, *Virtute meâ me, etc.*—we have done our best, and mortal can do no more.

In order to reach that church of the forbidden mosaic, we had sweated up several most steep and dusty streets—hot and dusty, although it was but nine o'clock in the morning. Thence the guide conducted us into some little dusty-powdered gardens, in which the people make believe to enjoy the verdure, and whence you look over a great part of the arid, dreary, stony city. There was no smoke, as in honest London, only dust—dust over the gaunt houses and the dismal yellow strips of gardens. Many churches were there, and tall, half-baked looking public edifices, that had a dry, uncomfortable, earthquaky look, to my idea. The ground-floors of the spacious houses by which we passed, seemed the coolest and pleasantest portions of the mansion. They were cellars or warehouses, for the most part, in which white-jacketed clerks sat smoking greasy cigars. The streets were plastered with placards of a bull-fight, to take place the next evening (there was no opera at that season) ; but it was not a real Spanish tauromachy — only a theatrical combat, as you could see by the picture, in which the horseman was cantering off at three miles an hour, the bull tripping after him with tips to his gentle horns. Mules interminable, and almost all excellently sleek and handsome, were pacing down every street : here and there, but later in the day, came clattering along a smart rider, on a prancing Spanish horse ; and in the afternoon a few families might be seen in the queerest, old-fashioned little carriages, drawn by their jolly mules, and swinging between, or rather before, enormous wheels.

The churches I saw were of the florid periwig architecture—I mean, of that pompous, cauliflower-kind-of-ornament, which was the fashion in Louis the Fifteenth's time, at which unlucky period a building mania seems to have seized upon many of the monarchs of Europe, and innumerable public edifices were erected. It seems to me to have been the period in all history when society was the least natural, and perhaps the most dissolute ; and I have always fancied that the bloated artificial forms of the architecture partake of the social disorganisation of the time. Who can respect a simpering ninny, grinning in a Roman dress and a full-bottomed wig, who is made to pass off for a hero ? or a fat woman in a hoop, and of a most doubtful virtue, who leers at you as a goddess ? In the palaces which we saw, several court-allegories were represented, which, atrocious as they were in point of art, might yet serve to attract the regard of the moraliser. There were Faith, Hope, and Charity restoring Don John to the arms of his happy Portugal : there were Virtue, Valour, and Victory saluting Don Emanuel : Reading, Writing, and Arithmetic (for what I know, or some mythologic nymphs) dancing before Don Miguel—the picture is there still, at the Ajuda ; and, ah me ! where is poor Mig ? Well, it is these state lies and ceremonies that we persist in going to see ; whereas a man would have a much better insight into Portuguese manners, by planting himself at a corner, like yonder beggar, and watching the real transactions of the day.

A drive to Belem is the regular route practised by the traveller who has to make only a short stay, and accordingly a couple of carriages were provided for our party, and we were driven through the long merry street of Belem, peopled by endless strings of mules, —by thousands of gallegos, with water-barrels on their shoulders, or lounging by the fountains to hire,—by the Lisbon and Belem omnibuses, with four mules, jingling along at a good pace ; and it seemed to me to present a far more lively and cheerful, though not so regular, an appearance as the stately quarters of the city we had left behind us. The little shops were at full work—the men brown, well-dressed, manly, and handsome : so much cannot, I am sorry to say, be said for the ladies, of whom, with every anxiety to do so, our party could not perceive a single good-looking specimen all day. The noble blue Tagus accompanies you all along these three miles of busy, pleasant street, whereof the chief charm, as I thought, was its look of genuine business—that appearance of comfort which the cleverest court-architect never knows how to give.

The carriages (the canvass one with four seats and the chaise in which I drove) were brought suddenly up to a gate with the royal arms over it ; and here we were introduced to as queer an exhibition as the eye has often looked on. This was the state-carriage house, where there is a museum of huge, old, tumble-down, gilded coaches of the last century, lying here, mouldy and dark, in a sort of limbo. The gold has vanished from the great, lumbering, old wheels and panels ; the velvets are wofully tarnished. When one thinks of the patches and powder that have simpered out of those plate glass windows—the mitred bishops, the big-wigged marshals, the shovel-hatted abbés which they have borne in their time—the human mind becomes affected in no ordinary degree. Some human minds heave a sigh for the glories of bygone days ; while others, considering rather the lies and humbug, the vice and servility, which went framed and glazed and enshrined, creaking along in those old Juggernaut cars, with fools worshipping under the wheels, console themselves for the decay of institutions that may have been splendid and costly, but were ponderous, clumsy, slow, and unfit for daily wear. The guardian of these defunct old carriages tells some prodigious fibs concerning them : he pointed out one carriage that was six hundred years old in his calendar ; but any connoisseur in bricabrac can see it was built at Paris in the Regent Orleans' time.

Hence it is but a step to an institution in full life and vigour, —a noble orphan school for one thousand boys and girls, founded by Don Pedro, who gave up to its use the superb convent of Belem, with its splendid cloisters, vast airy dormitories, and magnificent church. Some Oxford gentlemen would have wept to see the desecrated edifice,—to think that the shaven polls and white gowns were banished from it to give place to a thousand children, who have not even the clergy to instruct them. 'Every lad here may choose his trade,' our little informant said, who addressed us in better French than any of our party spoke, whose manners were perfectly gentlemanlike and respectful, and whose clothes, though of a common cotton stuff, were cut and worn with a military neatness and precision. All the children whom we remarked were dressed with similar neatness, and it was a pleasure to go through their various rooms for study, where some were busy at mathematics, some at drawing, some attending a lecture on tailoring, while others were sitting at the feet of a professor of the science of shoemaking. All the garments of the establishment were made by the pupils; even the deaf and dumb were drawing and reading, and the blind were, for the most part, set to perform on musical instruments, and got up a concert for the visiters. It was then we wished ourselves of the numbers of the deaf and dumb, for the poor fellows made noises so horrible, that even as blind beggars they could hardly get a livelihood in the musical way.

Hence we were driven to the huge palace of Necessidades, which is but a wing of a building that no king of Portugal ought ever to be rich enough to complete, and which, if perfect, might outvie the Tower of Babel. The mines of Brazil must have been productive of gold and silver, indeed, when the founder imagined this enormous edifice. From the elevation on which it stands it commands the noblest views,—the city is spread before it, with its many churches and towers, and for many miles you see the magnificent Tagus, rolling by banks crowned with trees and towers. But, to arrive at this enormous building you have to climb a steep suburb of wretched huts, many of them with dismal gardens of dry, cracked earth, where a few reedy sprouts of Indian corn seemed to be the chief cultivation, and which were guarded by huge plants of spiky aloes, on which the rags of the proprietors of the huts were sunning themselves. The terrace before the palace was similarly encroached upon by these wretched habitations. A few millions, judiciously expended, might make of this arid hill one of the most magnificent gardens in the world; and the palace seems to me to excel for situation any royal edifice I have ever seen. But the huts of these swarming poor have crawled up close to its gates,—the superb walls of hewn stone stop all of a sudden with a lath-and-plaster *hitch;* and capitals, and hewn stones for columns, still lying about on the deserted terrace, may lie there for ages to come, probably, and never take their places by the side of their brethren in yonder tall bankrupt galleries. The air of this pure sky has little effect upon the edifices,—the edges of the stone look as sharp as if the builders had just left their work; and close to the grand entrance stands an outbuilding, part of which may have been burnt fifty years ago, but is in such cheerful preservation, that you might fancy the fire had occurred yesterday. It must have been an awful sight from this hill to have looked at the city spread before it, and seen it reeling and swaying in the time of the earth-quake. I thought it looked so hot and shaky, that one might fancy a return of the fit. In several places still remain gaps and chasms, and ruins lie here and there as they cracked and fell.

Although the palace has not attained anything like its full growth, yet what exists is quite big enough for the monarch of such a little country ; and Versailles or Windsor has not apartments more nobly proportioned. The Queen resides in the Ajuda, a building of much less pretensions, of which the yellow walls and beautiful gardens are seen between Belem and the city. The Necessidades are only used for grand galas, receptions of ambassadors, and ceremonies of state. In the throne-room is a huge throne, surmounted by an enormous gilt crown, than which I have never seen anything larger in the finest pantomime at Drury Lane ; but the effect of this splendid piece is lessened by a shabby old Brussels carpet, almost the only other article of furniture in the apartment, and not quite large enough to cover its spacious floor. The looms of Kidderminster have supplied the web which ornaments the 'Ambassadors' Waiting-room,' and the ceilings are painted with huge allegories in distemper, which pretty well correspond with the other furniture. Of all the undignified objects in the world, a palace out at elbows is surely the meanest. Such places ought not to be seen in adversity,—splendour is their decency,—and when no longer able to maintain it, they should sink to the level of their means, calmly subside into manufactories, or go shabby in seclusion.

There is a picture-gallery belonging to the palace that is quite of a piece with the furniture, where are the mythological pieces relative to the kings before alluded to, and where the English visiter will see some astonishing pictures of the Duke of Wellington, done in a very characteristic style of Portuguese art. There is also a chapel, which has been decorated with much care and sumptuous-ness of ornament,—the altar surmounted by a ghastly and horrible carved figure in the taste of the time, when faith was strengthened by the shrieks of Jews on the rack, and enlivened by the roasting of heretics. Other such frightful images may be seen in the churches of the city ; those which we saw were still rich, tawdry, and splendid to outward show, although the French, as usual, had robbed their shrines of their gold and silver, and the statues of their jewels and crowns. But brass and tinsel look to the visiter full as well at a little distance,—as doubtless Soult and Junot thought, when they despoiled these places of worship, like French philosophers as they were.

A friend, with a classical turn of mind, was bent upon seeing the aqueduct, whither we went on a dismal excursion of three hours, in the worst carriages, over the most diabolical clattering roads, up and down dreary parched hills, on which grew a few grey olive-trees and many aloes. When we arrived, the gate leading to the aqueduct was closed, and we were entertained with a legend of some respectable character who had made a good livelihood there for some time past lately, having a private key to this very aqueduct, and lying in wait there for unwary travellers, like ourselves, whom he pitched down the arches into the ravines below, and there robbed them at leisure. So that all we saw was the door and the tall arches of the aqueduct, and by the time we returned to town it was time to go on board the ship again. If the inn at which we had sojourned was not of the best quality, the bill, at least, would have done honour to the first establishment in London. We all left the house of entertainment joyfully, glad to get out of the sunburnt city, and go *home*. Yonder in the steamer was home, with its black funnel and gilt portraiture of Lady Mary Wood at the bows ; and every soul on board felt glad to return to the friendly little vessel. But the authorities, however, of Lisbon are very suspicious of the departing stranger, and we were made to lie an hour in the river before the Sanita boat, where a passport is necessary to be procured before the traveller can quit the country. Boat after boat, laden with priests and peasantry, with handsome red-sashed gallegos clad in brown, and ill-favoured women, came and got their permits, and were off, as we lay bumping up against the old hull of the Sanita boat ; but the officers seemed to take a delight in keeping us there bumping, looked at us quite calmly over the ship's sides, and smoked their cigars without the least attention to the prayers which we shrieked out for release.

If we were glad to get away from Lisbon, we were quite as sorry to be obliged to quit Cadiz, which we reached the next night, and where we were allowed a couple of hours' leave to land and look about. It seemed as handsome within as it is stately without ; the long narrow streets of an admirable cleanliness, many of the tall houses of rich and noble decorations, and all looking as if the city were in full prosperity. I have seen no more cheerful and animated sight than the long street leading from the quay where we were landed, and the market blazing in sunshine, piled with fruit, fish, and poultry, under many-coloured awnings ; the tall white houses with their balconies and galleries shining round about, and the sky above so blue that the best cobalt in all the paint-box looks muddy and dim in comparison to it. There were pictures for a year in that market-place—from the copper-coloured old hags and beggars who roared to you for the love of heaven to give money, to the swaggering dandies of the market, with red sashes and tight clothes, looking on superbly, with a hand on the hip and a cigar in the mouth. These must be the chief critics at the great bull-fight house yonder, by the Alameda, with its scanty trees and cool breezes facing the water. Nor are there any corks to the bulls' horns here as at Lisbon. A small old English guide who seized upon me the moment my foot was on shore, had a store of agreeable legends regarding the bulls, men, and horses that had been killed with unbounded profusion in the late entertainments which have taken place.

It was so early an hour in the morning that the shops were scarcely opened as yet ; the churches, however, stood open for the faithful, and we met scores of women tripping towards them with pretty feet, and smart black mantilla, from which looked out fine dark eyes and handsome pale faces, very different from the coarse brown countenances we had seen at Lisbon. A very handsome modern cathedral, built by the present bishop at his own charges, was the finest of the public edifices we saw ; it was not, however, nearly so much frequented as another little church, crowded with altars and fantastic ornaments, and lights and gilding, where we were told to look behind a huge iron grille, and beheld a bevy of black nuns kneeling. Most of the good ladies in the front ranks stopped their devotions, and looked at the strangers with as much curiosity as we directed at them through the gloomy bars of their chapel. The men's convents are closed ; that which contains the famous Murillos has been turned into an academy of the fine arts ; but the English guide did not think the pictures were of sufficient interest to detain strangers, and so hurried us back to the shore, and grumbled at only getting three shillings at parting for his trouble and his information. And so our residence in Andalusia began and ended before breakfast, and we went on board and steamed for Gibraltar, looking, as we past, at Joinville's black squadron, and the white houses of Saint Mary's across the bay, with the hills of Medina Sidonia and Granada lying purple beyond them. There's something even in those names which is pleasant to write down ;—to have passed only two hours in Cadiz is something—to have seen real donnas with comb and mantle—real caballeros with cloak and cigar—real Spanish barbers lathering out of brass basins,—and to have heard guitars under the balconies ;—there was one that an old beggar was jangling in the market, whilst a huge leering fellow in bushy whiskers and a faded velvet dress came singing and jumping after our party,—not singing to a guitar, it is true, but imitating one capitally with his voice, and cracking his fingers by way of castanets, and performing a dance such as Figaro or Lablache might envy. How clear that fellow's voice thrums on the ear even now ; and how bright and pleasant remains the recollection of the fine city and the blue sea, and the Spanish flags floating on the boats that danced over it, and Joinville's band beginning to play stirring marches as we puffed out of the bay.

The next stage was Gibraltar, where we were to change horses. Before sunset we skirted along the dark savage mountains of the African coast, and came to the Rock just before gun-fire. It is the very image of an enormous lion, crouched between the Atlantic and the Mediterranean, and set there to guard the passage for its British mistress. The next British lion is Malta, four days further on in the midland sea, and ready to spring upon Egypt or pounce upon Syria, or roar so as to be heard at Marseilles in case of need.

To the eyes of the civilian, the first-named of these famous fortifications is by far the most imposing. The Rock looks so tremendous, that to ascend it, even without the compliment of shells or shot, seems a dreadful task—what would it be when all those mysterious lines of batteries were vomiting fire and brimstone ; when all those dark guns that you see poking their grim heads out of every imaginable cleft and zigzag should salute you with shot, both hot and cold ; and when, after tugging up the hideous perpendicular place, you were to find regiments of British grenadiers ready to plunge bayonets into your poor panting stomach, and let out artificially the little breath left there ? It is a marvel to think that soldiers will mount such places for a shilling—ensigns for five and ninepence—a day : a cabman would ask double the money to go half way ! One meekly reflects upon the above strange truths, leaning over the ship's side, and looking up the huge mountain, from the tower nestled at the foot of it to the thin flagstaff at the summit, up to which have been piled the most ingenious edifices for murder Christian science ever adopted. My hobby-horse is a quiet beast, suited for Park riding, or a gentle trot to Putney and back to a snug stable, and plenty of feeds of corn :—it can't abide climbing hills, and is not at all used to gunpowder. Some men's animals are so spirited that the very appearance of a stone wall sets them jumping at it ; regular chargers of hobbies, which snort and say—' Ha, ha ! ' at the mere notion of a battle.

CHAPTER III

THE 'LADY MARY WOOD'

OUR week's voyage is now drawing to a close.   We have just been to look at Cape Trafalgar, shining white over the finest blue sea. (We, who were looking at Trafalgar Square only the other day !) The sight of that cape must have disgusted Joinville and his fleet of steamers, as they passed yesterday into Cadiz bay, and to-morrow will give them a sight of St. Vincent.

One of their steam-vessels has been lost off the coast of Africa : they were obliged to burn her, lest the Moors should take possession of her.   She was a virgin vessel, just out of Brest.   Poor innocent ! to die in the very first month of her union with the noble whiskered god of war !

We Britons on board the English boat received the news of the *Groenenland's* abrupt demise with grins of satisfaction.   It was a sort of national compliment, and cause of agreeable congratulation. ' The lubbers ! ' we said ; ' the clumsy humbugs ! there's none but Britons to rule the waves !' and we gave ourselves piratical airs, and went down presently and were sick in our little buggy berths. It was pleasant, certainly, to laugh at Joinville's admiral's flag floating at his foremast, in yonder black ship, with its two thundering great guns at the bows and stern, its busy crew swarming on the deck, and a crowd of obsequious shore-boats bustling round the vessel—and to sneer at the Mogador warrior, and vow that we English, had we been inclined to do the business, would have performed it a great deal better.

Now yesterday at Lisbon we saw H.M.S. *Caledonia*. *This,* on the contrary, inspired us with feelings of respect and awful pleasure.   There she lay—the huge sea-castle—bearing the un-conquerable flag of our country.   She had but to open her jaws, as it were, and she might bring a second earthquake in the city —batter it into kingdom-come—with the Ajuda palace and the Necessidades, the churches, and the lean, dry, empty streets, and Don John, tremendous on horseback, in the midst of Black Horse Square.   Wherever we looked we could see that enormous *Caledonia*, with her flashing three lines of guns.   We looked at the little boats which ever and anon came out of this monster, with humble wonder.   There was the lieutenant who boarded us at midnight before we dropped anchor in the river ; ten white-jacketed men pulling as one, swept along with the barge, gig, boat, curricle, or coach-and-six, with which he came up to us. We examined him —his red whiskers—his collars turned down—his duck trowsers—his bullion epaulets—with awe. With the same reverential feeling we examined the seamen—the young gentleman in the bows of the boat—the handsome young officers of marines we met sauntering in the town next day—the Scotch surgeon who boarded us as we weighed anchor—every man, down to the broken-nosed mariner who was drunk in a wine-house, and had *Caledonia* written in his hat. Whereas at the Frenchmen we looked with undisguised contempt. We were ready to burst with laughter as we passed the Prince's vessel—there was a little French boy in a French boat alongside cleaning it, and twirling about a little French mop—we thought it the most comical, contemptible French boy, mop, boat, steamer, prince—Psha! it is of this wretched vapouring stuff that false patriotism is made. I write this as a sort of homily *apropos* of the day, and Cape Trafalgar, off which we lie. What business have I to strut the deck, and clap my wings, and cry 'cock-a-doodle-doo' over it? Some compatriots are at that work even now.

We have lost one by one all our jovial company. There were the five Oporto wine-merchants—all hearty English gentlemen —gone to their wine-butts, and their red-legged partridges, and their duels at Oporto. It appears that these gallant Britons fight every morning among themselves, and give the benighted people among whom they live an opportunity to admire the spirit national. There is the brave, honest major, with his wooden leg—the kindest and simplest of Irishmen: he has embraced his children, and reviewed his little invalid garrison of fifteen men, in the fort which he commands at Belem, by this time, and, I have no doubt, played to every soul of them the twelve tunes of his musical-box. It was pleasant to see him with that musical-box—how pleased he wound it up after dinner—how happily he listened to the little clinking tunes as they galloped, ding-dong, after each other. A man who carries a musical-box is always a good-natured man.

Then there was his grace, or his grandeur, the Archbishop of Beyrouth (in the parts of the infidels), his Holiness's Nuncio to the court of her most faithful Majesty, and who mingled among us like any simple mortal, — except that he had an extra smiling courtesy, which simple mortals do not always possess ; and when you passed him as such, and puffed your cigar in his face, took off his hat with a grin of such prodigious rapture, as to lead you to suppose that the most delicious privilege of his whole life, was that permission to look at the tip of your nose or of your cigar. With this most reverend prelate was his grace's brother and chaplain—a very greasy and good-natured ecclesiastic, whom, from his physiognomy, I would have imagined to be a dignitary of the Israelitish rather than the Romish church—as profuse in smiling courtesy as his lordship of Beyrout. These two had a meek little secretary between them, and a tall French cook and valet, who, at meal times, might be seen busy about the cabin where their reverences lay. They were on their backs for the greater part of the voyage; their yellow countenances were not only unshaven, but, to judge from appearances, unwashed. They ate in private; and it was only of evenings, as the sun was jetting over the western wave, and, comforted by the dinner, the cabin passengers assembled on the quarter-deck, that we saw the dark faces of the reverend gentlemen among us for a while. They sunk darkly into their berths when the steward's bell tolled for tea.

At Lisbon, where we came to anchor at midnight, a special boat came off, whereof the crew exhibited every token of reverence for the ambassador of the ambassador of heaven, and carried him off from our company. This abrupt departure in the darkness disappointed some of us, who had promised ourselves the pleasure of seeing His Grandeur depart in state in the morning, shaved, clean, and in full pontificals, the tripping little secretary swinging an incense-pot before him, and the greasy chaplain bearing his crosier.

Next day we had another bishop, who occupied the very same berth his grace of Beyrouth had quitted—was sick in the very same way—so much so that this cabin of the *Lady Mary Wood* is to be christened 'the bishop's berth' henceforth; and a handsome mitre is to be painted on the basin.

Bishop No. 2 was a very stout, soft, kind-looking old gentleman, in a square cap, with a handsome tassel of green and gold round his portly breast and back. He was dressed in black robes, and tight purple stockings: and we carried him from Lisbon to the little flat coast of Faro, of which the meek old gentleman was the chief pastor.

We had not been half-an-hour from our anchorage in the Tagus, when his lordship dived down into the episcopal berth. All that night there was a good smart breeze; it blew fresh all the next day, as we went jumping over the blue bright sea; and there was no sign of his lordship the bishop until we were opposite the purple hills of Algarve, which lay at some ten miles distant,—a yellow sunny shore stretching flat before them, whose long sandy flats and villages we could see with our telescopes from the steamer.

Presently a little vessel, with a huge shining lateen sail, and bearing the blue and white Portuguese flag, was seen playing a sort of leap-frog on the jolly waves, jumping over them, and ducking down as merry as could be. This little boat came towards the steamer as quick as ever she could jump ; and Captain Cooper roaring out, 'Stop her !' to *Lady Mary Wood*, her ladyship's paddles suddenly ceased twirling, and news was carried to the good bishop in the berth, that his boat was almost alongside, and that his hour was come.

It was rather an affecting sight to see the poor old fat gentleman, looking wistfully over the water as the boat now came up, and her eight seamen, with great noise, energy, and gesticulation laid her by the steamer. The steamer steps were let down ; his lordship's servant in blue and yellow livery (like the *Edinburgh Review,*) cast over the episcopal luggage into the boat, along with his own bundle and the jack-boots with which he rides postillion on one of the bishop's fat mules at Faro. The blue and yellow domestic went down the steps into the boat. Then came the bishop's turn ; but he couldn't do it for a long while. He went from one passenger to another, sadly shaking them by the hand, often taking leave and seeming loth to depart, until Captain Cooper, in a stern but respectful tone, touched him on the shoulder, and said, I know not with what correctness, being ignorant of the Spanish language, 'Senor Bispo ! Senor Bispo !' on which summons the poor old man, looking ruefully round him once more, put his square cap under his arm, tucked up his long black petticoats, so as to show his purple stockings and jolly fat calves, and went trembling down the steps towards the boat. The good old man ! I wish I had had a shake of that trembling, podgy hand somehow before he went upon his sea martyrdom. I felt a love for that soft-hearted old Christian. Ah ! let us hope his governante tucked him comfortably in bed when he got to Faro that night, and made him a warm gruel and put his feet in warm water. The men clung around him, and almost kissed him as they popped him into the boat, but he did not heed their caresses. Away went the boat scudding madly before the winds. Bang ! another lateen-sailed boat in the distance fired a gun in his honour ; but the wind was blowing away from the shore, and who knows when that meek bishop got home to his gruel ?

I think these were the notables of our party. I will not mention the laughing, ogling lady of Cadiz, whose manners, I very much regret to say, were a great deal too lively for my sense of propriety ; nor those fair sufferers, her companions, who lay on the deck with sickly, smiling, female resignation ; nor the heroic children, who no sooner eat biscuit than they were ill, and no sooner were ill than they began eating biscuit again ; but just allude to one other martyr, the kind lieutenant in charge of the mails, and who bore his cross with what I can't but think a very touching and noble resignation.

There's a certain sort of man whose doom in the world is disappointment,—who excels in it,—and whose luckless triumphs in his meek career of life, I have often thought, must be regarded by the kind eyes above with as much favour as the splendid successes and achievements of coarser and more prosperous men. As I sate with the lieutenant upon deck, his telescope laid over his lean legs, and he looking at the sunset with a pleased, withered old face, he gave me a little account of his history. I take it he is in nowise disinclined to talk about it, simple as it is : he has been seven-and-thirty years in the navy, being somewhat more mature in the service than Lieutenant Peel, Rear-Admiral Prince de Joinville, and other commanders, who need not be mentioned. He is a very well-educated man, and reads prodigiously,—travels, histories, lives of eminent worthies and heroes, in his simple way. He is not in the least angry at his want of luck in the profession. 'Were I a boy to-morrow,' he said, 'I would begin it again ; and when I see my schoolfellows, and how they have got on in life, if some are better off than I am, I find many are worse, and have no call to be discontented.' So he carries her Majesty's mails meekly through this world, waits upon port-admirals and captains in his old glazed hat, and is as proud of the pennon at the bow of his little boat, as if it were flying from the mainmast of a thundering man-of-war. He gets two hundred a year for his services, and has an old mother and a sister, living in England somewhere, who I will wager (though he never, I swear, said a word about it) have a good portion of this princely income.

Is it breaking a confidence to tell Lieutenant Bundy's history ? Let the motive excuse the deed. It is a good, kind, wholesome and noble character. Why should we keep all our admiration for those who win in this world, as we do, sycophants as we are ? When we write a novel, our great, stupid imaginations can go no further than to marry the hero to a fortune at the end, and to find out that he is a lord by right. Oh, blundering lick-spittle morality ! And yet I would like to fancy some happy retributive Utopia in the peaceful cloudland, where my friend the meek lieutenant should find the yards manned of his ship as he went on board, all the guns firing an enormous salute (only without the least noise or vile smell of powder), and he be saluted on the deck as Admiral Sir James, or Sir Joseph—aye, or Lord Viscount Bundy, knight of all the orders above the sun.

I think this is a sufficient, if not a complete catalogue, of the worthies on board the *Lady Mary Wood*. In the week we were on board—it seemed a year, by the way—we came to regard the ship quite as a home. We felt for the captain—the most good-humoured, active, careful, ready of captains—a filial, a fraternal regard ; for the providor, who provided for us with admirable comfort and generosity, a genial gratitude ; and for the brisk steward's lads—brisk in serving the banquet, sympathising in handing the basin—every possible sentiment of regard and goodwill. What winds blew, and how many knots we ran, are all noted down, no doubt, in the ship's log ; and as for what ships we saw—every one of them with their gunnage, tonnage, their nation, their direction whither they were bound, were not these all noted down with surprising ingenuity and precision by the lieutenant, at a family desk at which he sate, every night before a great paper, elegantly and mysteriously ruled off with his large ruler? I have a regard for every man on board that ship, from the captain down to the crew—down even to the cook, with tattooed arms, sweating among the saucepans in the galley, who used (with a touching affection) to send us locks of his hair in the soup. And so, while our feelings and recollections are warm, let us shake hands with this knot of good fellows, comfortably floating about in their little box of wood and iron, across Channel, Biscay Bay, and the Atlantic, from Southampton water to Gibraltar Straits.

CHAPTER IV

GIBRALTAR

SUPPOSE all the nations of the earth to send fitting ambassadors to represent them at Wapping or Portsmouth Point, with each, under its own national signboard and language, its appropriate house of call, and your imagination may figure the main street of Gibraltar ; almost the only part of the town, I believe, which boasts of the name of street at all, the remaining house-rows being modestly called lanes, such as Bomb Lane, Battery Lane, Fusee Lane, and so on. In Main Street the Jews predominate, the Moors abound ; and from the 'Jolly Sailor,' or the 'Brave Horse Marine,' where the people of our own nation are drinking British beer and gin, you hear choruses of 'Garry Owen' or 'The Lass I left behind me' ; while through the flaring lattices of the Spanish ventas come the clatter of castanets and the jingle and moan of

Spanish guitars and ditties. It is a curious sight at evening this thronged street, with the people, in a hundred different costumes, bustling to and fro under the coarse flare of the lamps; swarthy Moors, in white or crimson robes; dark Spanish smugglers in tufted hats, with gay silk handkerchiefs round their heads; fuddled seamen from men-of-war, or merchantmen; porters, Gallician and Genoese; and at every few minutes' interval, little squads of soldiers tramping to relieve guard at some one of the innumerable posts in the town.

Some of our party went to a Spanish venta, as a more convenient or romantic place of residence than an English house; others made choice of the club-house in Commercial Square, of which I formed an agreeable picture in my imagination; rather, perhaps, resembling the Junior United Service Club in Charles Street, by which every Londoner has passed ere this with respectful pleasure, catching glimpses of magnificent blazing candelabras, under which sit neat half-pay officers, drinking half-pints of port. The club-house of Gibraltar is not, however, of the Charles Street sort; it may have been cheerful once, and there are yet relics of splendour about it. When officers wore pigtails, and in the time of Governor O'Hara, it may have been a handsome place; but it is mouldy and decrepit now; and though his Excellency Mr. Bulwer, was living there, and made no complaints that I heard of, other less distinguished persons thought they had reason to grumble. Indeed, what is travelling made of? At least half its pleasures and incidents come out of inns; and of them the tourist can speak with much more truth and vivacity than of historical recollections compiled out of histories, or filched out of handbooks. But to speak of the best inn in a place needs no apology; that, at least, is useful information; as every person intending to visit Gibraltar cannot have seen the flea-bitten countenances of our companions, who fled from their Spanish venta to take refuge at the club the morning after our arrival: they may surely be thankful for being directed to the best house of accommodation in one of the most unromantic, uncomfortable, and prosaic of towns.

If one had a right to break the sacred confidence of the mahogany, I could entertain you with many queer stories of Gibraltar life, gathered from the lips of the gentlemen who enjoyed themselves round the dingy table-cloth of the club-house coffee-room, richly decorated with cold gravy and spilt beer. I heard there the very names of the gentlemen who wrote the famous letters from the *Warspite* regarding the French proceedings at Mogador; and met several refugee Jews from that place, who said that they were much more afraid of the Kabyles without the city, than of the guns of the French squadron, of which they seemed to make rather light. I heard the last odds on the ensuing match between Captain Smith's b. g. Bolter, and Captain Brown's ch. c. Roarer: how the gun-room of her Majesty's ship *Purgatory* had 'cobbed' a tradesman of the town, and of the row in consequence: I heard capital stories of the way in which Wilkins had escaped the guard, and Thompson had been locked up among the mosquitoes for being out after ten without a lantern. I heard how the governor was an old ——, but to say what, would be breaking a confidence; only this may be divulged, that the epithet was exceedingly complimentary to Sir Robert Wilson. All the while these conversations were going on, a strange scene of noise and bustle was passing in the market-place, in front of the window, where Moors, Jews, Spaniards, soldiers were thronging in the sun; and a ragged fat fellow, mounted on a tobacco-barrel, with his hat cocked on his ear, was holding an auction, and roaring with an energy and impudence that would have done credit to Covent Garden.

The Moorish castle is the only building about the Rock which has an air at all picturesque or romantic; there is a plain Roman Catholic cathedral, a hideous new Protestant church of the cigardivan architecture, and a Court-house with a portico which is said to be an imitation of the Parthenon: the ancient religious houses of the Spanish town are gone, or turned into military residences, and marked so that you would never know their former pious destination. You walk through narrow whitewashed lanes, bearing such martial names as are before-mentioned, and by-streets with barracks on either side; small Newgate-like looking buildings, at the doors of which you may see the serjeants' ladies conversing, or at the open windows of the officers' quarters, Ensign Fipps lying on his sofa and smoking his cigar, or Lieutenant Simson practising the flute to while away the weary hours of garrison dulness. I was surprised not to find more persons in the garrison library, where is a magnificent reading-room, and an admirable collection of books.

In spite of the scanty herbage and the dust on the trees, the Alameda is a beautiful walk; of which the vegetation has been as laboriously cared for as the tremendous fortifications which flank it on either side. The vast rock rises on one side with its interminable works of defence, and Gibraltar Bay is shining on the other, out on which from the terraces immense cannon are perpetually looking, surrounded by plantations of cannon-balls and beds of bomb-shells, sufficient, one would think, to blow away the whole Peninsula. The horticultural and military mixture is indeed very queer : here and there temples, rustic summer-seats, etc., have been erected in the garden, but you are sure to see a great squat mortar looking up from among the flower-pots ; and amidst the aloes and geraniums sprouts the green petticoat and scarlet coat of a Highlander ; fatigue-parties are seen winding up the hill, and busy about the endless cannon-ball plantations ; awkward squads are drilling in the open spaces ; sentries marching everywhere, and (this is a caution to artists) I am told have orders to run any man through who is discovered making a sketch of the place. It is always beautiful, especially at evening, when the people are sauntering along the walks, and the moon is shining on the waters of the bay and the hills and twinkling white houses of the opposite shore. Then the place becomes quite romantic : it is too dark to see the dust on the dried leaves ; the cannon-balls do not intrude too much, but have subsided into the shade ; the awkward squads are in bed ; even the loungers are gone, the fan-flirting Spanish ladies, the sallow black-eyed children, and the trim white-jacketed dandies. A fife is heard from some craft at roost on the quiet waters somewhere ; or a faint cheer from yonder black steamer at the Mole, which is about to set out on some night expedition. You forget that the town is at all like Wapping, and deliver yourself up entirely to romance ; the sentries look noble pacing there, silent in the moonlight, and Sandy's voice is quite musical, as he challenges with a ' Who goes there ? '

' All's Well ' is very pleasant when sung decently in tune ; and inspires noble and poetic ideas of duty, courage, and danger : but when you hear it shouted all the night through, accompanied by a clapping of muskets in a time of profound peace, the sentinel's cry becomes no more romantic to the hearer than it is to the sandy Connaught-man or the barelegged Highlander who delivers it. It is best to read about wars comfortably in *Harry Lorrequer* or Scott's novels, in which knights shout their war-cries, and jovial Irish bayoneteers hurrah, without depriving you of any blessed rest. Men of a different way of thinking, however, can suit themselves perfectly at Gibraltar ; where there is marching and counter-marching, challenging and relieving guard all the night through. And not here in Commercial Square alone, but all over the huge rock in the darkness—all through the mysterious zigzags, and round the dark cannon-ball pyramids, and along the vast rock-galleries, and up to the topmost flagstaff where the sentry can look out over two seas, poor fellows are marching and clapping muskets, and crying ' All's well,' dressed in cap and feather, in place of honest nightcaps best befitting the decent hours of sleep.

All these martial noises three of us heard to the utmost advantage, lying on iron bedsteads at the time in a cracked old room on the ground-floor, the open windows of which looked into the square. No spot could be more favourably selected for watching the humours of a garrison-town by night. About midnight, the door hard by us was visited by a party of young officers, who having had quite as much drink as was good for them, were naturally inclined for more; and when we remonstrated through the windows, one of them in a young tipsy voice asked after our mothers, and finally reeled away. How charming is the conversation of high-spirited youth! I don't know whether the guard got hold of them: but certainly if a civilian had been hiccuping through the street at that hour he would have been carried off to the guard-house, and left to the mercy of the mosquitoes there, and had up before the governor in the morning. The young men in the coffee-room tell me he goes to sleep every night with the keys of Gibraltar under his pillow. It is an awful image, and somehow completes the notion of the slumbering fortress. Fancy Sir Robert Wilson, his nose just visible over the sheets, his nightcap and the huge key (you see the very identical one in Reynolds's portrait of Lord Heathfield) peeping out from under the bolster!

If I entertain you with accounts of inns and nightcaps it is because I am more familiar with these subjects than with history and fortifications: as far as I can understand the former, Gibraltar is the great British depôt for smuggling goods into the Peninsula. You see vessels lying in the harbour, and are told in so many words they are smugglers; all those smart Spaniards with cigar and mantles are smugglers, and run tobaccos and cotton into Catalonia; all the respected merchants of the place are smugglers. The other day a Spanish revenue vessel was shot to death under the thundering great guns of the fort, for neglecting to bring to, but it so happened that it was in chase of a smuggler; in this little corner of her dominions Britain proclaims war to custom-houses, and protection to free-trade. Perhaps ere a very long day, England may be acting that part towards the world, which Gibraltar performs towards Spain now; and the last war in which we shall ever engage may be a custom-house war. For once establish railroads and abolish preventive duties through Europe, and what is there left to fight for? It will matter very little then under what flag people live, and foreign ministers and ambassadors may enjoy a dignified sinecure; the army will rise to the rank of peaceful constables, not having any more use for their bayonets than those worthy people have for their weapons now who accompany the law at assizes under the name of javelin-men. The apparatus of bombs and eighty-four pounders may disappear from the Alameda, and the crops of cannon-balls which now grow there, may give place to other plants more pleasant to the eye; and the great key of Gibraltar may be left in the gate for anybody to turn at will, and Sir Robert Wilson may sleep in quiet.

I am afraid I thought it was rather a release, when, having made up our minds to examine the rock in detail and view the magnificent excavations and galleries, the admiration of all military men, and the terror of any enemies who may attack the fortress, we received orders to embark forthwith in the *Tagus*, which was to carry us to Malta and Constantinople. So we took leave of this famous rock—this great blunderbuss—which we seized out of the hands of the natural owners a hundred and forty years ago, and which we have kept ever since tremendously loaded and cleaned and ready for use. To seize and have it is doubtless a gallant thing; it is like one of those tests of courage which one reads of in the chivalrous romances, when, for instance, Sir Huon, of Bordeaux, is called on to prove his knighthood by going to Babylon and pulling out the Sultan's beard and front teeth in the midst of his court there.

But, after all, justice must confess it was rather hard on the poor Sultan. If we had the Spaniards established at Land's End, with impregnable Spanish fortifications on St. Michael's Mount, we should perhaps come to the same conclusion. Meanwhile, let us hope during this long period of deprivation, the Sultan of Spain is reconciled to the loss of his front teeth and bristling whiskers— let us even try to think that he is better without them. At all events, right or wrong, whatever may be our title to the property, there is no Englishman but must think with pride of the manner in which his countrymen have kept it, and of the courage, endurance, and sense of duty with which stout old Eliot and his companions resisted Crillon and the Spanish battering ships and his fifty thousand men. There seems to be something more noble in the success of a gallant resistance than of an attack, however brave. After failing in his attack on the fort, the French General visited the English Commander who had foiled him, and parted from him and his garrison in perfect politeness and good-humour. The English troops, Drinkwater says, gave him thundering cheers as he went away, and the French in return complimented us on our gallantry, and lauded the humanity of our people. If we are to go on murdering each other in the old-fashioned way, what a pity it is that our battles cannot end in the old-fashioned way too.

One of our fellow-travellers, who had written a book, and had suffered considerably from sea-sickness during our passage along the coasts of France and Spain, consoled us all by saying that the very minute we got into the Mediterranean we might consider ourselves entirely free from illness; and, in fact, that it was unheard of in the inland sea. Even in the Bay of Gibraltar the water looked bluer than anything I have ever seen—except Miss Smith's eyes. I thought, somehow, the delicious faultless azure never could look angry—just like the eyes before alluded to—and under this assurance we passed the Strait, and began coasting the African shore calmly and without the least apprehension, as if we were as much used to the tempest as Mr. T. P. Cooke.

But when, in spite of the promise of the man who had written the book, we found ourselves worse than in the worst part of the Bay of Biscay, or off the storm-lashed rocks of Finisterre, we set down the author in question as a gross impostor, and had a mind to quarrel with him for leading us into this cruel error. The most provoking part of the matter, too, was, that the sky was deliciously clear and cloudless, the air balmy, the sea so insultingly blue that it seemed as if we had no right to be ill at all, and that the innumerable little waves that frisked round about our keel were enjoying an *anerithmon gelasma* (this is one of my four Greek quotations, depend on it, I will manage to introduce the other three before the tour is done)—seemed to be enjoying, I say, the above-named Greek quotation at our expense. Here is the dismal log of Wednesday, 4th of September :—'All attempts at dining very fruitless. Basins in requisition. Wind hard ahead. *Que diable allais je faire dans cette galère ?* Writing or thinking impossible, so read letters from the Ægean.' These brief words give, I think, a complete idea of wretchedness, despair, remorse, and prostration of soul and body. Two days previously we passed the forts and moles and yellow buildings of Algiers, rising very stately from the sea, and skirted by gloomy purple lines of African shore, with fires smoking in the mountains, and lonely settlements here and there.

On the 5th, to the inexpressible joy of all, we reached Valetta, the entrance to the harbour of which is one of the most stately and agreeable scenes ever admired by sea-sick traveller. The small basin was busy with a hundred ships, from the huge guard-ship, which lies there a city in itself ;—merchantmen loading and crews cheering, under all the flags of the world flaunting in the sunshine ; a half-score of busy black steamers perpetually coming and going, coaling and painting, and puffing and hissing in and out of harbour ; slim men-of-war's barges shooting to and fro, with long shining oars flashing like wings over the water ; hundreds of painted town-boats, with high heads and white awnings,—down to the little tubs in which some naked, tawny young beggars came paddling up to the steamer, entreating us to let them dive for halfpence. Round this busy blue water rise rocks, blazing in sunshine, and covered with every imaginable device of fortification: to the right, St. Elmo, with flag and lighthouse; and opposite, the Military Hospital, looking like a palace; and all round, the houses of the city, for its size the handsomest and most stately in the world.

Nor does it disappoint you on a closer inspection, as many a foreign town does. The streets are thronged with a lively, comfortable-looking population; the poor seem to inhabit handsome stone palaces, with balconies and projecting windows of heavy carved stone. The lights and shadows, the cries and stenches, the fruit-shops and fish-stalls, the dresses and chatter of all nations; the soldiers in scarlet, and women in black mantillas; the beggars, boatmen, barrels of pickled herrings and macaroni; the shovel-hatted priests and bearded capuchins; the tobacco, grapes, onions, and sunshine; the signboards, bottle-porter stores, the statues of saints and little chapels which jostle the stranger's eyes as he goes up the famous stairs from the water-gate, make a scene of such pleasant confusion and liveliness as I have never witnessed before. And the effect of the groups of multitudinous actors in this busy, cheerful drama, is heightened, as it were, by the decorations of the stage. The sky is delightfully brilliant; all the houses and ornaments are stately; castles and palaces are rising all around; and the flag, towers and walls of Fort St. Elmo look as fresh and magnificent as if they had been erected only yesterday.

The Strada Reale has a much more courtly appearance than that one described. Here are palaces, churches, court-houses and libraries, the genteel London shops, and the latest articles of perfumery. Gay young officers are strolling about in shell-jackets much too small for them; midshipmen are clattering by on hired horses; squads of priests, habited after the fashion of Don Basilio in the opera, are demurely pacing to and fro; professional beggars run shrieking after the stranger; and agents for horses, for inns, and for worse places still, follow him and insinuate the excellence of their goods. The houses where they are selling carpet-bags and pomatum were the palaces of the successors of the goodliest company of gallant knights the world ever heard tell of. It seems unromantic; but *these* were not the romantic knights of St. John. The heroic days of the order ended as the last Turkish galley lifted anchor after the memorable siege. The present stately houses were built in times of peace and splendour and decay. I doubt whether the 'Auberge de Provence,' where the Union Club flourishes now, has ever seen anything more romantic than the pleasant balls held in the great room there.

The church of Saint John, not a handsome structure without, is magnificent within : a noble hall covered with a rich embroidery of gilded carving, the chapels of the different nations on either side, but not interfering with the main structure, of which the whole is simple, and the details only splendid ; it seemed to me a fitting place for this wealthy body of aristocratic soldiers, who made their devotions as it were on parade, and though on their knees, never forgot their epaulets or their quarters of nobility. This mixture of religion and worldly pride seems incongruous at first ; but have we not at church at home similar relics of feudal ceremony ?—the verger with the silver mace who precedes the vicar to the desk ; the two chaplains of my lord archbishop, who bow over his grace as he enters the communion-table gate ; even poor John, who follows my lady with her coroneted prayer-book, and makes his *congé* as he hands it into the pew. What a chivalrous absurdity is the banner of some high and mighty prince, hanging over his stall in Windsor Chapel, when you think of the purpose for which men are supposed to assemble there ! The church of the knights of St. John is paved over with sprawling heraldic devices of the dead gentlemen of the dead order ; as if, in the next world, they expected to take rank in conformity with their pedigrees, and would be marshalled into heaven according to the orders of precedence. Cumbrous handsome paintings adorn the walls and chapels, decorated with pompous monuments of grand masters. Beneath is a crypt, where more of these honourable and reverend warriors lie, in a state that a Simpson would admire. In the altar are said to lie three of the most gallant relics in the world : the keys of Acre, Rhodes, and Jerusalem. What blood was shed in defending these emblems ! What faith, endurance, genius, and generosity ; what pride, hatred, ambition, and savage lust of blood were roused together for their guardianship !

In the lofty halls and corridors of the governor's house, some portraits of the late grand masters still remain ; a very fine one, by Caravaggio, of a knight in gilt armour, hangs in the dining-room, near a full-length of poor Louis XVI., in royal robes, the very picture of uneasy impotency. But the portrait of Vignacourt is the only one which has a respectable air ; the other chiefs of the famous society are pompous old gentlemen in black, with huge periwigs, and crowns round their hats, and a couple of melancholy pages in yellow and red. But pages and wigs and grand masters have almost faded out of the canvass, and are vanishing into Hades with a most melancholy indistinctness. The names of most of these gentlemen, however, live as yet in the forts of the place, which all seem to have been eager to build and christen : so that it seems as if, in the Malta mythology, they had been turned into freestone.

In the armoury is the very suit painted by Caravaggio, by the side of the armour of the noble old La Valette, whose heroism saved his island from the efforts of Mustapha and Dragut, and an army quite as fierce and numerous as that which was baffled before Gibraltar, by similar courage and resolution. The sword of the last-named famous corsair (a most truculent little scimitar), thousands of pikes and halberts, little old cannons and wall pieces, helmets and cuirasses, which the knights or their people wore, are trimly arranged against the wall, and, instead of spiking Turks or arming warriors, now serve to point morals and adorn tales. And here likewise are kept many thousand muskets, swords, and boarding pikes, for daily use, and a couple of ragged old standards of one of the English regiments, who pursued and conquered in Egypt the remains of the haughty and famous French republican army, at whose appearance the last knights of Malta flung open the gates of all their fortresses, and consented to be extinguished without so much as a remonstrance, or a kick, or a struggle.

We took a drive into what may be called the country ; where the fields are rocks, and the hedges are stones—passing by the stone gardens of the Florian, and wondering at the number and handsomeness of the stone villages and churches rising everywhere among the stony hills. Handsome villas were passed everywhere, and we drove for a long distance along the sides of an aqueduct, quite a royal work of the Caravaggio in gold armour, the grand master De Vignacourt. A most agreeable contrast to the arid rocks of the general scenery, was the garden at the governor's country house ; with the orange-trees and water, its beautiful golden grapes, luxuriant flowers, and thick cool shrubberies. The eye longs for this sort of refreshment, after being seared with the hot glare of the general country ; and St. Antonio was as pleasant after Malta, as Malta was after the sea.

We paid the island a subsequent visit in November, passing seventeen days at an establishment called Fort Manuel there, and by punsters the Manuel des Voyageurs ; where government accommodates you with quarters ; where the authorities are so attentive as to scent your letters with aromatic vinegar before you receive them, and so careful of your health as to lock you up in your room every night lest you should walk in your sleep, and so over the battlements into the sea ; if you escaped drowning in the sea, the sentries on the opposite shore would fire at you, hence the nature of the precaution. To drop, however, this satirical strain ; those who know what a quarantine is, may fancy that the place somehow becomes unbearable in which it has been endured. And though the November climate of Malta is like the most delicious May in England, and though there is every gaiety and amusement in the town, a comfortable little opera, a good old library filled full of good old books (none of your works of modern science, travel, and history, but good old *useless* books of the two last centuries), and nobody to trouble you in reading them ; and though the society of Valetta is most hospitable, varied, and agreeable, yet somehow one did not feel *safe* in the island, with perpetual glimpses of Fort Manuel from the opposite shore ; and, lest the quarantine authorities should have a fancy to fetch one back again, on a pretext of posthumous plague, we made our way to Naples by the very first opportunity—those who remained that is, of the little Eastern expedition. They were not all there. The Giver of life and death had removed two of our company : one was left behind to die in Egypt, with a mother to bewail his loss ; another we buried in the dismal lazaretto cemetery.

One is bound to look at this, too, as a part of our journey. Disease and death are knocking perhaps at your next cabin-door. Your kind and cheery companion has ridden his last ride and emptied his last glass beside you. And while fond hearts are yearning for him far away, and his own mind, if conscious, is turning eagerly towards the spot of the world whither affection or interest call it—the Great Father summons the anxious spirit from earth to himself, and ordains that the nearest and dearest shall meet here no more.

Such an occurrence as a death in a lazaretto, mere selfishness renders striking. We were walking with him but two days ago on deck. One has a sketch of him, another his card, with the address written yesterday, and given with an invitation to come and see him at home in the country, where his children are looking for him. He is dead in a day, and buried in the walls of the prison. A doctor felt his pulse by deputy—a clergyman comes from the town to read the last service over him—and the friends, who attend his funeral, are marshalled by lazaretto-guardians, so as not to touch each other. Every man goes back to his room and applies the lesson to himself. One would not so depart without seeing again the dear, dear faces. We reckon up those we love : they are but very few, but I think one loves them better than ever now. Should it be your turn next ?—and why not ? Is it pity or comfort to think of that affection which watches and survives you ?

The Maker has linked together the whole race of man with this chain of love. I like to think that there is no man but has had kindly feelings for some other, and he for his neighbour, until we bind together the whole family of Adam. Nor does it end here. It joins heaven and earth together. For my friend or my child of past days is still my friend or my child to me here, or in the home prepared for us by the Father of all. If identity survives the grave, as our faith tells us, is it not a consolation to think that there may be one or two souls among the purified and just, whose affection watches us invisible, and follows the poor sinner on earth!

CHAPTER V

ATHENS

Not feeling any enthusiasm myself about Athens, my bounden duty of course is clear, to sneer and laugh heartily at all who have. In fact, what business has a lawyer, who was in Pump Court this day three weeks, and whose common reading is law reports or the newspaper, to pretend to fall in love for the long vacation with mere poetry, of which I swear a great deal is very doubtful, and to get up an enthusiasm quite foreign to his nature and usual calling in life? What call have ladies to consider Greece 'romantic,' they who get their notions of mythology from the well-known pages of Tooke's *Pantheon?* What is the reason that blundering Yorkshire squires, young dandies from Corfu regiments, jolly sailors from ships in the harbour, and yellow old Indians returning from Bundelcund, should think proper to be enthusiastic about a country of which they know nothing; the mere physical beauty of which they cannot, for the most part, comprehend; and because certain characters lived in it two thousand four hundred years ago? What have these people in common with Pericles, what have these ladies in common with Aspasia (O fie)? Of the race of Englishmen who come wondering about the tomb of Socrates, do you think the majority would not have voted to hemlock him? Yes; for the very same superstition which leads men by the nose now, drove them onward in the days when the lowly husband of Xantippe died for daring to think simply and to speak the truth. I know of no quality more magnificent in fools than their faith; that perfect consciousness they have, that they are doing virtuous and meritorious actions, when they are performing acts of folly, murdering Socrates, or pelting Aristides with holy oyster-shells, all for Virtue's sake; and a 'History of Dulness in all Ages of the World,' is a book which a philosopher would surely be hanged, but as certainly blessed, for writing.

If papa and mamma (honour be to them!) had not followed the faith of their fathers, and thought proper to send away their only beloved son (afterwards to be celebrated under the name of Titmarsh) into ten years' banishment of infernal misery, tyranny, annoyance; to give over the fresh feelings of the heart of the little Michael Angelo to the discipline of vulgar bullies, who, in order to lead tender young children to the Temple of Learning (as they do in the spelling-books), drive them on with clenched fists and low abuse; if they fainted, revived them with a thump, or assailed them with a curse; if they were miserable, consoled them with a brutal jeer—if, I say, my dear parents, instead of giving me the inestimable benefit of a ten years' classical education, had kept me at home with my dear thirteen sisters, it is probable I should have liked this country of Attica, in sight of the blue shores of which the present pathetic letter is written: but I was made so miserable in youth by a classical education, that all connected with it is disagreeable in my eyes; and I have the same recollection of Greek in youth that I have of castor-oil.

So in coming in sight of the promontory of Sunium, where the Greek muse, in an awful vision, came to me, and said in a patronizing way, 'Why, my dear' (she always, the old spinster, adopts this high and mighty tone), 'Why, my dear, are you not charmed to be in this famous neighbourhood, in this land of poets and heroes, of whose history your classical education ought to have made you a master; if it did not, you have woefully neglected your opportunities, and your dear parents have wasted their money in sending you to school.' I replied, 'Madam, your company in youth was made so laboriously disagreeable to me, that I can't at present reconcile myself to you in age. I read your poets, but it was in fear and trembling; and a cold sweat is but an ill accompaniment to poetry. I blundered through your histories; but history is so dull (saving your presence) of herself, that when the brutal dulness of a schoolmaster is superadded to her own slow conversation, the union becomes intolerable; hence I have not the slightest pleasure in renewing my acquaintance with a lady who has been the source of so much bodily and mental discomfort to me.' To make a long story short, I am anxious to apologise for a want of enthusiasm in the classical line, and to excuse an ignorance which is of the most undeniable sort.

This is an improper frame of mind for a person visiting the land of Æschylus and Euripides ; add to which, we have been abominably overcharged at the Inn : and what are the blue hills of Attica, the silver calm basin of Piræus, the heathery heights of Pentelicus, and yonder rock crowned by the Doric columns of the Parthenon, and the thin Ionic shafts of the Erechtheum, to a man who has had little rest, and is bitten all over by bugs ? Was Alcibiades bitten by bugs, I wonder ; and did the brutes crawl over him as he lay in the rosy arms of Phryne ? I wished all night for Socrates' hammock or basket, as it is described in the *Clouds;* in which resting-place, no doubt, the abominable animals kept per force clear of him.

A French man-of-war, lying in the silvery little harbour, sternly eyeing out of its stern port-holes a saucy little English corvette beside, began playing sounding marches as a crowd of boats came

paddling up to the steamer's side to convey us travellers to shore. There were Russian schooners and Greek brigs lying in this little bay ; dumpy little windmills whirling round on the sunburnt heights round about it ; an improvised town of quays and marine taverns has sprung up on the shore ; a host of jingling barouches, more miserable than any to be seen even in Germany, were collected at the landing-place ; and the Greek drivers (how queer they looked in skull-caps, shabby jackets with profuse embroidery of worsted, and endless petticoats of dirty calico !) began, in a generous ardour for securing passengers, to abuse each other's horses and carriages in the regular London fashion. Satire could certainly hardly caricature the vehicle in which we were made to journey to Athens ; and it was only by thinking that, bad as they were, these coaches were much more comfortable contrivances than any Alcibiades or Cymon ever had, that we consoled ourselves along the road. It was flat for six miles along the plain to the city ; and you see for the greater part of the way the purple mount on which the Acropolis rises, and the gleaming houses of the town

spread beneath. Round this wide, yellow, barren plain,—a stunt
district of olive-trees is almost the only vegetation visible—there
rises, as it were, a sort of chorus of the most beautiful mountains ;
the most elegant, gracious, and noble the eye ever looked on.
These hills did not appear at all lofty or terrible, but superbly
rich and aristocratic. The clouds were dancing round about them ;
you could see their rosy, purple shadows sweeping round the clear,
serene summits of the hills. To call a hill aristocratic seems
affected or absurd ; but the difference between these hills and the
others, is the difference between Newgate Prison and the Travellers'
Club, for instance : both are buildings ; but the one stern, dark and
coarse ; the other rich, elegant, and festive. At least, so I thought.
With such a stately palace as munificent Nature had built for
these people, what could they be themselves but lordly, beautiful,
brilliant, brave, and wise ? We saw four Greeks on donkeys on
the road (which is a dust-whirlwind where it is not a puddle) ; and
other four were playing with a dirty pack of cards, at a barrack
that English poets have christened the half-way house. Does
external nature and beauty influence the soul to good ? You go
about Warwickshire, and fancy that from merely being born and
wandering in those sweet sunny plains and fresh woodlands, Shak-
spere must have drunk in a portion of that frank, artless sense of
beauty, which lies about his works like a bloom or dew ; but a
Coventry ribbon-maker, or a slang Leamington squire, are looking
on those very same landscapes too, and what do they profit ?
You theorise about the influence which the climate and appearance
of Attica must have had in ennobling those who were born there ;
yonder dirty swindling ragged blackguards, lolling over greasy
cards three hours before noon, quarrelling and shrieking, armed to
the teeth and afraid to fight, are bred out of the same land which
begot the philosophers and heroes. But the half-way house is
past by this time, and behold we are in the capital of king
Otho.

I swear solemnly that I would rather have two hundred a year
in Fleet Street, than be king of the Greeks, with Basileus written
before my name round their beggarly coin ; with the bother of
perpetual revolutions in my huge plaster-of-Paris palace, with no
amusement but a drive in the afternoon over a wretched arid
country, where roads are not made, with ambassadors (the deuce
knows why, for what good can the English, or the French, or the
Russian party get out of such a bankrupt alliance as this ?)
perpetually pulling and tugging at me, away from honest Germany,
where there is beer and æsthetic conversation, and operas at a
small cost. The shabbiness of this place actually beats Ireland,

and that is a strong word. The palace of the Basileus is an enormous edifice of plaster, in a square containing six houses, three donkies, no roads, no fountains (except in the picture of the inn); backwards it seems to look straight to the mountain—on one side is a beggarly garden—the king goes out to drive (revolutions permitting) at five—some four-and-twenty blackguards saunter up to the huge sandhill of a terrace, as his majesty passes by in a gilt barouche and an absurd fancy dress; the gilt barouche goes plunging down the sandhills: the two dozen soldiers, who have been presenting arms, slouch off to their quarters: the vast barrack of a palace remains entirely white, ghastly and lonely: and save the braying of a donkey now and then (which long-eared minstrels are more active and sonorous in Athens than in any place I know), all is entirely silent round Basileus's palace. How could people who knew Leopold fancy he would be so 'jolly green,' as to take such a birth? It was only a gobemouche of a Bavarian that could ever have been induced to accept it.

I beseech you to believe that it was not the bill and the bugs at the inn which induced the writer hereof to speak so slightingly of the residence of Basileus. These evils are now cured and forgotten. This is written off the leaden flats and mounds which they call the Troad. It is stern justice alone which pronounces this excruciating sentence. It was a farce to make this place into a kingly capital; and I make no manner of doubt that King Otho, the very day he can get away unperceived, and get together the passage-money, will be off for dear old Deutschland, Fatherland, Beerland!

I have never seen a town in England which may be compared to this; for though Herne Bay is a ruin now, money was once spent upon it and houses built; here, beyond a few scores of mansions comfortably laid out, the town is little better than a rickety agglomeration of larger and smaller huts, tricked out here and there with the most absurd cracked ornaments, and cheap attempts at elegance. But neatness is the elegance of poverty, and these people despise such a homely ornament. I have got a map with squares, fountains, theatres, public gardens, and Places d'Othon marked out; but they only exist in the paper capital—the wretched, tumble-down, wooden one boasts of none.

One is obliged to come back to the old disagreeable comparison of Ireland. Athens may be about as wealthy a place as Carlow or Killarney—the streets swarm with idle crowds, the innumerable little lanes flow over with dirty little children, they are playing and paddling about in the dirt everywhere, with great big eyes, yellow faces, and the queerest little gowns and skull-caps. But in the outer man, the Greek has far the advantage of the Irishman; most of them are well and decently dressed (if five-and-twenty yards of petticoat may not be called decent, what may?); they swagger to and fro with huge knives in their girdles. Almost all the men are handsome, but live hard, it is said, in order to decorate their backs with those fine clothes of theirs. I have seen but two or three handsome women, and these had the great drawback which is common to the race—I mean, a sallow, greasy, coarse complexion, at which it was not advisable to look too closely.

And on this score I think we English may pride ourselves on possessing an advantage (by *we*, I mean the lovely ladies to whom this is addressed with the most respectful compliments) over the most classical country in the world. I don't care for beauty which will only bear to be looked at from a distance like a scene in a theatre. What is the most beautiful nose in the world, if it be covered with a skin of the texture and colour of coarse whity-brown paper; and if Nature has made it as slippery and shining as though it had been anointed with pomatum? They may talk about beauty, but would you wear a flower that had been dipped in a grease-pot? No; give me a fresh, dewy, healthy rose out of Somersetshire; not one of those superb, tawdry, unwholesome exotics, which are only good to make poems about. Lord Byron wrote more cant of this sort than any poet I know of. Think of 'the peasant girls with dark blue eyes' of the Rhine—the brown-faced, flat-nosed, thick-lipped, dirty wenches! Think of 'filling high a cup of Samian wine'; small beer is nectar compared to it, and Byron himself always drank gin. That man *never* wrote from his heart. He got up rapture and enthusiasm with an eye to the public;—but this is dangerous ground, even more dangerous than to look Athens full in the face, and say that your eyes are not dazzled by its beauty. The Great Public admires Greece and Byron; the public knows best. Murray's *Guide-book* calls the latter 'our native bard.' Our native bard! *Mon Dieu! He* Shakspeare's, Milton's, Keats's, Scott's native bard! Well, woe be to the man who denies the public gods!

The truth is, then, that Athens is a disappointment; and I am angry that it should be so. To a skilled antiquarian, or an enthusiastic Greek scholar, the feelings created by a sight of the place of course will be different; but you who would be inspired by it must undergo a long preparation of reading, and possess, too, a particular feeling; both of which, I suspect, are uncommon in our busy commercial newspaper-reading country. Men only say they are enthusiastic about the Greek and Roman authors and history, because it is considered proper and respectable. And we know how gentlemen in Baker Street have editions of the classics handsomely bound in the library, and how they use them. Of course they don't retire to read the newspaper ; it is to look over a favourite ode of Pindar, or to discuss an obscure passage in Athenæus ! Of course country magistrates and members of Parliament are always studying Demosthenes and Cicero ; we know it from their continual habit of quoting the Latin grammar in Parliament. But it is agreed that the classics are respectable ; therefore we are to be enthusiastic about them. Also let us admit that Byron is to be held up as ' our native bard.'

I am not so entire a heathen as to be insensible to the beauty of those relics of Greek art, of which men much more learned and enthusiastic have written such piles of descriptions. I thought I could recognise the towering beauty of the prodigious columns of the temple of Jupiter ; and admire the astonishing grace, severity, elegance, completeness of the Parthenon. The little temple of Victory, with its fluted Corinthian shafts, blazed under the sun almost as fresh as it must have appeared to the eyes of its founders ; I saw nothing more charming and brilliant, more graceful, festive, and aristocratic than this sumptuous little building. The Roman remains which lie in the towns below, look like the works of barbarians beside these perfect structures. They jar strangely on the eye, after it has been accustoming itself to perfect harmony and proportions. If, as the schoolmaster tells us, the Greek writing is as complete as the Greek art ; if an ode of Pindar is as glittering and pure as the temple of Victory ; or a discourse of Plato as polished and calm as yonder mystical portico of the Erechtheum ; what treasures of the senses and delights of the imagination have those lost to whom the Greek books are as good as sealed !

And yet one meets with very dull first class-men. Genius won't transplant from one brain to another, or is ruined in the carriage like fine Burgundy. Sir Robert Peel and Sir John Hobhouse are both good scholars ; but their poetry in parliament does not strike one as fine. Muzzle, the schoolmaster, who is bullying poor trembling little boys, was a fine scholar when he was a sizar, and a ruffian then and ever since. Where is the great poet, since the days of Milton, who has improved the natural offshoots of his brain by grafting it from the Athenian tree ?

I had a volume of Tennyson in my pocket, which somehow settled that question, and ended the querulous dispute between me and Conscience, under the shape of the neglected and irritated Greek muse, which had been going on ever since I had commenced my walk about Athens. The old spinster saw me wince at the idea of the author of 'Dora' and 'Ulysses,' and tried to follow up her advantage by further hints of time lost, and precious opportunities thrown away—'You might have written poems like them,' said she ; 'or, no, not like them perhaps, but you might have done a neat prize poem, and pleased your papa and mamma. You might have translated Jack and Jill into Greek iambics, and been a credit to your college.' I turned testily away from her, 'Madam,' says I, 'because an eagle houses on a mountain, or soars to the sun, don't you be angry with a sparrow that perches on a garret-window, or twitters on a twig. Leave me to myself ; look, my beak is not aquiline by any means.'

And so, my dear friend, you who have been reading this last page in wonder, and who, instead of a description of Athens, have been accommodated with a lament on the part of the writer, that he was idle at school, and does not know Greek, excuse this momentary outbreak of egotistic despondency. To say truth, dear Jones, when one walks among the nests of the eagles, and sees the prodigious eggs they laid, a certain feeling of discomfiture must come over us smaller birds. You and I could not invent, it even stretches our minds painfully to try and comprehend part of the beauty of the Parthenon—ever so little of it—the beauty of a single column,—a fragment of a broken shaft lying under the astonishing blue sky there, in the midst of that unrivalled land-scape. There may be grander aspects of nature, but none more deliciously beautiful. The hills rise in perfect harmony, and fall in the most exquisite cadences,—the sea seems brighter, the islands more purple, the clouds more light and rosy than elsewhere. As you look up through the open roof, you are almost oppressed by the serene depth of the blue overhead. Look even at the fragments of the marble, how soft and pure it is, glittering and white like fresh snow ! 'I was all beautiful,' it seems to say, 'even the hidden parts of me were spotless, precious, and fair'—and so, musing over this wonderful scene, perhaps I get some feeble glimpse or idea of that ancient Greek spirit which peopled it with sublime races of heroes and gods ;[1] and which I never could get out of a Greek book,—no, not though Muzzle flung it at my head.

---

[1] Saint Paul speaking from the Areopagus, and rebuking these superstitions away, yet speaks tenderly to the people before him, whose devotions he had marked ; quotes their poets, to bring them to think of the God unknown, whom they had ignorantly worshipped ; and says, that the times of this ignorance *God winked at*, but that now it was time to repent. No rebuke can surely be more gentle than this delivered by the upright Apostle.

CHAPTER VI

SMYRNA—FIRST GLIMPSES OF THE EAST

I AM glad that the Turkish part of Athens was extinct, so that I should not be balked of the pleasure of entering an eastern town by an introduction to any garbled or incomplete specimen of one. Smyrna seems to me the most eastern of all I have seen; as Calais will probably remain to the Englishman the most French town in the world. The jack-boots of the postilions don't seem so huge elsewhere, or the tight stockings of the maid-servants so Gallic. The churches and the ramparts, and the little soldiers on them, remain for ever impressed upon your memory; from which larger temples and buildings, and whole armies have subsequently disappeared: and the first words of actual French heard spoken, and the first dinner at Quillacq's, remain after twenty years as clear as on the first day. Dear Jones, can't you remember the exact smack of the white hermitage, and the toothless old fellow singing 'Largo al factotum'?

The first day in the East is like that. After that there is nothing. The wonder is gone, and the thrill of that delightful shock, which so seldom touches the nerves of plain men of the world, though they seek for it everywhere. One such looked out at Smyrna from our steamer, and yawned without the least excitement, and did not betray the slightest emotion, as boats with real Turks on board came up to the ship. There lay the town with minarets and cypresses, domes and castles; great guns were firing off, and the blood-red flag of the Sultan flaring over the fort ever since sunrise; woods and mountains came down to the gulf's edge, and as you looked at them with the telescope, there peeped out of the general mass a score of pleasant episodes of Eastern life—there were cottages with quaint roofs; silent cool kiosks, where the chief of the eunuchs brings down the ladies of the harem. I saw Hassan, the fisherman, getting his nets; and Ali Baba going off with his donkey to the great forest for wood. Smith looked at these wonders quite unmoved; and I was surprised at his apathy: but he had been at Smyrna before. A man only sees the miracle once; though you yearn after it ever so, it won't come again. I saw nothing of Ali Baba and Hassan the next time we came to Smyrna, and had some doubts (recollecting the badness of the inn) about landing at all. A person who wishes to understand France and the East should come in a yacht to Calais or Smyrna, land for two hours, and never afterwards go back again.

But those two hours are beyond measure delightful. Some of us were querulous up to that time, and doubted of the wisdom of making the voyage. Lisbon, we owned, was a failure; Athens a dead failure. Malta very well, but not worth the trouble and sea-sickness; in fact, Baden-Baden or Devonshire would be a better move than this; when Smyrna came, and rebuked all mutinous cocknies into silence. Some men may read this who are in want of a sensation. If they love the odd and picturesque, if they loved the *Arabian Nights* in their youth, let them book themselves on board one of the Peninsular and Oriental vessels, and try one *dip* into Constantinople or Smyrna. Walk into the Bazaar, and the East is unveiled to you; how often and often have you tried to fancy this, lying out on a summer holiday at school! It is wonderful, too, how *like* it is; you may imagine that you have been in the place before, you seem to know it so well!

The beauty of that poetry is, to me, that it was never too hand-some; there is no fatigue of sublimity about it. Shacabac and the Little Barber play as great a part in it as the heroes; there are no uncomfortable sensations of terror; you may be familiar with the great Afreet, who was going to execute the travellers for killing his son with a date-stone. Morgiana, when she kills the forty robbers with boiling oil, does not seem to hurt them in the least; and though King Schahriar makes a practice of cutting off his wives' heads, yet you fancy they have got them on again in some of the back rooms of the palace, where they are dancing and playing on dulcimers. How fresh, easy, good-natured, is all this! How delightful is that notion of the pleasant Eastern people about knowledge, where the height of science is made to consist in the answering of riddles! and all the mathematicians and magicians bring their great beards to bear on a conundrum!

When I got into the bazaar among this race, somehow I felt as if they were all friends. There sat the merchants in their little shops, quiet and solemn, but with friendly looks. There was no smoking, it was the Ramazan; no eating, the fish and meats fizzing in the enormous pots of the cook-shops are only for the Christians. The children abounded; the law is not so stringent upon them, and many wandering merchants were there selling figs (in the name of the prophet, doubtless,) for their benefit, and elbowing onwards with baskets of grapes and cucumbers. Countrymen passed bristling over with arms, each with a huge bellyful of pistols and daggers in his girdle; fierce, but not the least dangerous. Wild swarthy Arabs, who had come in with the caravans, walked solemnly about, very different in look and demeanour from the sleek inhabitants of the town. Greeks and

Jews squatted and smoked, their shops tended by sallow-faced boys, with large eyes, who smiled and welcomed you in ; negroes bustled about in gaudy colours ; and women, with black nose-bags and shuffling yellow slippers, chattered and bargained at the doors of the little shops.   There was the rope quarter and the sweetmeat quarter, and the pipe bazaar and the arm bazaar, and the little turned-up shoe quarter and the shops where ready-made jackets and pelisses were swinging, and the region where, under the ragged awnings, regiments of tailors were at work.   The sun peeps through these awnings of mat or canvas, which are hung over the narrow lanes of the bazaar, and ornaments them with a thousand freaks of light and shadow.   Cogia Hassan Alhabbal's shop is in a blaze of light ; while his neighbour, the barber and coffee-house keeper, has his premises, his low seats and narghiles, his queer pots and basins, in the shade.   The cobblers are always good-natured ; there was one who, I am sure, has been revealed to me in my dreams, in a dirty old green turban, with a pleasant wrinkled face like an apple, twinkling his little grey eyes as he held them up to talk to the gossips, and smiling under a delightful old grey beard, which did the heart good to see.   You divine the conversation between him and the cucumber-man, as the Sultan used to understand the language of the birds.   Are any of those cucumbers stuffed with pearls, and is that Armenian with the black square turban Harun Alraschid in disguise, standing yonder by the fountain where the children are drinking—the gleaming marble fountain, chequered all over with light and shadow, and engraved with delicate Arabesques and sentences from the Koran ?

But the greatest sensation of all is when the camels come. Whole strings of real camels, better even than in the procession of Blue Beard, with soft rolling eyes and bended necks, swaying from one side of the bazaar to the other to and fro, and treading gingerly with their great feet.   O, you fairy dreams of boyhood ! O, you sweet meditations of half-holidays, here you are realised for half-an-hour !   The genius which presides over youth led us to do a good action that day.   There was a man sitting in an open room, ornamented with fine long-tailed sentences of the Koran ; some in red, some in blue ; some written diagonally over the paper ; some so shaped as to represent ships, dragons, or mysterious animals.   The man squatted on a carpet in the middle of this room, with folded arms, waggling his head to and fro, swaying about, and singing through his nose choice phrases from the sacred work.   But from the room above came a clear noise of many little shouting voices, much more musical than that of Naso in the matted parlour, and the guide told us it was a school, so we went upstairs to look.

I declare, on my conscience, the master was in the act of bastinadoing a little mulatto boy; his feet were in a bar, and the brute was laying on with a cane; so we witnessed the howling of the poor boy, and the confusion of the brute who was administering the correction. The other children were made to shout, I believe, to drown the noise of their little comrade's howling; but the punishment was instantly discontinued as our hats came up over the stair-trap, and the boy cast loose, and the bamboo huddled into a corner, and the schoolmaster stood before us abashed. All the small scholars in red caps, and the little girls in gaudy handkerchiefs, turned their big wondering dark eyes towards us; and the caning was over for *that* time, let us trust. I don't envy some schoolmasters in a future state. I pity that poor little blubbering Mahometan; he will never be able to relish the *Arabian Nights* in the original, all his life long.

From this scene we rushed off somewhat discomposed, to make a breakfast off red mullets and grapes, melons, pomegranates, and Smyrna wine, at a dirty little comfortable inn, to which we were recommended; and from the windows of which we had a fine cheerful view of the gulf and its busy craft, and the loungers and the merchants along the shore. There were camels unloading at one wharf, and piles of melons much bigger than the Gibraltar cannon-balls at another. It was the fig season, and we passed through several alleys encumbered with long rows of fig-dressers, children and women for the most part, who were packing the fruit diligently into drums, dipping them in salt water first, and spreading them neatly over with leaves; while the figs and leaves are drying, large white worms crawl out of them, and swarm over the decks of the ships which carry them to Europe and to England, where small children eat them with pleasure—I mean the figs, not the worms—and where they are still served at wine parties at the Universities. When fresh they are not better than elsewhere; but the melons are of admirable flavour, and so large, that Cinderella might almost be accommodated with a coach made of a big one, without any very great distention of its original proportions.

Our guide, an accomplished swindler, demanded two dollars as the fee for entering a mosque, which others of our party subsequently saw for sixpence, so we did not care to examine that place of worship. But there were other cheaper sights, which were to the full as picturesque, for which there was no call to pay money, or, indeed, for a day scarcely to move at all. I doubt whether a man who would smoke his pipe on a bazaar counter all day, and let the city flow by him, would not be almost as well employed as the most active curiosity-hunter.

To be sure he would not see the women. Those in the bazaar were shabby people for the most part, whose black masks nobody would feel a curiosity to remove. You could see no more of their figures than if they had been stuffed in bolsters; and even their feet were brought to a general splay uniformity by the double yellow slippers which the wives of true believers wear. But it is in the Greek and Armenian quarters, and among those poor Christians who were pulling figs, that you see the beauties; and a man of a generous disposition may lose his heart half-a-dozen times a day in Smyrna. There was the pretty maid at work at a tambour-frame in an open porch, with an old duenna spinning by her side, and a goat tied up to the railings of the little court-garden; there was the nymph who came down the stair with the pitcher on her head, and gazed with great, calm eyes, as large and stately as Juno's; there was the gentle mother, bending over a queer cradle, in which lay a small crying bundle of infancy. All these three charmers were seen in a single street in the Armenian quarter, where the house doors are all open, and the women of the families sit under the arches in the court. There was the fig-girl, beautiful beyond all others, with an immense coil of deep black hair twisted round a head of which Raphael was worthy to draw the outline, and Titian to paint the colour. I wonder the Sultan has not swept her off, or that the Persian merchants, who come with silks and sweetmeats, have not kidnapped her for the Shah of Tehran.

We went to see the Persian merchants at their Khan, and purchased some silks there from a swarthy black-bearded man, with a conical cap of lamb's wool. Is it not hard to think that silks bought of a man in a lamb's-wool cap, in a caravanserai, brought hither on the backs of camels, should have been manufactured after all at Lyons? Others of our party bought carpets, for which the town is famous; and there was one who absolutely laid in a stock of real Smyrna figs, and purchased three or four real Smyrna sponges for his carriage; so strong was his passion for the genuine article.

I wonder that no painter has given us familiar views of the East: not processions, grand sultans, or magnificent landscapes; but faithful transcripts of everyday Oriental life, such as each street will supply to him. The camels afford endless motives, couched in the market-places, lying by thousands in the camel square, snorting and bubbling after their manner, the sun blazing down on their backs, their slaves and keepers lying behind them in the shade : and the caravan-bridge, above all, would afford a painter subjects for a dozen of pictures. Over this Roman arch, which crosses the Meles river, all the caravans pass on their entrance to the town. On one side, as we sate and looked at it, was a great row of plane-trees; on the opposite bank a deep wood of tall cypresses : in the midst of which rose up innumerable grey tombs, surmounted with the turbans of the defunct believers. Beside the stream, the view was less gloomy. There was under the plane-trees a little coffee-house, shaded by a trellis-work, covered over with a vine, and ornamented with many rows of shining pots and water-pipes, for which there was no use at noonday now, in the time of Ramazan. Hard by the coffee-house was a garden and a bubbling marble fountain, and over the stream was a broken summer-house, to which amateurs may ascend, for the purpose of examining the river; and all round the plane-trees plenty of stools for those who were inclined to sit and drink sweet thick coffee, or cool lemonade made of fresh green citrons. The master of the house, dressed in a white turban, and light blue pelisse, lolled under the coffee-house awning; the slave, in white, with a crimson striped jacket, his face as black as ebony, brought us pipes and lemonade again, and returned to his station at the coffee-house, where he curled his black legs together, and began singing out of his flat nose, to the thrumming of a long guitar with wire strings. The instrument was not bigger than a soup-ladle, with a long straight handle, but its music pleased the performer; for his eyes rolled shining about, and his head wagged, and he grinned with an innocent intensity of enjoyment that did one good to look at. And there was a friend to share his pleasure : a Turk, dressed in scarlet, and covered all over with daggers and pistols, sate leaning forward on his little stool, rocking about, and grinning quite as eagerly as the black minstrel. As he sang and we listened, figures of women bearing pitchers went passing over the Roman bridge, which we saw between the large trunks of the planes; or grey forms of camels were seen stalking across it, the string preceded by the little donkey, who is always here their long-eared conductor.

These are very humble incidents of travel. Wherever the steamboat touches the shore adventure retreats into the interior, and what is called romance vanishes. It won't bear the vulgar gaze; or rather the light of common day puts it out, and it is only in the dark that it shines at all. There is no cursing and insulting of Giaours now. If a cockney looks or behaves in a particularly ridiculous way, the little Turks come out and laugh at him. A Londoner is no longer a spittoon for true believers : and now that dark Hassan sits in his divan and drinks champagne, and Selim has a French watch, and Zuleikha perhaps takes Morrison's pills, Byronism becomes absurd instead of sublime, and is only a foolish expression of cockney wonder. They still occasionally beat a man for going into a mosque, but this is almost the only sign of ferocious vitality left in the Turk of the Mediterranean coast, and strangers may enter scores of mosques without molestation. The paddle-wheel is the great conqueror. Wherever the captain cries 'Stop her,' Civilisation stops, and lands in the ship's boat, and makes a permanent acquaintance with the savages on shore. Whole hosts of crusaders have passed and died, and butchered here in vain. But to manufacture European iron into pikes and helmets was a waste of metal : in the shape of piston-rods and furnace-pokers it is irresistible ; and I think an allegory might be made showing how much stronger commerce is than chivalry, and finishing with a grand image of Mahomet's crescent being extinguished in Fulton's boiler.

This I thought was the moral of the day's sights and adventures. We pulled off to the steamer in the afternoon—the Inbat blowing fresh, and setting all the craft in the gulf dancing over its blue waters. We were presently under weigh again, the captain ordering his engines to work only at half-power, so that a French steamer which was quitting Smyrna at the same time might come up with us, and fancy she could beat the irresistible *Tagus*. Vain hope ! Just as the Frenchman neared us, the *Tagus* shot out like an arrow, and the discomfited Frenchman went behind. Though we all relished the joke exceedingly, there was a French gentleman on board who did not seem to be by any means tickled with it ; but he had received papers at Smyrna, containing news of Marshal Bugeaud's victory at Isly, and had this land victory to set against our harmless little triumph at sea.

That night we rounded the island of Mitylene : and the next day the coast of Troy was in sight, and the tomb of Achilles—a dismal-looking mound that rises on a low dreary barren shore—less lively and not more picturesque than the Scheldt or the mouth of the Thames. Then we passed Tenedos and the forts and town at the mouth of the Dardanelles : the weather was not too hot ; the water as smooth as at Putney ; and everybody happy and excited at the thought of seeing Constantinople to-morrow. We had music on board all the way from Smyrna. A German *commis-voyageur*, with a guitar, who had passed unnoticed until that time, produced his instrument about mid-day, and began to whistle waltzes.   He whistled so divinely that the ladies left their cabins, and the men laid down their books.   He whistled a polka so bewitchingly that two young Oxford men began whirling round the deck, and performed that popular dance with much agility until they sank down tired.   He still continued an unabated whistling, and as nobody would dance, pulled off his coat, produced a pair of castanets, and whistling a mazurka, performed it with tremendous agility.   His whistling made everybody gay and happy—made those acquainted who had not spoken before, and inspired such a feeling of hilarity in the ship, that that night, as we floated over the sea of Marmora, a general vote was expressed for broiled bones and a regular supper-party.   Punch was brewed, and speeches were made, and, after a lapse of fifteen years, I heard the 'Old English gentleman' and 'Bright chanticleer proclaims the morn,' sung in such style, that you would almost fancy the proctors must hear, and send us all home.

CHAPTER VII

CONSTANTINOPLE

WHEN we rose at sunrise to see the famous entry to Constantinople, we found, in the place of the city and the sun, a bright white fog, which hid both from sight, and which only disappeared as the vessel advanced towards the Golden Horn.   There the fog cleared off as it were by flakes ; and as you see gauze curtains lifted away, one by one, before a great fairy scene at the theatre, this will give idea enough of the fog : the difficulty is to describe the scene afterwards, which was in truth the great fairy scene, than which it is impossible to conceive anything more brilliant and magnificent. I can't go to any more romantic place than Drury Lane to draw my similes from—Drury Lane, such as we used to see it in our youth, when, to our sight, the grand last pictures of the melodrama or pantomime were as magnificent as any objects of nature we have seen with maturer eyes.   Well, the view of Constantinople is as fine as any of Stanfield's best theatrical pictures, seen at the best period of youth, when fancy had all the bloom on her—when all the heroines who danced before the scene appeared as ravishing beauties, when there shone an unearthly splendour about Baker and Diddear—and the sound of the bugles and fiddles, and the cheerful clang of the cymbals, as the scene unrolled, and the gorgeous procession meandered triumphantly through it—caused a thrill of pleasure, and awakened an innocent fulness of sensual enjoyment that is only given to boys.

The above sentence contains the following propositions :—The enjoyments of boyish fancy are the most intense and delicious in the world. Stanfield's panorama used to be the realisation of the most intense youthful fancy. I puzzle my brains and find no better likeness for the place. The view of Constantinople resembles the *ne plus ultra* of a Stanfield diorama, with a glorious accompaniment of music, spangled houris, warriors, and winding processions, feasting the eyes and the soul with light, splendour, and harmony. If you were never in this way during your youth ravished at the play-house, of course the whole comparison is useless ; and you have no idea, from this description, of the effect which Constantinople produces on the mind. But if you were never affected by a theatre, no words can work upon your fancy, and typographical attempts to move it are of no use. For, suppose we combine mosque, minaret, gold, cypress, water, blue, caïques, seventy-four, Galata, Tophana, Ramazan, Backallum, and so forth, together, in ever so many ways, your imagination will never be able to depict a city out of them. Or, suppose I say the Mosque of Saint Sophia is four hundred and seventy-three feet in height, measuring from the middle nail of the gilt crescent, surmounting the dome, to the ring in the centre stone ; the circle of the dome is one hundred and twenty-three feet in diameter, the windows ninety-seven in number—and all this may be true, for anything I know to the contrary ; yet who is to get an idea of Saint Sophia's from dates, proper names, and calculations with a measuring-line ? It can't be done by giving the age and measurement of all the buildings along the river, the names of all the boatmen who ply on it. Has your fancy, which pooh-poohs a simile, faith enough to build a city with a foot-rule ? Enough said about descriptions and similes (though whenever I am uncertain of one, I am naturally most anxious to fight for it) : it is a scene not perhaps sublime, but charming, magnificent, and cheerful beyond any I have ever seen—the most superb combination of city and gardens, domes and shipping, hills and water, with the healthiest breeze blowing over it, and above it the brightest and most cheerful sky.

It is proper they say to be disappointed on entering the town, or any of the various quarters of it ; because the houses are not so magnificent on inspection and seen singly, as they are when beheld *en masse* from the waters. But why form expectations so lofty ? If you see a group of peasants picturesquely disposed at a fair, you don't suppose that they are all faultless beauties, or that the men's coats have no rags, and the women's gowns are made of silk and velvet: the wild ugliness of the interior of Constantinople or Pera has a charm of its own, greatly more amusing than rows of red bricks or drab stones, however symmetrical. With brick or stone they could never form those fantastic ornaments, railings, balconies, roofs, galleries, which jut in and out of the rugged houses of the city. As we went from Galata to Pera up a steep hill, which newcomers ascend with some difficulty, but which a porter, with a couple of hundredweight on his back, paces up without turning a hair, I thought the wooden houses far from being disagreeable objects, sights quite as surprising and striking as the grand one we had just left.

I do not know how the Custom House of his Highness is made to be a profitable speculation. As I left the ship, a man pulled after my boat, and asked for backsheesh, which was given him to the amount of about twopence. He was a Custom-house officer, but I doubt whether this sum which he levied ever went to the revenue.

I can fancy the scene about the quays somewhat to resemble the river of London in olden times, before coal-smoke had darkened the whole city with soot, and when, according to the old writers, there really was bright weather. The fleets of caïques bustling along the shore, or scudding over the blue water, are beautiful to look at; in Hollar's print London river is so studded over with wherry-boats, which bridges and steamers have since destroyed. Here the caïque is still in full perfection: there are thirty thousand boats of the kind plying between the cities; every boat is neat and trimly carved and painted; and I scarcely saw a man pulling in one of them that was not a fine specimen of his race, brawny and brown, with an open chest and a handsome face. They wear a thin shirt of exceedingly light cotton, which leaves their fine brown limbs full play; and with a purple sea for a background, every one of these dashing boats forms a brilliant and glittering picture. Passengers squat in the inside of the boat; so that as it passes, you see little more than the heads of the true believers, with their red fez and blue tassel, and that placid gravity of expression which the sucking of a tobacco-pipe is sure to give to a man.

The Bosphorus is enlivened by a multiplicity of other kinds of craft. There are the dirty men-of-war's boats of the Russians, with unwashed mangy crews; the great ferry-boats carrying hundreds of passengers to the villages; the melon-boats piled up with enormous golden fruit; his Excellency the Pasha's boat,

with twelve men bending to their oars ; and his Highness's own
caïque, with a head like a serpent, and eight-and-twenty tugging
oarsmen, that goes shooting by amidst the thundering of the
cannon. Ships and steamers, with black sides and flaunting
colours, are moored everywhere, showing their flags, Russian and
English, Austrian, American, and Greek ; and along the quays
country ships from the Black Sea or the islands, with high carved
poops and bows, such as you see in the pictures of the shipping of
the 17th century. The vast groves and towers, domes and
quays, tall minarets and spired spreading mosques of the three
cities, rise all around in endless magnificence and variety, and
render this water-street a scene of such delightful liveliness and
beauty, that one never tires of looking at it. I lost a great
number of the sights in and round Constantinople, through the
beauty of this admirable scene : but what are sights after all ?
and isn't that the best sight which makes you most happy ?

We were lodged at Pera at Misseri's hotel, the host of which
has been made famous ere this time, by the excellent book
Eothen, a work for which all the passengers on board our ship
had been battling, and which had charmed all—from our great
statesman, our polished lawyer, our young Oxonian, who sighed
over certain passages that he feared were wicked, down to the
writer of this, who, after perusing it with delight, laid it down
with wonder, exclaiming, ' Aut Diabolus aut '—a book which
has since (greatest miracle of all) excited a feeling of warmth and
admiration in the bosom of the godlike, impartial, stony *Athenæum*.
Misseri, the faithful and chivalrous Tartar, is transformed into
the most quiet and gentlemanlike of landlords, a great deal more
gentlemanlike in manner and appearance than most of us, who sat
at his table, and smoked cool pipes on his house-top, as we looked
over the hill and the Russian palace to the water, and the Seraglio
gardens shining in the blue. We confronted Misseri, *Eothen* in
hand, and found, on examining him, that it *was* ' aut diabolus aut
amicus '—but the name is a secret ; I will never breathe it,
though I am dying to tell it.

The last good description of a Turkish bath, I think, was
Lady Mary Wortley Montagu's, which voluptuous picture must
have been painted at least a hundred and thirty years ago ; so
that another sketch may be attempted by a humbler artist in a
different manner. The Turkish bath is certainly a novel sensation
to an Englishman, and may be set down as a most queer and
surprising event of his life. I made the *valet de place* or dragoman
(it is rather a fine thing to have a dragoman in one's service)
conduct me forthwith to the best-appointed hummums in the

neighbourhood ; and we walked to a house at Tophana, and into a spacious hall lighted from above, which is the cooling-room of the bath.

The spacious hall has a large fountain in the midst, a painted gallery running round it ; and many ropes stretched from one gallery to another, ornamented with profuse draperies of towels and blue cloths, for the use of the frequenters of the place. All round the room and the galleries were matted enclosures, fitted with numerous neat beds and cushions for reposing on, where lay a dozen of true believers smoking, or sleeping, or in the happy half-dozing state. I was led up to one of these beds to rather a retired corner, in consideration of my modesty ; and to the next bed presently came a dancing dervish, who forthwith began to prepare for the bath.

When the dancing dervish had taken off his yellow sugar-loaf cap, his gown, shawl, etc., he was arrayed in two large blue cloths ; a white one being thrown over his shoulders, and another in the shape of a turban plaited neatly round his head ; the garments of which he divested himself were folded up in another linen, and neatly put by. I beg leave to state I was treated in precisely the same manner as the dancing dervish.

The reverend gentleman then put on a pair of wooden pattens, which elevated him about six inches from the ground ; and walked down the stairs, and paddled across the moist marble floor of the hall, and in at a little door, by the which also Titmarsh entered. But I had none of the professional agility of the dancing dervish ; I staggered about very ludicrously upon the high wooden pattens ; and should have been down on my nose several times, had not the dragoman and the master of the bath supported me down the stairs and across the hall. Dressed in three large cotton napkins, with a white turban round my head, I thought of Pall Mall with a sort of despair. I passed the little door, it was closed behind me—I was in the dark—I couldn't speak the language—in a white turban—Mon Dieu ! what was going to happen ?

The dark room was the tepidarium, a moist oozing arched den, with a light faintly streaming from an orifice in the domed ceiling. Yells of frantic laughter and song came booming and clanging through the echoing arches, the doors clapped to with loud reverberations. It was the laughter of the followers of Mahound, rollicking and taking their pleasure in the public bath. I could not go into that place ; I swore I would not ; they promised me a private room, and the dragoman left me. My agony at parting from that Christian cannot be described.

When you get into the Sudarium, or hot room, your first sensations only occur about half a minute after entrance, when you feel that you are choking. I found myself in that state, seated on a marble slab; the bath man was gone; he had taken away the cotton turban and shoulder shawl: I saw I was in a narrow room of marble, with a vaulted roof, and a fountain of warm and cold water; the atmosphere was in a steam, the choking sensation went off, and I felt a sort of pleasure presently in a soft boiling simmer, which, no doubt, potatoes feel when they are steaming. You are left in this state for about ten minutes; it is warm certainly, but odd and pleasant, and disposes the mind to reverie.

But let any delicate mind in Baker Street fancy my horror, when, on looking up out of this reverie, I saw a great brown wretch extended before me, only half dressed, standing on pattens, and exaggerated by them and the steam until he looked like an ogre, grinning in the most horrible way, and waving his arm, on which was a horse-hair glove. He spoke in his unknown nasal jargon, words which echoed through the arched room; his eyes seemed astonishingly large and bright, his ears stuck out, and his head was all shaved, except a bristling top-knot, which gave it a demoniac fierceness.

This description, I feel, is growing too frightful; ladies who read it will be going into hysterics, or saying, 'Well, upon my word, this is the most singular, the most extraordinary kind of language. Jane, my love, you will not read that odious book '— and so I will be brief. This grinning man belabours the patient violently with the horse-brush. When he has completed the horse-hair part, and you lie expiring under a squirting fountain of warm water, and fancying all is done, he reappears with a large brass basin, containing a quantity of lather, in the midst of which is something like old Miss MacWhirter's flaxen wig that she is so proud of, and that we have all laughed at. Just as you are going to remonstrate, the thing like the wig is dashed into your face and eyes, covered over with soap, and for five minutes you are drowned in lather; you can't see, the suds are frothing over your eyeballs; you can't hear, the soap is whizzing into your ears; you can't gasp for breath, Miss MacWhirter's wig is down your throat with half a pailful of suds in an instant—you are all soap. Wicked children in former days have jeered you, exclaiming, 'How are you off for soap?' You little knew what saponacity was till you entered a Turkish bath.

When the whole operation is concluded, you are led—with what heartfelt joy I need not say—softly back to the cooling-room, having been robed in shawls and turbans as before. You are laid gently on the reposing bed; somebody brings a narghilé, which tastes as tobacco must taste in Mahomet's Paradise ; a cool sweet dreamy languor takes possession of the purified frame ; and half-an-hour of such delicious laziness is spent over the pipe as is unknown in Europe, where vulgar prejudice has most shamefully maligned indolence, calls it foul names, such as the father of all evil, and the like ; in fact, does not know how to educate idleness as these honest Turks do, and the fruit which, when properly cultivated, it bears.

The after-bath state is the most delightful condition of laziness I ever knew, and I tried it wherever we went afterwards on our little tour.   At Smyrna the whole business was much inferior to the method employed in the capital.   At Cairo, after the soap, you are plunged into a sort of stone coffin, full of water, which is all but boiling.   This has its charms ; but I could not relish the Egyptian shampooing.   A hideous old blind man (but very dexterous in his art) tried to break my back and dislocate my shoulders, but I could not see the pleasure of the practice ; and another fellow began tickling the soles of my feet, but I rewarded him with a kick that sent him off the bench.   The pure idleness is the best, and I shall never enjoy such in Europe again.

Victor Hugo, in his famous travels on the Rhine, visiting Cologne, gives a learned account of what he *didn't* see there.   I have a remarkable catalogue of similar objects at Constantinople. I didn't see the dancing dervishes, it was Ramazan ; nor the howling dervishes at Scutari, it was Ramazan ; nor the interior of Saint Sophia, nor the women's apartment of the seraglio, nor the fashionable promenade at the Sweet Waters, always because it was Ramazan ; during which period the dervishes dance and howl but rarely, their legs and lungs being unequal to much exertion during a fast of fourteen hours.   On account of the same holy season, the royal palaces and mosques are shut ; and though the valley of the Sweet Waters is there, no one goes to walk ; the people remaining asleep all day, and passing the night in feasting and carousing. The minarets are illuminated at this season ; even the humblest mosque at Jerusalem, or Jaffa, mounted a few circles of dingy lamps ; those of the capital were handsomely lighted with many festoons of lamps, which had a fine effect from the water.   I need not mention other and constant illuminations of the city, which innumerable travellers have described—I mean the fires.   There were three in Pera during our eight days' stay there ; but they did not last long enough to bring the sultan out of bed to come and lend his aid.   Mr. Hobhouse (quoted in the Guide-book) says, if a fire lasts an hour, the sultan is bound to attend it in person ; and that people having petitions to present, have often set houses on fire for the purpose of forcing out this royal trump. The sultan can't lead a very 'jolly life,' if this rule be universal. Fancy his highness, in the midst of his moon-faced beauties, handkerchief in hand, and obliged to tie it round his face, and go out of his warm harem at midnight at the cursed cry of 'Yang en Var!'

We saw his highness in the midst of his people and their petitions, when he came to the mosque at Tophana ; not the largest, but one of the most picturesque of the public buildings of the city. The streets were crowded with people watching for the august arrival, and lined with the squat military in their bastard European costume ; the sturdy police, with bandeliers and brown surtouts, keeping order, driving off the faithful from the railings of the Esplanade through which their emperor was to pass, and only admitting (with a very unjust partiality I thought) us Europeans into that reserved space. Before the august arrival, numerous officers collected, colonels and pashas went by with their attendant running footmen ; the most active, insolent, and hideous of these great men, as I thought, being his highness's black eunuchs, who went prancing through the crowd, which separated before them with every sign of respect.

The common women were assembled by many hundreds, the yakmac, a muslin chin-cloth which they wear, makes almost every face look the same ; but the eyes and noses of these beauties are generally visible, and, for the most part, both these features are good. The jolly negresses wear the same white veil, but they are by no means so particular about hiding the charms of their good-natured black faces, and they let the cloth blow about as it lists, and grin unconfined. Wherever we went the negroes seemed happy. They have the organ of child-loving ; little creatures were always prattling on their shoulders, queer little things in nightgowns of yellow dimity, with great flowers, and pink, or red, or yellow shawls, with great eyes glistening underneath. Of such the black women seemed always the happy guardians. I saw one at a fountain, holding one child in her arms, and giving another a drink—a ragged little beggar—a sweet and touching picture of a black charity.

I am almost forgetting his highness the sultan. About a hundred guns were fired off at clumsy intervals from the esplanade facing the Bosphorus, warning us that the monarch had set off from his summer palace, and was on the way to his grand canoe. At last that vessel made its appearance ; the band struck up his favourite air ; his caparisoned horse was led down to the shore to receive him ; the eunuchs, fat pashas, colonels, and officers of state gathering round as the commander of the faithful mounted. I had the indescribable happiness of seeing him at a very short distance. The Padishah, or Father of all the Sovereigns on Earth, has not that majestic air which some sovereigns possess, and which makes the beholder's eyes wink, and his knees tremble under him : he has a black beard, and a handsome well-bred face, of a French cast ; he looks like a young French *roué* worn out by debauch ; his eyes bright, with black rings round them ; his cheeks pale and hollow. He was lolling on his horse as if he could hardly hold himself on the saddle ; or, as if his cloak, fastened with a blazing diamond clasp on his breast, and falling over his horse's tail, pulled him back. But the handsome sallow face of the Refuge of the World looked decidedly interesting and intellectual.   I have seen many a young Don Juan at Paris, behind a counter, with such a beard and countenance ; the flame of passion still burning in his hollow eyes, while on his damp brow was stamped the fatal mark of premature decay.   The man we saw cannot live many summers.   Women and wine are said to have brought the Zilullah to this state ; and it is whispered by the Dragomans, or *Laquais de Place* (from whom travellers at Constantinople generally get their political informa- tion,) that the sultan's mother and his ministers conspire to keep him plunged in sensuality, that they may govern the kingdom, according to their own fancies.   Mr. Urquhart, I am sure, thinks that Lord Palmerston has something to do with the business, and drugs the sultan's champagne for the benefit of Russia.

As the Pontiff of Mussulmans passed into the mosque, a shower of petitions was flung from the steps where the crowd was collected, and over the heads of the gendarmes in brown.   A general cry, as for justice, rose up ; and one old, ragged woman came forward, and burst through the throng, howling, and flinging about her lean arms, and baring her old, shrunken breast.   I never saw a finer action of tragic woe, or heard sounds more pitiful than those old, passionate groans of hers.   What was your prayer, poor old wretched soul ? The gendarmes hemmed her round, and hustled her away, but rather kindly.   The Padishah went on quite impassible—the picture of debauch and ennui.

I like pointing morals, and inventing for myself cheap consola- tions, to reconcile me to that state of life into which it has pleased heaven to call me ; and as the Light of the World disappeared round the corner, I reasoned pleasantly with myself about his highness, and enjoyed that secret selfish satisfaction a man has, who sees he is better off than his neighbour.   'Michael Angelo,' I said, 'you are still (by courtesy) young : if you had five hundred thousand a year, and were a great prince, I would lay a wager that men would discover in you a magnificent courtesy of demeanour, and a majestic presence that only belongs to the sovereigns of the world. If you had such an income, you think you could spend it with splendour ; distributing genial hospitalities, kindly alms, soothing misery, bidding humility be of good heart, rewarding desert. If you had such means of purchasing pleasure, you think, you rogue, you could relish it with gusto. But fancy being brought to the condition of the poor Light of the Universe, yonder ; and reconcile yourself with the idea that you are only a farthing rush-light. The cries of the poor widow fall as dead upon him, as the smiles of the brightest eyes out of Georgia. He can't stir abroad but those abominable cannon begin roaring and deafening his ears. He can't see the world but over the shoulders of a row of fat pashas, and eunuchs, with their infernal ugliness. His ears can never be regaled with a word of truth, or blessed with an honest laugh. The only privilege of manhood left to him, he enjoys but for a month in the year, at this time of Ramazan, when he is forced to fast for fifteen hours ; and, by consequence, has the blessing of feeling hungry.' Sunset during Lent appears to be his single moment of pleasure ; they say the poor fellow is ravenous by that time, and as the gun fires the dish-covers are taken off, so that for five minutes a day he lives and is happy over pillau, like another mortal.

And yet, when floating by the summer palace, a barbaric edifice of wood and marble, with gilded suns blazing over the porticoes, and all sorts of strange ornaments and trophies figuring on the gates and railings—when we passed a long row of barred and fillagreed windows, looking on the water—when we were told that those were the apartments of his highness's ladies, and actually heard them whispering and laughing behind the bars—a strange feeling of curiosity came over some ill-regulated minds—just to have *one* peep, one look at all those wondrous beauties, singing to the dulcimers, paddling in the fountains, dancing in the marble halls, or lolling on the golden cushions, as the gaudy black slaves brought pipes and coffee. This tumultuous movement was calmed, by thinking of that dreadful statement of travellers, that in one of the most elegant halls there is a trap-door, on peeping below which, you may see the Bosphorus running underneath, into which some luckless beauty is plunged occasionally, and the trap-door is shut, and the dancing and the singing and the smoking and the laughing go on as before. They say it is death to pick up any of the sacks thereabouts, if a stray one should float by you. There were none any day when I passed, *at least, on the surface of the water*.

It has been rather a fashion of our travellers to apologise for

Turkish life, of late, and paint glowing, agreeable pictures, of many of its institutions.   The celebrated author of *Palm-Leaves* (his name is famous under the date-trees of the Nile, and uttered with respect beneath the tents of the Bedawee) has touchingly described Ibraham Pasha's paternal fondness, who cut off a black slave's head for having dropped and maimed one of his children ; and has penned a melodious panegyric of *The Harem*, and of the fond and beautiful duties of the inmates of that place of love, obedience, and seclusion.   I saw, at the Mausoleum of the late Sultan Mahmoud's family, a good subject for a Ghazul, in the true new Oriental manner.

These royal burial-places are the resort of the pious Moslems. Lamps are kept burning there ; and in the ante-chambers, copies of the Koran are provided for the use of believers ; and you never pass these cemeteries but you see Turks washing at the cisterns, previous to entering for prayer, or squatted on the benches, chanting passages from the sacred volume.   Christians, I believe, are not admitted, but may look through the bars, and see the coffins of the defunct monarchs and children of the royal race.   Each lies in his narrow sarcophagus, which is commonly flanked by huge candles, and covered with a rich embroidered pall.   At the head of each coffin rises a slab, with a gilded inscription ; for the princesses, the slab is simple, not unlike our own monumental stones.   The headstones of the tombs of the defunct princes are decorated with a turban, or, since the introduction of the latter article of dress, with the red fez.   That of Mahmoud is decorated with the imperial aigrette.

In this dismal but splendid museum, I remarked two little tombs with little red fezzes, very small, and for very young heads evidently, which were lying under the little embroidered palls of state.   I forget whether they had candles too ; but their little flame of life was soon extinguished, and there was no need of many pounds of wax to typify it.   These were the tombs of Mahmoud's grandsons, nephews of the present Light of the Universe, and children of his sister, the wife of Halil Pacha.   Little children die in all ways ; these of the much-maligned Mahometan royal race perished by the bowstring.   Sultan Mahmoud (may he rest in glory !) strangled the one ; but, having some spark of human feeling, was so moved by the wretchedness and agony of the poor bereaved mother, his daughter, that his royal heart relented towards her, and he promised that, should she ever have another child, it should be allowed to live.   He died ; and Abdul Medjid (may his name be blessed !), the debauched young man whom we just saw riding to the mosque, succeeded.   His sister, whom he is said to have loved, became again a mother, and had a son. But she relied upon her father's word and her august brother's love, and hoped that this little one should be spared. The same accursed hand tore this infant out of its mother's bosom, and killed it. The poor woman's heart broke outright at this second calamity, and she died. But on her death-bed she sent for her brother, rebuked him as a perjurer and an assassin, and expired calling down the divine justice on his head. She lies now by the side of the two little fezzes.

Now, I say this would be a fine subject for an oriental poem. The details are dramatic and noble, and could be grandly touched by a fine artist. If the mother had borne a daughter, the child would have been safe ; that perplexity might be pathetically depicted as agitating the bosom of the young wife, about to become a mother. A son is born : you can see her despair and the pitiful look she casts on the child, and the way in which she hugs it every time the curtains of her door are removed. The sultan hesitated probably ; he allowed the infant to live for six weeks. He could not bring his royal soul to inflict pain. He yields at last ; he is a martyr—to be pitied, not to be blamed. If he melts at his daughter's agony, he is a man and a father. There are men and fathers too in the much-maligned orient.

Then comes the second act of the tragedy. The new hopes, the fond yearnings, the terrified misgivings, the timid belief, and weak confidence ; the child that is born—and dies smiling prettily —and the mother's heart is rent so, that it can love, or hope, or suffer no more. Allah is God ! She sleeps by the little fezzes. Hark ! the guns are booming over the water, and his highness is coming from his prayers.

After the murder of that little child, it seems to me one can never look with anything but horror upon the butcherly Herod who ordered it. The death of the seventy thousand Janissaries ascends to historic dignity, and takes rank as war. But a great prince and Light of the Universe, who procures abortions and throttles little babies, dwindles away into such a frightful insignificance of crime, that those may respect him who will. I pity their Excellencies the ambassadors, who are obliged to smirk and cringe to such a rascal. To do the Turks justice—and two days' walk in Constantinople will settle this fact as well as a year's residence in the city—the people do not seem in the least animated by this Herodian spirit. I never saw more kindness to children than among all classes, more fathers walking about with little solemn Mahometans in red caps and big trowsers, more business going on than in the toy quarter—and in the Atmeidan. Although you may

A STREET VIEW AT CONSTANTINOPLE.

see there the Thebaic stone set up by the Emperor Theodosius, and
the bronze column of serpents which Murray says was brought
from Delphi, but which my guide informed me was the very one
exhibited by Moses in the wilderness : yet I found the examination
of these antiquities much less pleasant than to look at the many
troops of children assembled on the plain to play ; and to watch
them as they were dragged about in little queer arobas, or painted
carriages, which are there kept for hire.   I have a picture of one
of them now in my eyes : a little green oval machine, with flowers
rudely painted round the window, out of which two smiling heads
are peeping, the pictures of happiness.   An old, good-humoured,
grey-bearded Turk is tugging the cart ; and behind it walks a lady
in a yakmac and yellow slippers, and a black female slave, grinning
as usual, towards whom the little coach-riders are looking.   A
small, sturdy, barefooted Mussulman is examining the cart with
some feelings of envy : he is too poor to purchase a ride for himself and the round-faced puppy-dog, which he is hugging in his
arms as young ladies in our country do dolls.

All the neighbourhood of the Atmeidan is exceedingly picturesque
—the mosque court and cloister, where the Persians have their
stalls of sweetmeats and tobacco ; a superb sycamore-tree grows
in the middle of this, overshadowing aromatic fountain : great
flocks of pigeons are settling in corners of the cloister, and barley
is sold at the gates, with which the good-natured people feed them.
From the Atmeidan you have a fine view of Saint Sophia : and
here stands a mosque which struck me as being much more
picturesque and sumptuous—the mosque of Sultan Achmed, with
its six gleaming white minarets, and its beautiful courts and trees.
Any infidels may enter the court without molestation, and, looking
through the barred windows of the mosque, have a view of its
airy and spacious interior.   A small audience of women was collected
there when I looked in, squatted on the mats, and listening to a
preacher, who was walking among them, and speaking with great
energy.   My dragoman interpreted to me the sense of a few words
of his sermon : he was warning them of the danger of gadding
about to public places, and of the immorality of too much talking ;
and, I dare say, we might have had more valuable information
from him, regarding the follies of womankind, had not a tall Turk
clapped my interpreter on the shoulder, and pointed him to be off.

Although the ladies are veiled, and muffled with the ugliest
dresses in the world, yet it appears their modesty is alarmed in
spite of all the coverings which they wear.   One day, in the bazaar,
a fat old body, with diamond rings on her fingers, that were tinged
with henné, of a logwood colour, came to the shop where I was

purchasing slippers, with her son, a young Aga of six years of age, dressed in a braided frock-coat, with a huge tassel to his fez, exceeding fat, and of a most solemn demeanour.   The young Aga came for a pair of shoes, and his contortions were so delightful as he tried them, that I remained looking on with great pleasure, wishing for Leech to be at hand to sketch his lordship and his fat mamma, who sat on the counter.   That lady fancied I was looking at her, though, as far as I could see, she had the figure and com- plexion of a roly-poly pudding ; and so, with quite a premature bashfulness, she sent me a message by the shoemaker, ordering me to walk away if I had made my purchases, for that ladies of her rank did not choose to be stared at by strangers ; and I was obliged to take my leave, though with sincere regret, for the little lord had just squeezed himself into an attitude than which I never saw anything more ludicrous in General Tom Thumb.   When the ladies of the seraglio come to that bazaar with their *cortége* of infernal black eunuchs, strangers are told to move on briskly.   I saw a bevy of about eight of these, with their aides-de-camp ; but they were wrapped up, and looked just as vulgar and ugly as the other women, and were not, I suppose, of the most beautiful sort.   The poor devils are allowed to come out, half-a-dozen times in the year, to spend their little wretched allowance of pocket-money in pur- chasing trinkets and tobacco ; all the rest of the time they pursue the beautiful duties of their existence in the walls of the sacred harem.

Though strangers are not allowed to see the interior of the cage in which these birds of Paradise are confined, yet many parts of the seraglio are free to the curiosity of visiters who choose to drop a backsheesh here and there.   I landed one morning at the seraglio point from Galata, close by an ancient pleasure-house of the defunct sultan ; a vast broad-brimmed pavilion, that looks agreeable enough to be a dancing-room for ghosts now : there is another summer-house, the Guide-book cheerfully says, whither the sultan goes to sport with his women and *mutes*.   A regiment of infantry, with their music at their head, were marching to exercise in the outer grounds of the seraglio ; and we followed them, and had an opportunity of seeing their evolutions, and hearing their bands, upon a fine green plain under the seraglio walls, where stands one solitary column, erected in memory of some triumph of some Byzantian emperor.

There were three battalions of the Turkish infantry exercising here ; and they seemed to perform their evolutions in a very satisfactory manner : that is, they fired altogether, and charged and halted in very straight lines, and bit off imaginary cartridge- tops with great fierceness and regularity, and made all their ramrods ring to measure, just like so many Christians. The men looked small, young, clumsy, and ill-built; uncomfortable in their shabby European clothes; and about the legs, especially, seemed exceedingly weak and ill-formed. Some score of military invalids were lolling in the sunshine, about a fountain and a marble summer-house, that stand on the ground, watching their comrades' manœuvres (as if they could never have enough of that delightful pastime); and these sick were much better cared for than their healthy companions. Each man had two dressing-gowns, one of white cotton, and an outer wrapper of warm brown woollen. Their heads were accommodated with wadded cotton nightcaps; and it seemed to me from their condition, and from the excellent character of the military hospitals, that it would be much more wholesome to be ill than to be well in the Turkish service.

Facing this green esplanade, and the Bosphorus shining beyond it, rise the great walls of the outer seraglio gardens; huge masses of ancient masonry, over which peep the roofs of numerous kiosks and outhouses, amongst thick evergreens, planted so as to hide the beautiful frequenters of the place from the prying eyes and telescopes. We could not catch a glance of a single figure moving in these great pleasure-grounds. The road winds round the walls; and the outer park, which is likewise planted with trees, and diversified by garden-plots and cottages, had more the air of the outbuildings of a homely English park, than of a palace which we must all have imagined to be the most stately in the world. The most commonplace water-carts were passing here and there; roads were being repaired in the Macadamite manner; and carpenters were mending the park-palings, just as they do in Hampshire. The next thing you might fancy would be the sultan walking out with a spud and a couple of dogs, on the way to meet the post-bag and the *Saint James's Chronicle*.

The palace is no palace at all. It is a great town of pavilions, built without order, here and there, according to the fancy of succeeding lights of the universe, or their favourites. The only row of domes which looked particularly regular or stately, were the kitchens. As you examined the buildings they had a ruinous, dilapidated look,—they are not furnished, it is said, with particular splendour,—not a bit more elegantly than Miss Jones's seminary for young ladies, which we may be sure is much more comfortable than the extensive establishment of his Highness Abdul Medjid.

In the little stable I thought to see some marks of royal magnificence, and some horses worthy of the king of all kings. But the Sultan is said to be a very timid horseman: the animal that is always kept saddled for him did not look to be worth twenty pounds ; and the rest of the horses in the shabby, dirty stalls, were small, ill-kept, common-looking brutes.   You might see better, it seemed to me, at a country inn stable of any market-day.

The kitchens are the most sublime part of the seraglio.   There are nine of these great halls, for all ranks, from his highness downwards ; where many hecatombs are roasted daily, according to the accounts ; and where cooking goes on with a savage Homeric grandeur.   Chimneys are despised in these primitive halls ; so that the roofs are black with the smoke of hundreds of furnaces, which escapes through apertures in the domes above.   These, too, give the chief light in the rooms, which streams downwards, and thickens and mingles with the smoke, and so murkily lights up hundreds of swarthy figures busy about the spits and the cauldrons. Close to the door by which we entered, they were making pastry for the sultanas ; and the chief pastrycook, who knew my guide, invited us courteously to see the process, and partake of the delicacies prepared for those charming lips.   How those sweet lips must shine after eating these puffs !   First, huge sheets of dough are rolled out till the paste is about as thin as silver paper : then an artist forms the dough-muslin into a sort of drapery, curling it round and round in many fanciful and pretty shapes, until it is all got into the circumference of a round metal tray in which it is baked.   Then the cake is drenched in grease most profusely ; and, finally, a quantity of syrup is poured over it, when the delectable mixture is complete.   The moon-faced ones are said to devour immense quantities of this wholesome food ; and, in fact, are eating grease and sweetmeats from morning till night.   I don't like to think what the consequences may be, or allude to the agonies which the delicate creatures must inevitably suffer.

The good-natured chief pastrycook filled a copper basin with greasy puffs ; and, dipping a dubious ladle into a large cauldron, containing several gallons of syrup, poured a liberal portion over the cakes, and invited us to eat.   One of the tarts was quite enough for me ; and I excused myself on the plea of ill-health from imbibing any more grease and sugar.   But my companion, the dragoman, finished some forty puffs in a twinkling.   They slipped down his opened jaws as the sausages do down Clown's throat in a pantomime.   His moustachios shone with grease, and it dripped down his beard and fingers.   We thanked the smiling chief pastrycook, and rewarded him handsomely for the tarts.   It is something to have eaten of the dainties prepared for the ladies of the harem ; but I think Mr. Cockle ought to get the names of the chief sultanas among the exalted patrons of his Antibilious Pills.

From the kitchens we passed into the second court of the

seraglio, beyond which is death. The Guide-book only hints at the dangers which would befal a stranger caught prying in the mysterious *first* court of the palace. I have read Bluebeard, and don't care for peeping into forbidden doors; so that the second court was quite enough for me; the pleasure of beholding it being heightened, as it were, by the notion of the invisible danger sitting next door, with uplifted scimetar ready to fall on —present though not seen.

A cloister runs along one side of this court; opposite is the hall of the divan, 'large but low, covered with lead, and gilt, after the Moorish manner, plain enough.' The Grand Vizir sits in this place, and the ambassadors used to wait here, and be conducted hence on horseback, attired with robes of honour. But the ceremony is now, I believe, discontinued; the English envoy, at any rate, is not allowed to receive any backsheesh, and goes away as he came, in the habit of his own nation. On the right is a door leading into the interior of the seraglio; *none pass through it but such as are sent for*, the Guide-book says: it is impossible to top the terror of that description.

About this door lads and servants were lolling, ichoglans and pages, with lazy looks and shabby dresses; and among them, sunning himself sulkily on a bench, a poor old, fat, wrinkled, dismal white eunuch, with little fat white hands, and a great head sunk into his chest, and two sprawling little legs that seemed incapable to hold up his bloated old body. He squeaked out some surly reply to my friend the Dragoman, who, softened and sweetened by the tarts he had just been devouring, was, no doubt, anxious to be polite; and the poor worthy fellow walked away rather crestfallen at this return of his salutation, and hastened me out of the place.

The palace of the seraglio, the cloister with marble pillars, the hall of the ambassadors, the impenetrable gate guarded by eunuchs and ichoglans, has a romantic look in print; but not so in reality. Most of the marble is wood, almost all the gilding is faded, the guards are shabby, the foolish perspectives painted on the walls are half cracked off. The place looks like Vauxhall in the daytime.

We passed out of the second court under THE SUBLIME PORTE, which is like a fortified gate of a German town of the middle ages, into the outer court, round which are public offices, hospitals, and dwellings of the multifarious servants of the palace. The place is very wide and picturesque; there is a pretty church of Byzantine architecture at the further end; and in the midst of the court a magnificent plane-tree, of prodigious dimensions and fabulous age, according to the guides; Saint Sophia tower, in the further distance: and from here, perhaps, is the best view of its light swelling domes and beautiful proportions. The Porte itself, too, forms an excellent subject for the sketcher, if the officers of the court will permit him to design it. I made the attempt, and a couple of Turkish beadles looked on very good-naturedly for some time at the progress of the drawing; but a good number of other spectators speedily joined them, and made a crowd, which is not permitted, it would seem, in the seraglio; so I was told to pack up my portfolio, and remove the cause of the disturbance, and lost my drawing of the Ottoman Porte.

I don't think I have anything more to say about the city, which has not been much better told by graver travellers. I with them could see (perhaps it was the preaching of the politicians that warned me of the fact) that we are looking on at the last days of an empire; and heard many stories of weakness, disorder, and oppression. I even saw a Turkish lady drive up to Sultan Achmet's mosque *in a Brougham*. Is not that a subject to moralise upon? And might one not draw endless conclusions from it, that the knell of the Turkish dominion is rung; that the European spirit and institutions once admitted can never be rooted out again; and that the scepticism prevalent amongst the higher orders must descend ere very long to the lower; and the cry of the Muezim from the mosque become a mere ceremony?

But as I only staid eight days in this place, and knew not a syllable of the language, perhaps it is as well to pretermit any disquisitions about the spirit of the people. I can only say that they looked to be very good-natured, handsome, and lazy; that the women's yellow slippers are very ugly : that the kabobs at the shop, hard by the rope bazaar, are very hot and good; and that at the Armenian cook-shops they serve you delicious fish, and a stout raisin wine of no small merit. There came in, as we sat and dined there at sunset, a good old Turk, who called for a penny fish, and sat down under a tree very humbly, and ate it with his own bread. We made that jolly old Mussulman happy with a quart of the raisin wine; and his eyes twinkled with every fresh glass, and he wiped his old beard delighted, and talked and chirped a good deal, and, I dare say, told us the whole state of the empire. He was the only Mussulman with whom I attained any degree of intimacy during my stay in Constantinople; and you will see that, for obvious reasons, I cannot divulge the particulars of our conversation.

'You have nothing to say, and you own it,' says somebody; 'then why write?' That question perhaps (between ourselves) I have put likewise; and yet, my dear sir, there are *some* things worth remembering even in this brief letter : that woman in the brougham is an idea of significance; that comparison of the seraglio to Vauxhall in the daytime, is a true and real one; from both of which your own great soul and ingenious philosophic spirit may draw conclusions, that I myself have modestly forborne to press. You are too clever to require a moral to be tacked to all the fables you read, as it is done for children in the spelling-books; else I would tell you that the government of the Ottoman Porte seems to be as rotten, as wrinkled and as feeble as the old eunuch I saw crawling about it in the sun; that when the lady drove up in a brougham to Sultan Achmet, I felt that the schoolmaster was really abroad; and that the crescent will go out before that luminary, as meekly as the moon does before the sun.

CHAPTER VIII

RHODES

THE sailing of a vessel direct for Jaffa, brought a great number of passengers together, and our decks were covered with Christian, Jew, and Heathen. In the cabin we were Poles and Russians, Frenchmen, Germans, Spaniards, and Greeks; on the deck were squatted several little colonies of people of different race and persuasion. There was a Greek Papa, a noble figure with a flowing and venerable white beard, who had been living on bread-and-water for I don't know how many years, in order to save a little money to make the pilgrimage to Jerusalem. There were several families of Jewish Rabbies, who celebrated their 'feast of tabernacles' on board; their chief men performing worship twice or thrice a day, dressed in their pontifical habits, and bound with phylacteries : and there were Turks, who had their own ceremonies and usages, and wisely kept aloof from their neighbours of Israel.

The dirt of these children of captivity exceeds all possibility of description ; the profusion of stinks which they raised, the grease of their venerable garments and faces, the horrible messes cooked in the filthy pots, and devoured with the nasty fingers, the squalor

of mats, pots, old bedding, and foul carpets of our Hebrew friends, could hardly be painted by Swift, in his dirtiest mood, and cannot be, of course, attempted by my timid and genteel pen. What would they say in Baker Street to some sights with which our new friends favoured us ? What would your ladyship have said if you had seen the interesting Greek nun combing her hair over the cabin— combing it with the natural fingers, and averse to slaughter, flinging the delicate little intruders, which she found in the course of her investigation, gently into the great cabin ? Our attention was a good deal occupied in watching the strange ways and customs of the various comrades of ours.

The Jews were refugees from Poland, going to lay their bones to rest in the valley of Jehoshaphat, and performing with exceeding rigour the offices of their religion. At morning and evening you were sure to see the chiefs of the families, arrayed in white robes, bowing over their books, at prayer. Once a week, on the eve before the Sabbath, there was a general washing in Jewry, which sufficed until the ensuing Friday. The men wore long gowns and caps of fur, or else broad-brimmed hats, or in service time, bound on their heads little iron boxes, with the sacred name engraved on them. Among the lads there were some beautiful faces ; and among the women your humble servant discovered one who was a perfect rosebud of beauty, when first emerging from her Friday's toilette, and for a day or two afterwards, until each succeeding day's smut darkened those fresh and delicate cheeks of hers. We had some very rough weather in the course of the passage from Constantinople to Jaffa, and the sea washed over and over our Israelitish friends and their baggages and bundles; but though they were said to be rich, they would not afford to pay for cabin shelter. One father of a family, finding his progeny half-drowned in a squall, vowed he *would* pay for a cabin; but the weather was somewhat finer the next day, and he could not squeeze out his dollars, and the ship's authorities would not admit him except upon payment.

This unwillingness to part with money is not only found amongst the followers of Moses, but in those of Mahomet, and Christians too. When we went to purchase in the bazaars, after offering money for change, the honest fellows would frequently keep back several piastres, and when urged to refund, would give most dismally; and begin doling out penny by penny, and utter pathetic prayers to their customer not to take any more. I bought five or six pounds' worth of Broussa silks for the womankind, in the bazaar at Constantinople, and the rich Armenian who sold them, begged for three-halfpence to pay his boat to Galata. There is something naïf and amusing in this exhibition of cheatery—this simple cringing and wheedling and passion for twopence-halfpenny. It was pleasant to give a millionaire beggar an alms, and laugh in his face, and say, 'There, Dives, there's a penny for you: be happy, you poor old swindling scoundrel, as far as a penny goes.' I used to watch these Jews on shore, and making bargains with one another as soon as they came on board; the battle between vendor and purchaser was an agony—they shrieked, clasped hands, appealed to one another passionately; their handsome, noble faces assumed a look of woe—quite an heroic eagerness and sadness about a farthing.

Ambassadors from our Hebrews descended at Rhodes to buy provisions, and it was curious to see their dealings: there was our venerable Rabbi, who, robed in white and silver, and bending over his book at the morning service, looked like a patriarch, and whom I saw chaffering about a fowl with a brother Rhodian Israelite. How they fought over the body of that lean animal! The street swarmed with Jews—goggling eyes looked out from the old carved casements—hooked noses issued from the low, antique doors—Jew boys driving donkeys—Hebrew mothers nursing children; dusky, tawdry, ragged young beauties—and most venerable grey-bearded fathers—were all gathered round about the affair of the hen! And at the same time that our Rabbi was arranging the price of it, his children were instructed to procure bundles of green branches to decorate the ship during their feast. Think of the centuries during which these wonderful people have remained unchanged; and how, from the days of Jacob downwards, they have believed and swindled!

The Rhodian Jews, with their genius for filth, have made their quarter of the noble, desolate old town, the most ruinous and wretched of all. The escutcheons of the proud old knights are still carved over the doors, whence issue these miserable greasy hucksters and pedlars. The Turks respected these emblems of the brave enemies whom they had overcome, and left them untouched ; when the French seized Malta they were by no means so delicate. They effaced armorial bearings with their usual hot-headed eagerness ; and a few years after they had torn down the coats-of-arms of the gentry, the heroes of Malta and Egypt were busy devising heraldry for themselves, and were wild to be barons and counts of the empire.

The chivalrous relics at Rhodes are very superb. I know of no buildings whose stately and picturesque aspect seems to correspond better with one's notions of their proud founders. The towers and gates are warlike and strong, but beautiful and aristocratic : you see that they must have been high-bred gentlemen who built them. The edifices appear in almost as perfect a condition as when they were in the occupation of the noble knights of St. John ; and they have this advantage over modern fortifications, that they are a thousand times more picturesque. Ancient war condescended to ornament itself, and built fine carved castles and vaulted gates : whereas, to judge from Gibraltar and Malta, nothing can be less romantic than the modern military architecture ; which sternly regards the fighting, without in the least heeding the war-paint. Some of the huge artillery, with which the place was defended, still lies in the bastions ; and the touch-holes of the guns are preserved by being covered with rusty old corslets, worn by defenders of the fort three hundred years ago. The Turks, who battered down chivalry, seem to be waiting their turn of destruction now. In walking through Rhodes one is strangely affected by witnessing the signs of this double decay. For instance, in the streets of the knights, you see noble houses, surmounted by noble escutcheons of superb knights, who lived there, and prayed, and quarrelled, and murdered the Turks ; and were the most gallant pirates of the inland seas ; and made vows of chastity, and robbed and ravished ; and, professing humility, would admit none but nobility into their order ; and died recommending themselves to sweet St. John, and calmly hoping for heaven in consideration of all the heathen they had slain. When this superb fraternity was obliged to yield to courage as great as theirs, faith as sincere, and to robbers even more dexterous and audacious than the noblest knight who ever sang a canticle to the Virgin, these halls were filled by magnificent Pashas and Agas, who lived here in the intervals of war, and, having conquered its best champions, despised Christendom and chivalry pretty much as an Englishman despises a Frenchman. Now the famous house is let to a shabby merchant, who has his little beggarly shop in the bazaar; to a small officer, who ekes out his wretched pension by swindling, and who gets his pay in bad coin. Mahometanism pays in pewter now, in place of silver and gold. The lords of the world have run to seed. The powerless old sword frightens nobody now—the steel is turned to pewter too, somehow, and will no longer shear a Christian head off any shoulders. In the Crusades my wicked sympathies have always been with the Turks. They seem to me the best Christians of the two; more humane, less brutally presumptuous about their own merits, and more generous in esteeming their neighbours. As far as I can get at the authentic story, Saladin is a pearl of refinement compared to the brutal beef-eating Richard—about whom Sir Walter Scott has led all the world astray. When shall we have a real account of those times and heroes—no good-humoured pageant, like those of the Scott romances—but a real authentic story to instruct and frighten honest people of the present day, and make them thankful that the grocer governs the world now in place of the baron? Meanwhile a man of tender feelings may be pardoned for twaddling a little over this sad spectacle of the decay of two of the great institutions of the world. Knighthood is gone—amen; it expired with dignity, its face to the foe: and old Mahometanism is lingering, about just ready to drop. But it is unseemly to see such a Grand Potentate in such a state of decay: the son of Bajazet Ilderim insolvent; the descendants of the Prophets bullied by Calmucs and English and whipper-snapper Frenchmen; the Fountain of Magnificence done up, and obliged to coin pewter! Think of the poor dear houris in Paradise, how sad they must look as the arrivals of the Faithful become less and less frequent every day. I can fancy the place beginning to wear the fatal Vauxhall look of the seraglio, and which has pursued me ever since I saw it: the fountains of eternal wine are beginning to run rather dry, and of a questionable liquor; the ready-roasted meat-trees may cry 'Come, eat me,' every now and then, in a faint voice, without any gravy in it—but the Faithful begin to doubt about the quality of the victuals. Of nights you may see the houris sitting sadly under them, darning their faded muslins: Ali, Omar, and the Imaums are reconciled and have gloomy consultations: and the Chief of the Faithful himself, the awful camel-driver, the supernatural husband of Kadisheh, sits alone in a tumble-down kiosk, thinking moodily of the destiny that is impending over him; and of the day when his gardens of bliss shall be as vacant as the bankrupt Olympus.

All the town of Rhodes has this appearance of decay and ruin, except a few consuls' houses planted on the seaside, here and there, with bright flags flaunting in the sun; fresh paint; English crockery; shining mahogany, etc.,—so many emblems of the new prosperity of *their* trade, while the old inhabitants were going to rack—the fine church of St. John, converted into a mosque, is a ruined church, with a ruined mosque inside; the fortifications are mouldering away, as much as time will let them.   There was considerable bustle and stir about the little port; but it was a bustle of people, who looked for the most part to be beggars; and I saw no shop in the bazaar that seemed to have the value of a pedlar's pack.

I took, by way of guide, a young fellow from Berlin, a journey-man shoemaker, who had just been making a tour in Syria, and who professed to speak both Arabic and Turkish quite fluently, which I thought he might have learned when he was a student at college, before he began his profession of shoemaking; but I found he only knew about three words of Turkish, which were produced on every occasion, as I walked under his guidance through the desolate streets of the noble old town.   We went out upon the lines of fortification, through an ancient gate and guard-house, where once a chapel probably stood, and of which the roofs were richly carved and gilded.   A ragged squad of Turkish soldiers lolled about the gate now—a couple of boys on a donkey; a grinning slave on a mule; a pair of women flapping along in yellow papooshes; a basket-maker sitting under an antique carved portal, and chanting or howling as he platted his osiers; a peaceful well of water, at which knights' chargers had drunk, and at which the double-boyed donkey was now refreshing himself—would have made a pretty picture for a sentimental artist.   As he sits, and endeavours to make a sketch of this plaintive little comedy, a shabby dignitary of the island comes clattering by on a thirty-shilling horse, and two or three of the ragged soldiers leave their pipes to salute him as he passes under the Gothic archway.

The astonishing brightness and clearness of the sky under which the island seemed to bask, struck me as surpassing anything I had seen—not even at Cadiz, or the Piræus, had I seen sands so yellow, or water so magnificently blue.   The houses of the people along the shore were but poor tenements, with humble courtyards and gardens; but every fig-tree was gilded and bright, as if it were in a Hesperian orchard; the palms, planted here and there, rose with a sort of halo of light round about them; the creepers on the walls quite dazzled with the brilliancy of their flowers and leaves; the people lay in the cool shadows, happy and idle, with handsome solemn faces; nobody seemed to be at work; they only talked a very little, as if idleness and silence were a condition of the delightful shining atmosphere in which they lived.

We went down to an old mosque by the seashore, with a cluster of ancient domes hard by it, blazing in the sunshine, and carved all over with names of Allah, and titles of old pirates and generals who reposed there. The guardian of the mosque sat in the garden-court, upon a high wooden pulpit, lazily wagging his body to and fro, and singing the praises of the prophet gently through his nose, as the breeze stirred through the trees overhead, and cast chequered and changing shadows over the paved court, and the little fountains, and the nasal psalmist on his perch. On one side was the mosque, into which you could see, with its white walls and cool matted floor, and quaint carved pulpit and ornaments, and nobody at prayers. In the middle distance rose up the noble towers and battlements of the knightly town, with the deep sea line behind them.

It really seemed as if everybody was to have a sort of sober cheerfulness, and must yield to indolence under this charming atmosphere. I went into the courtyard by the seashore (where a few lazy ships were lying, with no one on board), and found it was the prison of the place. The door was as wide open as Westminster Hall. Some prisoners, one or two soldiers and functionaries, and some prisoners' wives, were lolling under an arcade by a fountain; other criminals were strolling about here and there, their chains clinking quite cheerfully: and they and the guards and officials came up chatting quite friendly together, and gazed languidly over the portfolio, as I was endeavouring to get the likeness of one or two of these comfortable malefactors. One old and wrinkled she-criminal, whom I had selected on account of the peculiar hideousness of her countenance, covered it up with a dirty cloth, at which there was a general roar of laughter among this good-humoured auditory of cut-throats, pickpockets, and policemen. The only symptom of a prison about the place was a door, across which a couple of sentinels were stretched, yawning; while within lay three freshly-caught pirates, chained by the leg. They had committed some murders of a very late date, and were awaiting sentence; but their wives were allowed to communicate freely with them: and it seemed to me, that if half-a-dozen friends would set them free, and they themselves had energy enough to move, the sentinels would be a great deal too lazy to walk after them.

The combined influence of Rhodes and Ramazan, I suppose, had taken possession of my friend, the *schuster-gesell* from Berlin. As soon as he received his fee, he cut me at once, and went and lay down by a fountain near the port, and ate grapes out of a dirty pocket-handkerchief.   Other Christian idlers lay near him, dozing, or sprawling in the boats, or listlessly munching water-melons. Along the coffee-houses of the quay sat hundreds more, with no better employment ; and the captain of the *Iberia* and his officers, and several of the passengers in that famous steamship, were in this company, being idle with all their might.   Two or three adventurous young men went off to see the valley where the dragon was killed ; but others, more susceptible of the real influence of the island, I am sure would not have moved, though we had been told that the Colossus himself was taking a walk half a mile off.

CHAPTER IX

THE WHITE SQUALL

On deck, beneath the awning,
I dozing lay and yawning ;
It was the grey of dawning,
　　Ere yet the sun arose ;
And above the funnel's roaring,
And the fitful wind's deploring,
I heard the cabin snoring
　　With universal nose.
I could hear the passengers snorting,
I envied their disporting,
Vainly I was courting
　　The pleasure of a doze.

So I lay, and wondered why light
Came not, and watched the twilight
And the glimmer of the skylight,
　　That shot across the deck ;
And the binnacle pale and steady,
And the dull glimpse of the dead-eye,
And the sparks in fiery eddy,
　　That whirled from the chimney neck :
In our jovial floating prison
There was sleep from fore to mizen,
And never a star had risen
　　The hazy sky to speck.

Strange company we harboured ;
We'd a hundred Jews to larboard,
Unwashed, uncombed, unbarbered,
    Jews black, and brown, and grey ;
With terror it would seize ye,
And make your souls uneasy,
To see those Rabbis greasy,
    Who did nought but scratch and pray :
Their dirty children puking,
Their dirty saucepans cooking,
Their dirty fingers hooking
    Their swarming fleas away.

To starboard Turks and Greeks were,
Whiskered, and brown their cheeks were,
Enormous wide their breeks were,
    Their pipes did puff alway ;
Each on his mat allotted,
In silence smoked and squatted,
Whilst round their children trotted,
    In pretty, pleasant play.
He can't but smile who traces
The smiles on those brown faces,
And the pretty prattling graces
    Of those small heathens gay.

And so the hours kept tolling,
And through the ocean rolling,
Went the brave *Iberia* bowling
    Before the break of day——

When a SQUALL upon a sudden,
Came o'er the waters scudding ;
And the clouds began to gather,
And the sea was lashed to lather,
And the lowering thunder grumbled,
And the lightning jumped and tumbled,
And the ship, and all the ocean,
Woke up in wild commotion.
Then the wind set up a howling,
And the poodle-dog a yowling,
And the cocks began a crowing,
And the old cow raised a lowing,
As she heard the tempest blowing ;

And fowls and geese did cackle,
And the cordage and the tackle
Began to shriek and crackle ;
And the spray dashed o'er the funnels,
And down the deck in runnels ;
And the rushing water soaks all,
From the seamen in the fo'ksal,
To the stokers, whose black faces
Peer out of their bed-places ;
And the captain he was bawling,
And the sailors pulling, hauling ;
And the quarter-deck tarpauling
Was shivered in the squalling ;
And the passengers awaken,
Most pitifully shaken ;
And the steward jumps up, and hastens
For the necessary basins.

Then the Greeks they groaned and quivered,
And they knelt, and moaned, and shivered,
As the plunging waters met them,
And splashed and overset them ;
And they call in their emergence
Upon countless saints and virgins ;
And their marrowbones are bended,
And they think the world is ended.

And the Turkish women for'ard
Were frightened and behorror'd ;
And, shrieking and bewildering,
The mothers clutched their children ;
The men sung, ' Allah ! Illah !
Mashallah Bismillah ! '
As the warring waters doused them,
And splashed them and soused them ;
And they called upon the Prophet,
And thought but little of it.

Then all the fleas in Jewry
Jumped up and bit like fury ;
And the progeny of Jacob
Did on the main-deck wake up
(I wot those greasy Rabbins
Would never pay for cabins) ;

And each man moaned and jabbered in
His filthy Jewish gaberdine,
In woe and lamentation,
And howling consternation.
And the splashing water drenches
Their dirty brats and wenches ;
And they crawl from bales and benches,
In a hundred thousand stenches.

This was the White Squall famous,
Which latterly o'ercame us,
And which all will well remember
On the 28th September ;
When a Prussian captain of Lancers
(Those tight-laced, whiskered prancers)
Came on the deck astonished,
By that wild squall admonished,
And wondering cried, 'Potz tausend,
Wie ist der Stürm jetzt brausend ?'
And looked at Captain Lewis,
Who calmly stood and blew his
Cigar in all the bustle,
And scorned the tempest's tussle.
And oft we've thought hereafter
How he beat the storm to laughter ;
For well he knew his vessel
With that vain wind could wrestle ;
And when a wreck we thought her,
And doomed ourselves to slaughter,
How gaily he fought her,
And through the hubbub brought her,
And, as the tempest caught her,
Cried, 'GEORGE ! SOME BRANDY-AND-WATER !'

And when, its force expended,
The harmless storm was ended,
And, as the sunrise splendid
    Came blushing o'er the sea ;
I thought, as day was breaking,
My little girls were waking,
And smiling, and making
    A prayer at home for me.

CHAPTER X

THERE should have been a poet in our company to describe that charming little bay of Glaucus, into which we entered on the 26th of September, in the first steamboat that ever disturbed its beautiful waters. You can't put down in prose that delicious episode of natural poetry; it ought to be done in a symphony, full of sweet melodies and swelling harmonies; or sung in a strain of clear crystal iambics, such as Milnes knows how to write. A mere map, drawn in words, gives the mind no notion of that exquisite nature. What do mountains become in type, or rivers in Mr. Vizetelly's best brevier? Here lies the sweet bay, gleaming peaceful in the rosy sunshine: green islands dip here and there in its waters: purple mountains swell circling round it; and towards them, rising from the bay, stretches a rich green plain, fruitful with herbs and various foliage, in the midst of which the white houses twinkle. I can see a little minaret, and some spreading palm-trees; but, beyond these, the description would answer as well for Bantry Bay as well as Makri. You could write so far, nay, much more particularly and grandly, without seeing the place at all, and after reading Beaufort's *Caramania*, which gives you not the least notion of it.

Suppose the great hydrographer of the Admiralty himself can't describe it, who surveyed the place; suppose Mr. Fellowes, who discovered it afterwards—suppose I say Sir John Fellowes, Knt.—can't do it (and I defy any man of imagination to get an impression of Telmessus from his book)—can you, vain man, hope to try? The effect of the artist, as I take it, ought to be, to produce upon his hearer's mind, by his art, an effect something similar to that produced on his own, by the sight of the natural object. Only music, or the best poetry, can do this. Keats's 'Ode to the Grecian Urn' is the best description I know of that sweet, old, silent ruin of Telmessus. After you have once seen it, the remembrance remains with you, like a tune from Mozart, which he seems to have caught out of heaven, and which rings sweet harmony in your ears for ever after! It's a benefit for all after life! You have but to shut your eyes, and think, and recall it, and the delightful vision comes smiling back, to your order!— the divine air—the delicious little pageant, which nature set before you on this lucky day.

Here is the entry made in the note-book on the eventful day:
—In the morning steamed into the bay of Glaucus—landed at
Makri—cheerful old desolate village—theatre by the beautiful
seashore—great fertility, oleanders—a palm-tree in the midst of
the village, spreading out like a sultan's aigrette—sculptured
caverns, or tombs, up the mountain—camels over the bridge.

Perhaps it is best for a man of fancy to make his own landscape
out of these materials: to group the couched camels under the
plane-trees; the little crowd of wandering, ragged heathens come
down to the calm water, to behold the nearing steamer; to fancy
a mountain, in the sides of which some scores of tombs are rudely
carved; pillars and porticos, and Doric entablatures. But it is
of the little theatre that he must make the most beautiful picture
—a charming little place of festival, lying out on the shore, and
looking over the sweet bay and the swelling purple islands. No
theatre-goer ever looked out on a fairer scene. It encourages
poetry, idleness, delicious sensual reverie. O, Jones! friend of my
heart! would you not like to be a white-robed Greek, lolling
languidly on the cool benches here, and pouring compliments (in
the Ionic dialect) into the rosy ears of Neæra? Instead of Jones,
your name should be Ionides; instead of a silk hat, you should
wear a chaplet of roses in your hair: you would not listen to the
choruses they were singing on the stage, for the voice of the fair
one would be whispering a rendezvous for the *mesonuktiais horais*,
and my Ionides would have no ear for aught beside. Yonder, in
the mountain, they would carve a Doric cave temple, to receive
your urn when all was done; and you would be accompanied
thither by a dirge of the surviving Ionidæ. The caves of the dead
are empty now, however, and their place knows them not any
more among the festal haunts of the living. But, by way of
supplying the choric melodies, sung here in old time, one of our
companions mounted on the scene and spouted,

' My name is Norval.'

On the same day we lay to for a while at another ruined
theatre, that of Antiphilos. The Oxford men, fresh with recollections of the little-go, bounded away up the hill on which it lies, to
the ruin, measured the steps of the theatre, and calculated the
width of the scene; while others, less active, watched them with
telescopes from the ship's sides, as they plunged in and out of the
stones and hollows.

Two days after, the scene was quite changed. We were out of
sight of the classical country, and lay in St. George's Bay, behind
a huge mountain, upon which St. George fought the dragon, and

rescued the lovely lady Sabra, the king of Babylon's daughter. The Turkish fleet was lying about us, commanded by that Halil Pacha, whose two children the two last sultans murdered. The crimson flag, with the star and crescent, floated at the stern of his ship. Our diplomatist put on his uniform and cordons, and paid his excellency a visit. He spoke in rapture, when he returned, of the beauty and order of the ship, and the urbanity of the infidel admiral. He sent us bottles of ancient Cyprus wine to drink: and the captain of her Majesty's ship, *Trump*, alongside which we were lying, confirmed that good opinion of the Capitan Pasha, which the reception of the above present led us to entertain, by relating many instances of his friendliness and hospitalities. Captain G—— said, the Turkish ships were as well manned, as well kept, and as well manœuvred, as any vessels in any service; and intimated a desire to command a Turkish seventy-four, and a perfect willingness to fight her against a French ship of the same size. But I heartily trust he will neither embrace the Mahometan opinions, nor be called upon to engage any seventy-four whatever. If he do, let us hope he will have his own men to fight with. If the crew of the *Trump* were all like the crew of the captain's boat, they need fear no two hundred and fifty men out of any country, with any Joinville at their head. We were carried on shore by this boat. For two years, during which the *Trump* had been lying off Beyrout, none of the men but these eight had ever set foot on shore. Mustn't it be a happy life? We were landed at the busy quay of Beyrout, flanked by the castle that the fighting old commodore half battered down.

Along the Beyrout quays civilisation flourishes under the flags of the consul, which are streaming out over the yellow buildings in the clear air. Hither she brings from England her produce of marine-stores and woollens, her crockeries, her portable soups, and her bitter ale. Hither she has brought politeness, and the last modes from Paris. They were exhibited in the person of a pretty lady, superintending the great French store, and who seeing a stranger sketching on the quay, sent forward a man with a chair, to accommodate that artist, and greeted him with a bow and a smile, such as only can be found in France. Then she fell to talking with a young French officer, with a beard, who was greatly smitten with her. They were making love just as they do on the Boulevard. An Arab porter left his bales, and the camel he was unloading, to come and look at the sketch. Two stumpy, flat-faced Turkish soldiers, in red caps and white undresses, peered over the paper. A noble little Lebanonian girl, with a deep yellow face, and curly dun-coloured hair, and a blue tattooed chin, and for all clothing, a little ragged shift of blue cloth, stood by like a little statue, holding her urn, and stared with wondering brown eyes. How magnificently blue the water was!—how bright the flags and buildings as they shone above it, and the lines of the rigging tossing in the bay! The white crests of the blue waves jumped and sparkled like quicksilver; the shadows were as broad and cool as the lights were brilliant and rosy; the battered old towers of the commodore looked quite cheerful in the delicious atmosphere; and the mountains beyond were of an amethyst colour. The French officer and the

lady went on chattering quite happily about love, the last new bonnet, or the battle of Isly, or the 'Juif Errant'; how neatly her gown and sleeves fitted her pretty little person! We had not seen a woman for a month, except honest Mrs. Flanigan, the stewardess, and the ladies of our party, and the tips of the noses of the Constantinople beauties, as they passed by leering from their yakmacs, waddling and plapping in their odious yellow papooshes.

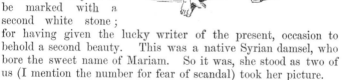

And this day is to be marked with a second white stone; for having given the lucky writer of the present, occasion to behold a second beauty. This was a native Syrian damsel, who bore the sweet name of Mariam. So it was, she stood as two of us (I mention the number for fear of scandal) took her picture.

So it was, that the good-natured black cook looked behind her young mistress, with a benevolent grin, that only the admirable Leslie could paint.

Mariam was the sister of the young guide, whom we hired to show us through the town; and to let us be cheated in the purchase of gilt scarfs and handkerchiefs, which strangers think proper to buy. And before the above authentic drawing could be made, many were the stratagems the wily artists were obliged to employ, to subdue the shyness of the little Mariam. In the first place, she would stand behind the door (from which in the darkness her beautiful black eyes gleamed out like penny tapers); nor could the entreaties of her brother and mamma, bring her from that hiding-place. In order to conciliate the latter, we began by making a picture of her too—that is, not of her, who was an enormous old fat woman in yellow, quivering all over with strings of pearls, and necklaces of sequins, and other ornaments, the which descended from her neck, and down her ample stomacher—we did not depict that big old woman, who would have been frightened at an accurate representation of her own enormity; but an ideal being, all grace and beauty, dressed in her costume, and still simpering before me in my sketch-book, like a lady in a book of fashions.

This portrait was shown to the old woman, who handed it over to the black cook, who, grinning, carried it to little Mariam—and the result is, that the young creature stepped forward, and submitted; and has come over to Europe, as you see.

A very snug and happy family did this of Mariam's appear to be. If you could judge by all the laughter and giggling, by the splendour of the women's attire, by the neatness of the little house, prettily decorated with arabesque paintings, neat mats, and gay carpets; they were a family well to do in the Beyrout world, and lived with as much comfort as any Europeans. They had one book; and, on the wall of the principal apartment, a black picture of the Virgin, whose name is borne by pretty Mariam.

The camels and the soldiers, the bazaars and khans, the fountains and awnings, which chequer, with such delightful variety of light and shade, the alleys and markets of an Oriental town, are to be seen in Beyrout in perfection; and an artist might here employ himself for months with advantage and pleasure. A new costume was here added to the motley and picturesque assembly of dresses. This was the dress of the blue-veiled women from the Lebanon, stalking solemnly through the markets, with huge horns, near a yard high, on their foreheads. For thousands of years since the time the Hebrew prophets wrote, these horns have so been exalted in the Lebanon.

At night Captain Lewis gave a splendid ball and supper to the *Trump*. We had the *Trump's* band to perform the music; and a grand sight it was to see the captain himself enthusiastically leading on the drum. Blue lights and rockets were burned from the yards of our ship; which festive signals were answered presently from the *Trump*, and from another English vessel in the harbour,

They must have struck the Capitan Pasha with wonder, for he sent his secretary on board of us to inquire what the fireworks meant. And the worthy Turk had scarcely put his foot on the deck, when he found himself seized round the waist by one of the *Trump's* officers, and whirling round the deck in a waltz, to his own amazement, and the huge delight of the company. His face of wonder and gravity, as he went on twirling, could not have been exceeded by that of a dancing dervish at Scutari ; and the manner in which he managed to *enjamber* the waltz excited universal applause.

I forget whether he accommodated himself to European ways so much further as to drink champagne at supper-time ; to say that he did would be telling tales out of school, and might interfere with the future advancement of that jolly dancing Turk.

We made acquaintance with another of the sultan's subjects, who, I fear, will have occasion to doubt of the honour of the English nation, after the foul treachery with which he was treated.

Among the occupiers of the little bazaar watch-boxes, venders of embroidered handkerchiefs and other articles of showy Eastern haberdashery, was a good-looking, neat young fellow, who spoke English very fluently, and was particularly attentive to all the passengers on board our ship. This gentleman was not only a pocket-handkerchief merchant in the bazaar, but earned a further livelihood by letting out mules and donkeys ; and he kept a small lodging-house, or inn, for travellers, as we were informed.

No wonder he spoke good English, and was exceedingly polite and well bred ; for the worthy man had passed some time in England, and in the best society too. That humble haberdasher at Beyrout had been a lion here, at the very best houses of the great people, and had actually made his appearance at Windsor, where he was received as a Syrian Prince, and treated with great hospitality by royalty itself.

I don't know what waggish propensity moved one of the officers of the *Trump* to say, that there was an equerry of his Royal Highness the Prince on board, and to point me out as the dignified personage in question. So the Syrian Prince was introduced to the royal equerry, and a great many compliments passed between us. I even had the audacity to state, that on my very last interview with my royal master, his Royal Highness had said, ' Colonel Titmarsh, when you go to Beyrout, you will make special inquiries regarding my interesting friend Cogia Hassan.'

Poor Cogia Hassan (I forget whether that was his name, but it is as good as another) was overpowered with this royal message ;

and we had an intimate conversation together, at which the waggish officer of the *Trump* assisted with the greatest glee.

But see the consequences of deceit! The next day, as we were getting under way, who should come on board but my friend the Syrian Prince, most eager for a last interview with the Windsor equerry; and he begged me to carry his protestations of unalterable fidelity to the gracious consort of her Majesty. Nor was this all. Cogia Hassan actually produced a great box of sweetmeats, of which he begged my excellency to accept, and a little figure of a doll, dressed in the costume of Lebanon. Then the punishment of imposture began to be felt severely by me. How to accept the poor devil's sweetmeats? How to refuse them? And as we know that one fib leads to another, so I was obliged to support the first falsehood by another; and putting on a dignified air—'Cogia Hassan,' says I, 'I am surprised you don't know the habits of the British court better, and are not aware that our gracious master solemnly forbids his servants to accept any sort of backsheesh upon our travels.'

So Prince Cogia Hassan went over the side with his chest of sweetmeats, but insisted on leaving the doll, which may be worth twopence-halfpenny; of which, and of the costume of the women of Lebanon, the following is an accurate likeness:—

CHAPTER XI

A DAY AND NIGHT IN SYRIA

WHEN, after being for five whole weeks at sea, with a general belief that at the end of a few days the marine malady leaves you for good, you find that a brisk wind and a heavy rolling swell create exactly the same inward effects which they occasioned at the very commencement of the voyage—you begin to fancy that you are unfairly dealt with : and I, for my part, had thought of complaining to the Company of this atrocious violation of the rules of their prospectus ; but we were perpetually coming to anchor in various ports, at which intervals of peace good-humour was restored to us.

On the 3rd of October our cable rushed with a huge rattle into the blue sea before Jaffa, at a distance of considerably more than a mile of the town, which lay before us very clear, with the flags of the consuls flaring in the bright sky, and making a cheerful and hospitable show. The houses a great heap of sun-baked stones, surmounted here and there by minarets and countless little white-washed domes ; a few date-trees spread out their fan-like heads over these dull-looking buildings ; long sands stretched away on either side, with low purple hills behind them ; we could see specks of camels crawling over these yellow plains ; and those persons who were about to land, had the leisure to behold the sea-spray flashing over the sands, and over a heap of black rocks which lie before the entry to the town. The swell is very great, the passage between the rocks narrow, and the danger sometimes considerable. So the guide began to entertain the ladies and other passengers in the huge country boat which brought us from the steamer, with an agreeable story of a lieutenant and eight sea-men of one of her Majesty's ships, who were upset, dashed to pieces, and drowned upon these rocks, through which two men and two boys, with a very moderate portion of clothing, each standing and pulling half an oar—there were but two oars between them, and another by way of rudder—were endeavouring to guide us.

When the danger of the rocks and surf was passed, came another danger of the hideous brutes in brown skins and the briefest shirts, who came towards the boat, straddling through the water with outstretched arms, grinning and yelling their Arab invitations to mount their shoulders. I think these fellows frightened the ladies still more than the rocks and the surf; but the poor creatures were obliged to submit, and trembling were accommodated somehow upon the mahogany backs of these ruffians, carried through the shallows, and flung up to a ledge before the city gate, where crowds more of dark people were swarming, howling after their fashion. The gentlemen, meanwhile, were having arguments about the eternal backsheesh with the roaring Arab boatmen; and I recall with wonder and delight especially, the curses and screams of one small and extremely loud-lunged fellow, who expressed discontent at receiving a five, instead of a six piastre piece. But how is one to know, without possessing the language? Both coins are made of a greasy pewtery sort of tin; and I thought the biggest was the most valuable: but the fellow showed a sense of their value, and a disposition seemingly to cut any man's throat who did not understand it. Men's throats have been cut for a less difference before now.

Being cast upon the ledge, the first care of our gallantry was to look after the ladies, who were scared and astonished by the naked savage brutes, who were shouldering the poor things to and fro: and bearing them through these and a dark archway, we came into a street crammed with donkeys and their packs and drivers, and towering camels with leering eyes looking into the second-floor rooms, and huge splay feet, through which *mesdames et mesde-moiselles* were to be conducted. We made a rush at the first open door, and passed comfortably under the heels of some horses gathered under the arched court, and up a stone staircase, which turned out to be that of the Russian consul's house. His people welcomed us most cordially to his abode, and the ladies and the luggage (objects of our solicitude) were led up many stairs and across several terraces to a most comfortable little room, under a dome of its own, where the representative of Russia sat. Women with brown faces and draggle-tailed coats and turbans, and wondering eyes, and no stays, and blue beads and gold coins hanging round their necks, came to gaze, as they passed, upon the fair neat English women; blowsy black cooks puffing over fires, and the strangest pots and pans on the terraces; children paddling about in long striped robes, interrupted their sports or labours, to come and stare; and the consul, in his cool domed chamber, with a lattice overlooking the sea, with clean mats, and pictures of the Emperor, the Virgin, and St. George, received the strangers with smiling courtesies, regaling these with pomegranates and sugar, those with pipes of tobacco, whereof the fragrant tubes were three yards long.

The Russian amenities concluded, we left the ladies still under the comfortable, cool dome of the Russian consulate, and went to see our own representative. The streets of the little town are neither agreeable to horse or foot travellers. Many of the streets are mere flights of rough steps, leading abruptly into private houses; you pass under archways and passages numberless; a steep, dirty labyrinth of stone-vaulted stables and sheds occupy the ground-floor of the habitations; and you pass from flat to flat of the terraces; at various irregular corners of which, little chambers, with little private domes, are erected, and the people live seemingly as much upon the terrace as in the room.

We found the English consul in a queer little arched chamber, with a strange old picture of the king's arms to decorate one side of it; and here the consul, a demure old man, dressed in red flowing robes, with a feeble janissary, bearing a shabby tin-mounted staff, or mace, to denote his office, received such of our nation as came to him for hospitality. He distributed pipes and coffee to all and every one; he made us a present of his house and all his beds for the night, and went himself to lie quietly on the terrace; and for all this hospitality he declined to receive any reward from us, and said he was but doing his duty in taking us in. This worthy man, I thought, must doubtless be very well paid by our government for making such sacrifices; but it appears, that he does not get one single farthing, and that the greater number of our Levant consuls are paid at a similar rate of easy remuneration. If we have bad consular agents, have we a right to complain? If the worthy gentlemen cheat occasionally, can we reasonably be angry? But in travelling through these countries, English people, who don't take into consideration the miserable poverty and scanty resources of their country, and are apt to brag and be proud of it, have their vanity hurt by seeing the representatives of every nation but their own well and decently maintained, and feel ashamed at sitting down under the shabby protection of our mean consular flag.

The active young men of our party had been on shore long before us, and seized upon all the available horses in the town; but we relied upon a letter from Halil Pacha, enjoining all governors and pachas to help us in all ways: and hearing we were the bearers of this document, the Cadi and Vice-Governor of Jaffa came to wait upon the head of our party, declared that it was his delight and honour to set eyes upon us; that he would do everything in the world to serve us; that there were no horses, unluckily, but he would send and get some in three hours; and so left us with a world of grinning bows and many choice compliments, from one side to the other, which came to each filtered through an obsequious interpreter. But hours passed, and the clatter of horses' hoofs was not heard. We had our dinner of eggs and flaps of bread, and the sunset gun fired : we had our pipes and coffee again, and the night fell. Is this man throwing dirt upon us ? we began to think. Is he laughing at our beards, and are our mother's graves ill-treated by this smiling, swindling cadi ? We determined to go and seek in his own den this shuffling dispenser of infidel justice. This time we would be no more bamboozled by compliments ; but we would use the language of stern expostulation, and, being roused, would let the rascal hear the roar of the indignant British lion : so we rose up in our wrath. The poor consul got a lamp for us with a bit of wax candle, such as I wonder his means could afford ; the shabby janissary marched ahead with his tin mace, the two *laquais de place*, that two of our company had hired, stepped forward, each with an old sabre, and we went clattering and stumbling down the streets of the town, in order to seize upon this cadi in his own divan. I was glad, for my part (though outwardly majestic and indignant in demeanour), that the horses had not come, and that we had a chance of seeing this little, queer glimpse of oriental life, which the magistrate's faithlessness procured for us.

As piety forbids the Turks to eat during the weary daylight hours of the Ramazan, they spend their time profitably in sleeping until the welcome sunset, when the town wakens : all the lanterns are lighted up ; all the pipes begin to puff, and the narghiles to bubble ; all the sour-milk-and-sherbet-men begin to yell out the excellence of their wares ; all the frying-pans in the little, dirty cook-shops begin to friz, and the pots to send forth a steam : and through this dingy, ragged, bustling, beggarly, cheerful scene, we began now to march towards the Bow Street of Jaffa. We bustled through a crowded narrow archway which led to the cadi's police-office, entered the little room, atrociously perfumed with musk, and passing by the rail-board, where the common sort stood, mounted up the stage on which his worship and friends sat, and squatted down on the divans in stern and silent dignity. His honour ordered us coffee, his countenance evidently showing considerable alarm. A black slave, whose duty seemed to be to prepare this beverage in a side-room with a furnace, prepared for each of us about a teaspoonful of the liquor : his worship's clerk, I presume, a tall Turk of a noble aspect, presented it to us, and having lapped up the little modicum of drink, the British lion began to speak.

All the other travellers (said the lion with perfect reason) have good horses and are gone ; the Russians have got horses, the

Spaniards have horses, the English have horses, but we, we vizirs in our country, and coming with letters of Halil Pacha, are laughed at, spit upon! Are Halil Pacha's letters dirt, that you attend to them in this way? Are British lions dogs that you treat them so?—and so on. This speech with many variations was made on our side for a quarter of an hour; and we finally swore, that unless the horses were forthcoming, we would write to Halil Pacha the next morning, and to his Excellency the English minister at the Sublime Porte. Then you should have heard the chorus of Turks in reply: a dozen voices rose up from the divan, shouting, screaming, ejaculating, expectorating (the Arabic spoken language seems to require a great employment of the two latter oratorical methods), and uttering what the meek interpreter did not translate to us, but what I dare say were by no means complimentary phrases towards us and our nation. Finally, the palaver concluded by the Cadi declaring, that by the will of heaven horses should be forthcoming at three o'clock in the morning; and that if not, why then we might write to Halil Pacha.

This posed us, and we rose up and haughtily took leave. I should like to know that fellow's real opinion of us lions very much: and especially to have had the translation of the speeches of a huge-breeched turbaned roaring infidel, who looked and spoke as if he would have liked to fling us all into the sea, which was hoarsely murmuring under our windows an accompaniment to the concert within.

We then marched through the bazaars, that were lofty and grim, and pretty full of people. In a desolate broken building, some hundreds of children were playing and singing; in many corners sat parties over their water-pipes, one of whom every now and then would begin twanging out a most queer chant; others there were playing at casino—a crowd squatted round the squalling gamblers, and talking and looking on with eager interest. In one place of the bazaar we found a hundred people at least listening to a story-teller, who delivered his tale with excellent action, voice and volubility: in another they were playing a sort of thimble-rig with coffee-cups, all intent upon the game, and the player himself very wild lest one of our party, who had discovered where the pea lay, should tell the company. The devotion and energy with which all these pastimes were pursued, struck me as much as anything. These people have been playing thimble-rig and casino; that story-teller has been shouting his tale of Antar, for forty years; and they are just as happy with this amusement now as when first they tried it. Is there no ennui in the Eastern countries, and are the blue devils not allowed to go abroad there?

From the bazaars we went to see the house of Mustapha, said to be the best house and the greatest man of Jaffa. But the great man had absconded suddenly, and had fled into Egypt. The sultan had made a demand upon him for sixteen thousand purses, £80,000—Mustapha retired—the sultan pounced down upon his house, and his goods, his horses, and his mules. His harem was desolate. Mr. Milnes could have written six affecting poems, had he been with us, on the dark loneliness of that violated sanctuary. We passed from hall to hall, terrace to terrace—a few fellows were slumbering on the naked floors, and scarce turned as we went by them. We entered Mustapha's particular divan—there was the raised floor, but no bearded friends squatting away the night of Ramazan; there was the little coffee furnace, but where was the slave and the coffee and the glowing embers of the pipes? Mustapha's favourite passages from the Koran were still painted up on the walls, but nobody was the wiser for them. We walked over a sleeping negro, and opened the windows which looked into his gardens. The horses and donkeys, the camels and mules were picketed there below, but where is the said Mustapha? From the frying-pan of the Porte, has he not fallen into the fire of Mehemet Ali? And which is best, to broil or to fry? If it be but to read the *Arabian Nights* again on getting home, it is good to have made this little voyage and seen these strange places and faces.

Then we went out through the arched lowering gateway of the town into the plain beyond, and that was another famous and brilliant scene of the *Arabian Nights*. The heaven shone with a marvellous brilliancy—the plain disappeared far in the haze—the towers and battlements of the town rose black against the sky—old outlandish trees rose up here and there—clumps of camels were couched in the rare herbage—dogs were baying about—groups of men lay sleeping under their haicks round about—round about the tall gates many lights were twinkling—and they brought us water-pipes and sherbet—and we wondered to think that London was only three weeks off.

Then came the night at the consul's. The poor demure old gentleman brought out his mattresses; and the ladies sleeping round on the divans, we lay down quite happy; and I for my part intended to make as delightful dreams as Alnaschar; but—lo, the delicate mosquito sounded his horn: the active flea jumped up, and came to feast on Christian flesh (the eastern flea bites more bitterly than the most savage bug in Christendom), and the bug—oh, the accursed! Why was he made? What duty has that infamous ruffian to perform in the world, save to make people wretched? Only Bulwer in his most pathetic style could describe the miseries of that night—the moaning, the groaning, the cursing, the tumbling, the blistering, the infamous despair and degradation! I heard all the cocks in Jaffa crow; the children crying, and the mothers hushing them; the donkeys braying fitfully in the moonlight; at last, I heard the clatter of hoofs below, and the hailing of men. It was three o'clock, the horses were actually come; nay, there were camels likewise; asses and mules, pack-saddles and drivers, all bustling together under the moonlight in the cheerful street—and the first night in Syria was over.

CHAPTER XII

FROM JAFFA TO JERUSALEM

It took an hour or more to get our little caravan into marching order, to accommodate all the packs to the horses, the horses to the riders; to see the ladies comfortably placed in their litter, with a sleek and large black mule fore and aft, a groom to each mule, and a tall and exceedingly good-natured and mahogany-coloured infidel to walk by the side of the carriage, to balance it as it swayed to and fro, and to offer his back as a step to the inmates whenever they were minded to ascend or alight. These three fellows, fasting through the Ramazan, and over as rough a road, for the greater part, as ever shook mortal bones, performed their fourteen hours' walk of near forty miles with the most admirable courage, alacrity, and good-humour. They once or twice drank water on the march, and so far infringed the rule; but they refused all bread or edible refreshment offered to them, and tugged on with an energy that the best camel, and I am sure the best Christian, might envy. What a lesson of good-humoured endurance it was to certain Pall Mall Sardanapaluses, who grumble if club sofa cushions are not soft enough!

If I could write sonnets at leisure, I would like to chronicle in fourteen lines my sensations on finding myself on a high Turkish saddle, with a pair of fire-shovel stirrups and worsted reins, red padded saddle-cloth, and innumerable tags, fringes, glass beads, ends of rope, to decorate the harness of the horse, the gallant steed on which I was about to gallop into Syrian life. What a figure we cut in the moonlight, and how they would have stared in the Strand! Aye, or in Leicestershire, where I warrant such a horse and rider are not often visible! The shovel stirrups are deucedly short; the clumsy leathers cut the shins of some equestrians abominably; you sit over your horse as it were on a tower, from which the descent would be very easy, but for the big peak of the saddle. A good way for the inexperienced is to put a stick or umbrella across the saddle peak again, so that it is next to impossible to go over your horse's neck. I found this a vast comfort in going down the hills, and recommend it conscientiously to other dear simple brethren of the city.

Peaceful men, we did not ornament our girdles with pistols, yataghans, etc., such as some pilgrims appeared to bristle all over with; and as a lesson to such rash people, a story may be told which was narrated to us at Jerusalem, and carries a wholesome moral. The Honourable Hoggin Armer, who was lately travelling in the East, wore about his stomach two brace of pistols, of such exquisite finish and make, that a Sheikh, in the Jericho country, robbed him merely for the sake of the pistols. I don't know whether he has told the story to his friends at home.

Another story about Sheikhs may here be told *apropos*. That celebrated Irish Peer, Lord Oldgent (who was distinguished in the Buckinghamshire Dragoons), having paid a sort of blackmail to the Sheikh of Jericho country, was suddenly set upon by another Sheikh, who claimed to be the real Jerichonian governor; and these twins quarrelled over the body of Lord Oldgent, as the widows for the innocent baby before Solomon. There was enough for both—but these digressions are interminable.

The party got under weigh at near four o'clock: the ladies in the litter, the French *femme de chambre* manfully caracoling on a grey horse; the cavaliers, like your humble servant, on their high saddles; the domestics, flunkies, guides, and grooms, on all sorts of animals,—some fourteen in all. Add to these, two most grave and stately Arabs in white beards, white turbans, white haicks and raiments; sabres curling round their military thighs, and immense long guns at their backs. More venerable warriors I never saw; they went by the side of the litter soberly prancing. When we emerged from the steep clattering streets of the city into the grey plains, lighted by the moon and starlight, these militaries rode onward, leading the way through the huge avenues of strange diabolical-looking prickly pears (plants that look as if they had grown in Tartarus), by which the first mile or two of route from the city is bounded; and as the dawn arose before us, exhibiting first a streak of grey, then of green, then of red in the sky, it was fine to see these martial figures defined against the rising light. The sight of that little cavalcade, and of the nature around it, will always remain with me, I think, as one of the freshest and most delightful sensations I have enjoyed since the day I first saw Calais pier. It was full day when they gave their horses a drink at a large pretty oriental fountain, and then presently we entered the open plain—the famous plain of Sharon —so fruitful in roses once, now hardly cultivated, but always beautiful and noble.

Here presently, in the distance, we saw another cavalcade pricking over the plain. Our two white warriors spread to the right and left, and galloped to reconnoitre. We, too, put our steeds to the canter, and handling our umbrellas as Richard did his lance against Saladin, went undaunted to challenge this caravan. The fact is, we could distinguish that it was formed of the party of our pious friends the Poles, and we hailed them with cheerful shouting, and presently the two caravans joined company, and scoured the plain at the rate of near four miles per hour. The horse-master, a courier of this company, rode three miles for our one. He was a broken-nosed Arab, with pistols, a sabre, a fusee, a yellow Damascus cloth flapping over his head, and his nose ornamented with diachylon. He rode a hog-necked grey Arab, bristling over with harness, and jumped, and whirled, and reared, and halted, to the admiration of all.

Scarce had the diachylonian Arab finished his evolutions, when, lo! yet another cloud of dust was seen, and another party of armed and glittering horsemen appeared. They, too, were led by an Arab, who was followed by two Janissaries, with silver maces shining in the sun. 'Twas the party of the new American Consul-General of Syria and Jerusalem, hastening to that city, with the inferior consuls of Ramleh and Jaffa to escort him. He expects to see the millennium in three years, and has accepted the office of consul at Jerusalem, so as to be on the spot in readiness.

When the diachylon Arab saw the American Arab, he straightway galloped his steed towards him, took his pipe, which he delivered at his adversary in guise of a jereed, and galloped round and round, and in and out, and there and back again, as in a play of war. The American replied in a similar playful ferocity—the two warriors made a little tournament for us there on the plains before Jaffa, in the which diachylon, being a little worsted, challenged his adversary to a race, and fled away on his grey, the American following on his bay. Here poor sticking-plaister was again worsted, the Yankee contemptuously riding round him, and then declining further exercise.

What more could mortal man want? A troop of knights and paladins could have done no more. In no page of Walter Scott have I read a scene more fair and sparkling. The sober warriors of our escort did not join in the gambols of the young men. There they rode soberly, in their white turbans, by their ladies' litter, their long guns rising up behind them.

There was no lack of company along the road : donkeys numberless, camels by twos and threes ; now a mule-driver, trudging along the road, chanting a most queer melody ; now a lady, in white veil, black mask, and yellow *papooshes*, bestriding her ass, and followed by her husband,—met us on the way ; and most people gave a salutation. Presently we saw Ramleh, in a smoking mist, on the plain before us, flanked to the right by a tall lonely tower, that might have held the bells of some moustier of Caen or Evreux. As we entered, about three hours and a half after starting, among the white domes and stone houses of the little town, we passed the place of tombs. Two women were sitting on one of them,—the one bending her head towards the stone, and rocking to and fro, and moaning out a very sweet, pitiful lamentation. The American Consul invited us to breakfast at the house of his subaltern, the hospitable one-eyed Armenian, who represents the United States at Jaffa. The stars and stripes were flaunting over his terraces, to which we ascended, leaving our horses to the care of a multitude of roaring, ragged Arabs beneath, who took charge of and fed the animals, though I can't say in the least why ; but, in the same way as getting off my horse on entering Jerusalem, I gave the rein into the hand of the first person near me, and have never heard of the worthy brute since. At the American Consul's we were served first with rice soup in pishpash, flavoured with cinnamon and spice ; then with boiled mutton, then with stewed ditto and tomatoes ; then with fowls swimming in grease ; then with brown ragouts belaboured with onions ; then with a smoking pilaff of rice : several of which dishes I can pronounce to be of excellent material and flavour. When the gentry had concluded this repast it was handed to a side table, where the commonalty speedily discussed it. We left them licking their fingers as we hastened away upon the second part of the ride.

As we quitted Ramleh, the scenery lost that sweet and peaceful look which characterises the pretty plain we had traversed ; and the sun, too, rising in the heaven, dissipated all those fresh, beautiful tints in which God's world is clothed of early morning, and which city people have so seldom the chance of beholding. The plain over which we rode looked yellow and gloomy ; the cultivation little or none ; the land across the roadside fringed, for the most part, with straggling wild carrot plants ; a patch of green only here and there. We passed several herds of lean, small,

well-conditioned cattle ; many flocks of black goats, tended now
and then by a ragged negro shepherd, his long gun slung over his
back, his hand over his eyes to shade them as he stared at our
little cavalcade. Most of the half-naked country folks we met had
this dismal appendage to eastern rustic life ; and the weapon could
hardly be one of mere defence, for, beyond the faded skull-cap, or
tattered coat of blue or dirty white, the brawny, brown-chested,
solemn-looking fellows had nothing seemingly to guard. As before,
there was no lack of travellers on the road : more donkeys trotting
by, looking sleek and strong ; camels singly and by pairs, laden
with a little humble ragged merchandise, on their way between the
two towns. About noon we halted eagerly at a short distance
from an Arab village and well, where all were glad of a drink
of fresh water. A village of beavers, or a colony of ants, make
habitations not unlike these dismal huts piled together on the plain
here. There were no single huts along the whole line of road ;
poor and wretched as they are, the Fellahs huddle all together for
protection from the other thieves, their neighbours. The government (which we restored to them) has no power to protect them,
and is only strong enough to rob them. The women, with their
long blue gowns and ragged veils, came to and fro with pitchers
on their heads. Rebecca had such a one when she brought drink
to the lieutenant of Abraham. The boys came staring round,
bawling after us with their fathers for the inevitable backsheesh.
The village dogs barked round the flocks, as they were driven to
water or pasture.

We saw a gloomy, not very lofty-looking ridge of hills in front
of us ; the highest of which the guide pointing out to us, told us
that from it we should see Jerusalem. It looked very near, and
we all set up a trot of enthusiasm to get into this hill country.

But that burst of enthusiasm (it may have carried us nearly a
quarter of a mile in three minutes) was soon destined to be checked
by the disagreeable nature of the country we had to traverse.
Before we got to the real mountain district, we were in a manner
prepared for it, by the mounting and descent of several lonely outlying hills, up and down which our rough stony track wound.
Then we entered the hill district, and our path lay through the
clattering bed of an ancient stream, whose brawling waters have
rolled away into the past, along with the fierce and turbulent race
who once inhabited these savage hills. There may have been
cultivation here two thousand years ago. The mountains, or huge
stony mounds environing this rough path, have level ridges all the
way up to their summits ; on these parallel ledges there is still
some verdure and soil : when water flowed here and the country

was thronged with that extraordinary population, which, according to the Sacred Histories, was crowded into the region, these mountain steps may have been gardens and vineyards, such as we see now thriving along the hills of the Rhine. Now the district is quite deserted, and you ride among what seem to be so many petrified waterfalls. We saw no animals moving among the stony brakes; scarcely even a dozen little birds in the whole course of the ride. The sparrows are all at Jerusalem, among the house-tops, where their ceaseless chirping and twittering forms the most cheerful sound of the place.

The company of Poles, the company of Oxford men, and the little American army, travelled too quick for our caravan, which was made to follow the slow progress of the ladies' litter, and we had to make the journey through the mountains in a very small number. Not one of our party had a single weapon more dreadful than an umbrella ; and a couple of Arabs, wickedly inclined, might have brought us all to the halt, and rifled every carpet-bag and pocket belonging to us. Nor can I say that we journeyed without certain qualms of fear. When swarthy fellows, with girdles full of pistols and yataghans, passed us without unslinging their long guns ; when scowling camel-riders, with awful long bending lances, decorated with tufts of rags, or savage plumes of scarlet feathers, went by without molestation, I think we were rather glad that they did not stop and parley : for after all, a British lion with an umbrella is no match for an Arab with his infernal long gun. What, too, would have become of our women ? So we tried to think that it was entirely out of anxiety for them that we were inclined to push on.

There is a shady resting-place and village in the midst of the mountain district where the travellers are accustomed to halt for an hour's repose and refreshment ; and the other caravans were just quitting this spot, having enjoyed its cool shades and waters when we came up. Should we stop ? Regard for the ladies (of course no other earthly consideration) made us say, No ! What admirable self-denial and chivalrous devotion ! So our poor devils of mules and horses got no rest and no water, our panting litter-men no breathing-time, and we staggered desperately after the procession ahead of us. It wound up the mountain in front of us : the Poles with their guns and attendants, the American with his janissaries ; fifty or sixty all riding slowly like the procession in Bluebeard.

But alas, they headed us very soon ; when we got up the weary hill they were all out of sight ; perhaps thoughts of Fleet Street did cross the minds of some of us then, and a vague desire to see

a few policemen. The district now seemed peopled, and with an
ugly race. Savage personages peered at us out of huts, and grim
holes in the rocks. The mules began to loiter most abominably—
water the muleteers must have—and, behold, we came to a pleasant-
looking village of trees standing on a hill; children were shaking
figs from the trees—women were going about—before us was the
mosque of a holy man—the village, looking like a collection of
little forts, rose up on the hill to our right, with a long view of
the fields and gardens stretching from it, and camels arriving with
their burthens. Here we must stop; Paolo the chief servant,
knew the Sheikh of the village—he very good man—give him
water and supper—water very good here—in fact we began to
think of the propriety of halting here for the night, and making
our entry into Jerusalem on the next day.

A man on a handsome horse dressed in red came prancing up
to us, looking hard at the ladies in the litter, and passed away.
Then two others sauntered up, one handsome, and dressed in red
too, and he stared into the litter without ceremony, began to
play with a little dog that lay there, asked if we were Inglees,
and was answered by me in the affirmative. Paolo had brought
the water, the most delicious draught in the world. The gentle-
folks had had some, the poor muleteers were longing for it. The
French maid, the courageous Victoire (never since the days of
Joan of Arc has there surely been a more gallant and virtuous
female of France) refused the drink; when suddenly a servant of
the party scampers up to his master and says: 'Abou Gosh says
the ladies must get out and show themselves to the women of the
village.'

It was Abou Gosh himself, the redoubted robber Sheikh about
whom we had been laughing and crying 'Wolf' all day.
Never was seen such a skurry—'March!' was the instant
order given. When Victoire heard who it was and the message,
you should have seen how she changed countenance; trembling
for her virtue in the ferocious clutches of a Gosh: 'Un verre
d'eau pour l'amour de Dieu!' gasped she, and was ready to faint
on her saddle. 'Ne buvez plus, Victoire!' screamed a little
fellow of our party. 'Push on, push on!' cried one and all.
'What's the matter!' exclaimed the ladies in the litter, as they
saw themselves suddenly jogging on again. But we took care not
to tell them what had been the designs of the redoubtable Abou
Gosh. Away then we went—Victoire was saved—and her
mistresses rescued from dangers they knew not of, until they were
a long way out of the village.

Did he intend insult or goodwill? Did Victoire escape the

odious chance of becoming Madame Abou Gosh? Or did the mountain chief simply propose to be hospitable after his fashion? I think the latter was his desire; if the former had been his wish, a half-dozen of his long guns could have been up with us in a minute, and had all our party at their mercy. But now, for the sake of the mere excitement, the incident was, I am sorry to say, rather a pleasant one than otherwise; especially for a traveller, who is in the happy condition of being able to sing before robbers, as is the case with the writer of the present.

A little way out of the land of Goshen we came upon a long stretch of gardens and vineyards, slanting towards the setting sun, which illuminated numberless golden clusters of the most delicious grapes, of which we stopped and partook. Such grapes were never before tasted; water so fresh as that which a countryman fetched for us from a well, never sluiced parched throats before. It was the ride, the sun, and above all Abou Gosh, who made that refreshment so sweet: and hereby I offer him my best thanks. Presently in the midst of a most diabolical ravine, down which our horses went sliding, we heard the evening gun: it was fired from Jerusalem. The twilight is brief in this country, and in a few minutes the landscape was grey round about us, and the sky lighted up by a hundred thousand stars, which made the night beautiful.

Under this superb canopy we rode for a couple of hours to our journey's end. The mountains round about us dark, lonely, and sad; the landscape as we saw it at night (it is not more cheerful in the daytime), the most solemn and forlorn I have ever seen. The feelings of almost terror, with which riding through the night we approached this awful place, the centre of the world's past and future history, have no need to be noted down here. The recollection of those sensations must remain with a man as long as his memory lasts; and he should think of them as often, perhaps, as he should talk of them little.

CHAPTER XIII

JERUSALEM

THE ladies of our party found excellent quarters in readiness for them at the Greek convent in the city; where airy rooms, and plentiful meals, and wines and sweetmeats delicate and abundant, were provided to cheer them after the fatigues of their journey. I don't know whether the worthy fathers of the convent share in the good things which they lavish on their guests ; but they look as if they do. Those whom we saw bore every sign of easy conscience and good living ; there were a pair of strong, rosy, greasy, lazy lay-brothers, dawdling in the sun on the convent terrace, or peering over the parapet into the street below, whose looks gave one a notion of anything but asceticism.

In the principal room of the strangers' house (the lay traveller is not admitted to dwell in the sacred interior of the convent), and over the building, the Russian double-headed eagle is displayed. The place is under the patronage of the Emperor Nicholas : an imperial Prince has stayed in these rooms : the Russian Consul performs a great part in the city ; and a considerable annual stipend is given by the Emperor towards the maintenance of the great establishment in Jerusalem. The Great Chapel of the Church of the Holy Sepulchre is by far the richest, in point of furniture, of all the places of worship under that roof. We were in Russia, when we came to visit our friends here ; under the protection of the Father of the Church and the Imperial Eagle ! This butcher and tyrant, who sits on his throne only through the crime of those who held it before him—every step in whose pedigree is stained by some horrible mark of murder, parricide, adultery—this padded and whiskered pontiff—who rules in his jack-boots over a system of spies and soldiers, of deceit, ignorance, dissoluteness, and brute force, such as surely the history of the world never told of before—has a tender interest in the welfare of his spiritual children : in the Eastern Church ranks after the divinity, and is worshipped by millions of men. A pious exemplar of Christianity, truly ! and of the condition to which its union with politics has brought it ! Think of the rank to which he pretends, and gravely believes that he possesses, no doubt !—think of those who assumed the same ultra-sacred character before him !—and then of the Bible and the Founder of the Religion, of which the Emperor assumes to be the chief priest and defender !

We had some Poles of our party ; but these poor fellows went to the Latin convent, declining to worship after the Emperor's fashion. The next night after our arrival, two of them passed in the Sepulchre. There we saw them, more than once on subsequent visits, kneeling in the Latin Church before the pictures, or marching solemnly with candles in processions, or lying flat on the stones, or passionately kissing the spots which their traditions have consecrated as the authentic places of the Saviour's sufferings. More honest or more civilised, or from opposition, the Latin

z

fathers have long given up and disowned the disgusting mummery of the Eastern Fire,—which lie the Greeks continue annually to tell.

Their travellers' house and convent, though large and commodious, are of a much poorer and shabbier condition than those of the Greeks. Both make believe not to take money ; but the traveller is expected to pay in each. The Latin fathers enlarge their means by a little harmless trade in beads and crosses, and mother-of-pearl shells, on which figures of saints are engraved ; and which they purchase from the manufacturers, and vend at a small profit. The English, until of late, used to be quartered in these sham inns ; but last year two or three Maltese took houses for the reception of tourists, who can now be accommodated with cleanly and comfortable board, at a rate not too heavy for most pockets.

To one of these we went very gladly ; giving our horses the bridle at the door, which went off of their own will to their stables, through the dark, inextricable labyrinths of streets, archways, and alleys, which we had threaded after leaving the main street from the Jaffa gate. There, there was still some life. Numbers of persons were collected at their doors, or smoking before the dingy coffee-houses, where singing and story-telling was going on ; but out of this great street everything was silent, and no sign of a light from the windows of the low houses which we passed.

We ascended from a lower floor up to a terrace, on which were several little domed chambers, or pavilions. From this terrace, whence we looked in the morning, a great part of the city spread before us :—white domes upon domes, and terraces of the same character as our own. Here and there, from among these white-washed mounds round about, a minaret rose, or a rare date-tree ; but the chief part of the vegetation near was that odious tree the prickly pear,—one huge green wart growing out of another, armed with spikes, as inhospitable as the aloe, without shelter or beauty. To the right the Mosque of Omar rose ; the rising sun behind it. Yonder steep tortuous lane before us, flanked by ruined walls on either side, has borne, time out of mind, the title of Via Dolorosa ; and tradition has fixed the spots where the Saviour rested, bearing his cross to Calvary. But of the mountain, rising immediately in front of us, a few grey olive-trees speckling the yellow side here and there, there can be no question. That is the Mount of Olives. Bethany lies beyond it. The most sacred eyes that ever looked on this world, have gazed on those ridges : it was there He was used to walk and teach. With shame and humility one looks towards the spot where that inexpressible Love and Benevolence lived and breathed ; where the great yearning heart of the Saviour interceded for all our race ; and whence the bigots and traitors of his day led him away to kill him !

That company of Jews whom we had brought with us from Constantinople, and who had cursed every delay on the route, not from impatience to view the Holy City, but from rage at being obliged to purchase dear provisions for their maintenance on ship-board, made what bargains they best could at Jaffa, and journeyed to the Valley of Jehoshaphat at the cheapest rate. We saw the tall form of the old Polish Patriarch, venerable in filth, stalking among the stinking ruins of the Jewish quarter. The sly old Rabbi, in the greasy folding hat, who would not pay to shelter his children from the storm off Beyrout, greeted us in the Bazaars ; the younger Rabbis were furbished up with some smartness. We met them on Sunday at the kind of promenade, by the walls of the Bethlehem gate ; they were in company of some red-bearded co-religionists, smartly attired in eastern raiment ; but their voice was the voice of the Jews of Berlin, and of course as we passed they were talking about so many hundert thaler. You may track one of the people, and be sure to hear mention of that silver calf that they worship.

The English mission has been very unsuccessful with these religionists. I don't believe the Episcopal apparatus—the Chaplains, and the Colleges, and the Beadles—have succeeded in converting a dozen of them ; and a sort of martyrdom is in store for the luckless Hebrew at Jerusalem who shall secede from his faith. Their old community spurn them with horror ; and I heard of the case of one unfortunate man, whose wife, in spite of her husband's change of creed, being resolved, like a true woman, to cleave to him, was spirited away from him in his absence ; was kept in privacy in the city, in spite of all exertions of the mission, of the Consul and the Bishop, and the Chaplains and the Beadles ; was passed away from Jerusalem to Beyrout, and thence to Constantinople ; and from Constantinople was whisked off into the Russian territories, where she still pines after her husband. May that unhappy convert find consolation away from her. I could not help thinking as my informant, an excellent and accomplished gentleman of the mission, told me the story, that the Jews had done only what the Christians do under the same circumstances. The woman was the daughter of a most learned

Rabbi, as I gathered. Suppose a daughter of the Rabbi of Exeter, or Canterbury, were to marry a man who turned Jew, would not her Right Reverend Father be justified in taking her out of the power of a person likely to hurl her soul to perdition ? Those poor converts should surely be sent away to England out of the way of persecution. We could not but feel a pity for them, as they sat there on their benches in the church conspicuous ; and thought of the scorn and contumely which attended them without, as they passed in their European dresses and shaven beards, among their grisly, scowling, long-robed countrymen.

As elsewhere in the towns I have seen, the Ghetto of Jerusalem is pre-eminent in filth. The people are gathered round about the dung-gate of the city. Of a Friday you may hear their wailings and lamentations for the lost glories of their city. I think the Valley of Jehoshaphat is the most ghastly sight I have seen in the world. From all quarters they come hither to bury their dead. When his time is come yonder hoary old miser, with whom we made our voyage, will lay his carcase to rest here. To do that and to claw together money, has been the purpose of that strange, long life.

We brought with us one of the gentlemen of the mission, a Hebrew convert, the Rev. Mr. E——— ; and lest I should be supposed to speak with disrespect above, of any of the converts of the Hebrew faith, let me mention this gentleman as the only one whom I had the fortune to meet on terms of intimacy. I never saw a man whose outward conduct was more touching, whose sincerity was more evident, and whose religious feeling seemed more deep, real, and reasonable.

Only a few feet, of the walls of the Anglican Church of Jerusalem, rise up from their foundations, on a picturesque open spot, in front of the Bethlehem Gate. The English Bishop has his church hard by : and near it is the house where the Christians of our denomination assemble and worship.

There seem to be polyglot services here. I saw books of prayer, or Scripture, in Hebrew, Greek, and German : in which latter language Dr. Alexander preaches every Sunday. A gentleman, who sat near me at church, used all these books indifferently ; reading the first lesson from the Hebrew book, and the second from the Greek. Here we all assembled on the Sunday after our arrival : it was affecting to hear the music and language of our country sounding in this distant place ; to have the decent and manly ceremonial of our service ; the prayers delivered in that noble language. Even that stout anti-prelatist, the American

Consul, who has left his house and fortune in America in order to witness the coming of the Millennium, who believes it to be so near that he has brought a dove with him from his native land (which bird he solemnly informed us was to survive the expected Advent), was affected by the good old words and service. He swayed about and moaned in his place at various passages ; during the sermon he gave especial marks of sympathy and approbation. I never heard the service more excellently and impressively read than by the Bishop's Chaplain, Mr. Veitch. But it was the music that was most touching, I thought,—the sweet old songs of home.

There was a considerable company assembled : near a hundred people, I should think. Our party made a large addition to the usual congregation. The Bishop's family is proverbially numerous : the Consul, and the gentlemen of the mission, have wives, and children, and English establishments. These, and the strangers, occupied places down the room, to the right and left of the desk and communion-table. The converts, and the members of the college, in rather a scanty number, faced the officiating clergyman ; before whom the silver maces of the Janissaries were set up, as they set up the Beadles' maces in England.

I made many walks round the city to Olivet and Bethany, to the tombs of the kings, and the fountains sacred in story. These are green and fresh, but all the rest of the landscape seemed to me to be *frightful*. Parched mountains, with a grey bleak olive-tree trembling here and there ; savage ravines and valleys, paved with tombstones—a landscape unspeakably ghastly and desolate, meet the eye wherever you wander round about the city. The place seems quite adapted to the events which are recorded in the Hebrew histories. It and they, as it seems to me, can never be regarded without terror. Fear and blood, crime and punishment, follow from page to page in frightful succession. There is not a spot at which you look, but some violent deed has been done there : some massacre has been committed, some victim has been murdered, some idol has been worshipped with bloody and dreadful rites. Not far from hence is the place where the Jewish conqueror fought for the possession of Jerusalem. "The sun stood still, and hasted not to go down about a whole day ;" so that the Jews might have daylight to destroy the Amorites, whose iniquities were full, and whose land they were about to occupy. The fugitive heathen king, and his allies, were discovered in their hiding-place, and hanged : 'and the children of Judah smote Jerusalem with the edge of the sword, and set the city on fire ; and they left none remaining, but utterly destroyed all that breathed.'

I went out at the Zion gate, and looked at the so-called tomb of David. I had been reading all the morning in the Psalms, and his history in Samuel and Kings. *'Bring thou down Shimei's hoar head to the grave with blood,'* are the last words of the dying monarch as recorded by the history. What they call the tomb, is now in a crumbling old mosque ; from which Jew and Christian are excluded alike. As I saw it, blazing in the sunshine, with the purple sky behind it, the glare only served to mark the surrounding desolation more clearly. The lonely walls and towers of the city rose hard by. Dreary mountains, and declivities of naked stones, were round about : they are burrowed with holes in which Christian hermits lived and died. You see one green place far down in the valley : it is called En Rogel. Adonijah feasted there, who was killed by his brother Solomon, for asking for Abishag for wife. The Valley of Hinnom skirts the hill : the dismal ravine was a fruitful garden once. Ahaz, and the idolatrous kings, sacrificed to idols under the green trees there, and 'caused their children to pass through the fire.' On the mountain opposite Solomon, with the thousand women of his harem, worshipped the gods of all their nations, 'Ashtoreth,' and 'Milcom, and Molech, the abomination of the Ammonites.' An enormous charnel-house stands on the hill where the bodies of dead pilgrims used to be thrown ; and common belief has fixed upon this spot as the Aceldama, which Judas purchased with the price of his treason. Thus you go on from one gloomy place to another, each seared with its bloody tradition. Yonder is the Temple, and you think of Titus's soldiery storming its flaming porches, and entering the city, in the savage defence of which two million human souls perished. It was on Mount Zion that Godfrey and Tancred had their camp : when the Crusaders entered the mosque, they rode knee-deep in the blood of its defenders, and of the women and children, who had fled thither for refuge : it was the victory of Joshua over again. Then, after three days of butchery, they purified the desecrated mosque and went to prayer. In the centre of this history of crime, rises up the Great Murder of all. . . .

I need say no more about this gloomy landscape. After a man has seen it once, he never forgets it—the recollection of it seems to me to follow him like a remorse, as it were to implicate him in the awful deed which was done there. Oh ! with what unspeakable shame and terror should one think of that crime, and prostrate himself before the image of that Divine Blessed Sufferer !

Of course the first visit of the traveller is to the famous Church of the Sepulchre.

In the archway, leading from the street to the court and church, there is a little bazaar of Bethlehemites, who must interfere considerably with the commerce of the Latin fathers. These men bawl to you from their stalls, and hold up for your purchase their devotional baubles,—bushels of rosaries and scented beads, and carved mother-of-pearl shells, and rude stone salt-cellars and figures. Now that inns are established,—envoys of these pedlers attend them on the arrival of strangers, squat all day on the terraces before your door, and patiently entreat you to buy of their goods. Some worthies there are who drive a good trade by tattooing pilgrims with the five crosses, the arms of Jerusalem ; under which the name of the city is punctured in Hebrew, with the auspicious year of the Hadgi's visit. Several of our fellow-travellers submitted to this queer operation, and will carry, to their grave, this relic of their journey. Some of them had engaged a servant, a man, at Beyrout, who had served as a lad on board an English ship in the Mediterranean. Above his tattooage of the five crosses, the fellow had a picture of two hearts united, and the pathetic motto, 'Betsy, my dear.' He had parted with Betsy, my dear, five years before, at Malta. He had known a little English there, but had forgotten it. Betsy, my dear, was forgotten too. Only her name remained engraved with a vain simulacrum of constancy on the faithless rogue's skin : on which was now printed another token of equally effectual devotion. The beads and the tattooing, however, seem essential ceremonies attendant on the Christian pilgrim's visit ; for many hundreds of years, doubtless, the palmers have carried off with them these simple reminiscences of the sacred city. That symbol has been engraven upon the arms of how many Princes, Knights, and Crusaders ! Don't you see a moral as applicable to them as to the swindling Beyrout horse-boy ? I have brought you back that cheap and wholesome apologue, in lieu of any of the Bethlehemite shells and beads.

After passing through the porch of the pedlers, you come to the courtyard in front of the noble old towers of the Church of the Sepulchre, with pointed arches and gothic traceries, rude, but rich and picturesque in design. Here crowds are waiting in the sun, until it shall please the Turkish guardians of the church-door to open. A swarm of beggars sit here permanently : old tattered hags with long veils, ragged children, blind old bearded beggars, who raise up a chorus of prayers for money, holding out their wooden bowls, or clattering with their sticks on the stones, or pulling your coat-skirts, and moaning and whining : yonder sit a group of coal-black Coptish pilgrims, with robes and turbans of dark blue, fumbling their perpetual beads. A party of Arab Christians have come up from their tents or villages: the men half-naked, looking as if they were beggars, or banditti, upon occasion; the women have flung their head-cloths back, and are looking at the strangers under their tattooed eyebrows. As for the strangers, there is no need to describe *them*; that figure of the Englishman, with his hands in his pockets, has been seen all the world over: staring down the crater of Vesuvius, or into a

Hottentot kraal; or at a pyramid, or a Parisian coffee-house, or an Esquimaux hut, with the same insolent calmness of demeanour. When the gates of the church are open, he elbows in among the first, and flings a few scornful piastres to the Turkish door-keeper; and gazes round easily at the place, in which people of every other nation in the world are in tears, or in rapture, or wonder. He has never seen the place until now, and looks as indifferent as the Turkish guardian who sits in the doorway, and swears at the people as they pour in.

Indeed, I believe, it is impossible for us to comprehend the source and nature of the Roman Catholic devotion. I once went into a church at Rome at the request of a Catholic friend, who described the interior to be so beautiful and glorious, that he thought (he said) it must be like heaven itself. I found walls hung with cheap stripes of pink and white calico, altars covered with artificial flowers, a number of wax candles, and plenty of gilt paper ornaments. The place seemed to me like a shabby theatre; and here was my friend on his knees at my side, plunged in a rapture of wonder and devotion.

I could get no better impression out of this the most famous Church in the world. The deceits are too open and flagrant; the inconsistencies and contrivances too monstrous. It is hard even to sympathise with persons who receive them as genuine; and though (as I know and saw in the case of my friend at Rome) the believer's life may be passed in the purest exercise of faith and charity, it is difficult even to give him credit for honesty, so bare-faced seem the impostures which he professes to believe and reverence. It costs one no small effort even to admit the possibility of a Catholic's credulity : to share in his rapture and devotion is still further out of your power ; and I could get from this Church no other emotions but those of shame and pain.

The Legends with which the Greeks and Latins have garnished the spot, have no more sacredness for you than the hideous, unreal, barbaric pictures and ornaments which they have lavished on it. Look at the fervour with which pilgrims kiss and weep over a tawdry Gothic painting, scarcely better fashioned than an idol in a South Sea Morai. The histories, which they are called upon to reverence, are of the same period and order,—savage Gothic carica-tures. In either, a saint appears in the costume of the middle ages, and is made to accommodate himself to the fashion of the tenth century.

The different churches battle for the possession of the various relics. The Greeks show you the Tomb of Melchisedec, while the Armenians possess the Chapel of the Penitent Thief; the poor Copts (with their little cabin of a chapel) can yet boast of possess-ing the thicket in which Abraham caught the Ram, which was to serve as the vicar of Isaac ; the Latins point out the Pillar to which the Lord was bound. The place of the Invention of the Sacred Cross, the Fissure in the Rock of Golgotha, the Tomb of Adam himself—are all here within a few yards' space. You mount a few steps, and are told it is Calvary upon which you stand. All this in the midst of flaring candles, reeking incense, savage pictures of Scripture story, or portraits of kings who have been benefactors to the various chapels ; a din and clatter of strange people,—these weeping, bowing, kissing,—those utterly indifferent ; and the priests clad in outlandish robes, snuffling and chanting incompre-hensible litanies, robing, disrobing, lighting up candles or ex-

tinguishing them, advancing, retreating, bowing with all sorts of
unfamiliar genuflexions. Had it pleased the inventors of the
Sepulchre topography to have fixed on fifty more spots of ground,
as the places of the events of the sacred story, the pilgrim would
have believed just as now. The priest's authority has so mastered
his faith, that it accommodates itself to any demand upon it ; and
the English stranger looks on the scene, for the first time, with a
feeling of scorn, bewilderment, and shame, at that grovelling
credulity, those strange rites and ceremonies, that almost confessed
imposture.

Jarred and distracted by these, the Church of the Holy
Sepulchre, for some time, seems to an Englishman the least sacred
spot about Jerusalem. It is the lies, and the legends, and the
priests, and their quarrels, and their ceremonies, which keep the
Holy Place out of sight. A man has not leisure to view it, for the
brawling of the guardians of the spot. The Roman conquerors,
they say, raised up a statue of Venus in this sacred place, intending to destroy all memory of it. I don't think the heathen was
as criminal as the Christian is now. To deny and disbelieve, is
not so bad as to make belief a ground to cheat upon. The liar
Ananias perished for that ; and yet out of these gates, where angels
may have kept watch—out of the tomb of Christ—Christian
priests issue with a lie in their hands. What a place to choose
for imposture, good God ! to sully, with brutal struggles for self-
aggrandisement, or shameful schemes of gain !

The situation of the Tomb (into which, be it authentic or not,
no man can enter without a shock of breathless fear, and deep and
awful self-humiliation) must have struck all travellers. It stands
in the centre of the arched rotunda, which is common to all deno-
minations, and from which branch off the various chapels belonging
to each particular sect. In the Coptic Chapel I saw one coal-black
Copt, in blue robes, cowering in the little cabin, surrounded by
dingy lamps, barbarous pictures, and cheap, faded trumpery. In
the Latin Church, there was no service going on, only two fathers
dusting the mouldy gewgaws along the brown walls, and laughing
to one another. The gorgeous church of the Fire impostors, hard
by, was always more fully attended ; as was that of their wealthy
neighbours, the Armenians. These three main sects hate each
other : their quarrels are interminable : each bribes and intrigues
with the heathen lords of the soil, to the prejudice of his neighbour.
Now it is the Latins who interfere, and allow the common church
to go to ruin, because the Greeks purpose to roof it : now the
Greeks demolish a monastery on Mount Olivet, and leave the ground
to the Turks, rather than allow the Armenians to possess it. On

another occasion, the Greeks having mended the Armenian steps, which led to the (so-called) Cave of the Nativity at Bethlehem, the latter asked for permission to destroy the work of the Greeks, and did so.   And so round this sacred spot, the centre of Christendom, the representatives of the three great sects worship under one roof, and hate each other !

Above the Tomb of the Saviour, the cupola *is open*, and you see the blue sky overhead.   Which of the builders was it that had the grace to leave that under the high protection of heaven, and not confine it under the mouldering old domes and roofs, which cover so much selfishness, and uncharitableness, and imposture !

We went to Bethlehem, too ; and saw the apocryphal wonders there.

Five miles' ride brings you from Jerusalem to it, over naked wavy hills ; the aspect of which, however, grows more cheerful as you approach the famous village.   We passed the Convent of Mar Elyas on the road, walled and barred like a fort.   In spite of its strength, however, it has more than once been stormed by the Arabs, and the luckless fathers within put to death.   Hard by was Rebecca's Well : a dead body was lying there, and crowds of male and female mourners dancing and howling round it.   Now and then a little troop of savage scowling horsemen—a shepherd driving his black sheep, his gun over his shoulder—a troop of camels —or of women, with long blue robes and white veils, bearing pitchers, and staring at the strangers with their great solemn eyes —or a company of labourers, with their donkeys, bearing grain or grapes to the city,—met us and enlivened the little ride.   It was a busy and cheerful scene.   The Church of the Nativity, with the adjoining Convents, forms a vast and noble Christian structure. A party of travellers were going to the Jordan that day, and scores of their followers,—of the robbing Arabs, who profess to protect them, (magnificent figures some of them, with flowing haicks and turbans, with long guns and scimitars, and wretched horses, covered with gaudy trappings,) were standing on the broad pavement before the little Convent gate.   It was such a scene as Cattermole might paint.   Knights and Crusaders may have witnessed a similar one. You could fancy them issuing out of the narrow little portal, and so greeted by the swarms of swarthy clamorous women and merchants and children.

The scene within the building was of the same Gothic character.   We were entertained by the Superior of the Greek Convent, in a fine refectory, with ceremonies and hospitalities that pilgrims of the middle ages might have witnessed.   We were

shown over the magnificent Barbaric Church, visited of course
the Grotto where the Blessed Nativity is said to have taken place,
and the rest of the idols set up for worship by the clumsy legend.
When the visit was concluded, the party going to the Dead Sea
filed off with their armed attendants; each individual traveller
making as brave a show as he could, and personally accoutred
with warlike swords and pistols. The picturesque crowds, and
the Arabs and the horsemen, in the sunshine; the noble old
convent, and the grey-bearded priests, with their feast; and the
church, and its pictures, and columns, and incense; the wide
brown hills spreading round the village; with the accidents of
the road,—flocks and shepherds, wells, and funerals, and camel-
trains, have left on my mind a brilliant, romantic, and cheerful
picture. But you, dear M——, without visiting the place, have
imagined one far finer; and Bethlehem, where the Holy Child
was born, and the angels sang, 'Glory to God in the highest,
and peace and goodwill on earth,' is the most sacred and beautiful
spot in the earth to you.

By far the most comfortable quarters in Jerusalem, are those
of the Armenians, in their convent of St. James. Wherever we
have been, these Eastern quakers look grave, and jolly, and sleek.
Their convent at Mount Zion is big enough to contain two or
three thousand of their faithful; and their church is ornamented
by the most rich and hideous gifts ever devised by uncouth piety.
Instead of a bell, the fat monks of the convent beat huge noises
on a board, and drub the faithful in to prayers. I never saw
men more lazy and rosy than these reverend fathers, kneeling in
their comfortable matted church, or sitting in easy devotion.
Pictures, images, gilding, tinsel, wax candles, twinkle all over the
place; and ten thousand ostriches' eggs (or any lesser number
you may allot) dangle from the vaulted ceiling. There were
great numbers of people at worship in this gorgeous church; they
went on their knees, kissing the walls with much fervour, and
paying reverence to the most precious relic of the convent,—the
chair of St. James, their Patron, the first Bishop of Jerusalem.

The chair pointed out with greatest pride in the church of the
Latin Convent, is that shabby red damask one appropriated to
the French Consul,—the representative of the king of that
nation,—and the protection which it has from time immemorial
accorded to the Christians of the Latin rite in Syria. All
French writers and travellers speak of this protection with
delightful complacency. Consult the French books of travel on
the subject, and any Frenchman whom you may meet; he says,

La France, Monsieur, de tous les temps protège les Chrétiens d'Orient; and the little fellow looks round the church with a sweep of the arm, and protects it accordingly. It is *bon ton* for them to go in processions; and you see them on such errands, marching with long candles, as gravely as may be. But I have never been able to edify myself with their devotion : and the religious outpourings of Lamartine and Chateaubriand, which we have all been reading *à propos* of the journey we are to make, have inspired me with an emotion anything but respectful. *Voyez comme M. de Chateaubriand prie Dieu,* the Viscount's eloquence seems always to say. There is a sanctified grimace about the little French pilgrim, which it is very difficult to contemplate gravely.

The pictures, images, and ornaments of the principal Latin Convent, are quite mean and poor, compared to the wealth of the Armenians. The convent is spacious, but squalid. Many hopping and crawling plagues are said to attack the skins of pilgrims who sleep there. It is laid out in courts and galleries, the mouldy doors of which are decorated with twopenny pictures of favourite saints and martyrs ; and so great is the shabbiness and laziness, that you might fancy yourself in a convent in Italy. Brown-clad fathers, dirty, bearded, and sallow, go gliding about the corridors. The relic manufactory, before mentioned, carries on a considerable business ; and dispatches bales of shells, crosses, and beads, to believers in Europe. These constitute the chief revenue of the convent now. *La France* is no longer the most Christian kingdom, and her protection of the Latins is not good for much since Charles X. was expelled ; and Spain, which used likewise to be generous on occasions (the gifts, arms, candlesticks, baldaquins, of the Spanish Sovereigns, figure pretty frequently in the various Latin chapels), has been stingy since the late disturbances, the spoliation of the clergy, etc. After we had been taken to see the humble curiosities of the place, the Prior treated us in his wooden parlour with little glasses of pink rosolio, brought with many bows and genuflexions by his reverence, the convent butler.

After this community of holy men, the most important perhaps is the American Convent, a Protestant congregation of Independents chiefly, who deliver tracts, propose to make converts, have meetings of their own, and also swell the little congregation that attends the Anglican service. I have mentioned our fellow-traveller, the Consul-General for Syria of the United States. He was a tradesman, who had made a considerable fortune, and lived at a country house in comfortable retirement. But his opinion is, that the prophecies of Scripture are about to be accomplished ;

that the day of the return of the Jews is at hand, and the glorification of the restored Jerusalem. He is to witness this; he and a favourite dove with which he travels; and he forsook home and comfortable country house, in order to make this journey. He has no other knowledge of Syria but what he derives from the prophecy; and this (as he takes the office gratis) has been considered a sufficient reason for his appointment by the United States Government. As soon as he arrived, he sent and demanded an interview with the Pasha; explained to him his interpretation of the Apocalypse, in which he has discovered that the Five Powers and America are about to intervene in Syrian affairs, and the infallible return of the Jews to Palestine. The news must have astonished the Lieutenant of the Sublime Porte; and since the days of the Kingdom of Munster, under his Anabaptist Majesty, John of Leyden, I doubt whether any Government has received or appointed so queer an ambassador. The kind, worthy, simple man, took me to his temporary Consulate House at the American Missionary Establishment; and, under pretence of treating me to white wine, expounded his ideas; talked of futurity as he would about an article in the *Times;* and had no more doubt of seeing a divine kingdom established in Jerusalem, than you that there will be a levée next spring at St. James's. The little room in which we sat, was padded with Missionary tracts, but I heard of scarce any converts—not more than are made by our own Episcopal establishment.

But if the latter's religious victories are small, and very few people are induced by the American tracts, and the English preaching and catechising, to forsake their own manner of worshipping the Divine Being, in order to follow ours; yet surely our religious colony of men and women can't fail to do good, by the sheer force of good example, pure life, and kind offices. The ladies of the mission have numbers of clients, of all persuasions, in the town, to whom they extend their charities. Each of their houses is a model of neatness, and a dispensary of gentle kindnesses; and the ecclesiastics have formed a modest centre of civilisation in the place. A dreary joke was made in the House of Commons about Bishop Alexander and the Bishopess his lady, and the Bishoplings his numerous children, who were said to have scandalised the people of Jerusalem. That sneer evidently came from the Latins and Greeks; for what could the Jews and Turks care because an English clergyman had a wife and children as their own priests have? There was no sort of ill-will exhibited towards them, as far as I could learn; and I saw the Bishop's children riding about the town as safely as they could about

Hyde Park. All Europeans, indeed, seemed to me to be received with forbearance, and almost courtesy, within the walls. As I was going about making sketches, the people would look on very good-humouredly, without offering the least interruption; nay,

two or three were quite ready to stand still for such a humble portrait as my pencil could make of them; and the sketch done, it was passed from one person to another, each making his comments, and signifying a very polite approval. Here are a pair of them, — Fath Allah and Ameenut Daoodee, his father, horse-dealers by trade, who came and sat with us at the Inn, and smoked pipes (the sun being down), while the original of the

above masterpiece was made. With the Arabs outside the walls, however, and the freshly arriving country people, this politeness was not so much exhibited. There was a certain tattooed girl, with black eyes, and huge silver earrings, and a chin delicately picked out with blue, who formed one of a group of women outside the great convent, whose likeness I longed to carry off;—there was a woman, with a little child, with wondering eyes, drawing water at the Pool of Siloam, in such an attitude and dress as Rebecca may have had when Isaac's lieutenant asked her for drink:—both of these parties standing still for half a minute, at the next cried out for backsheesh; and not content with the five piastres which I gave them individually, screamed out for more, and summoned their friends, who screamed out backsheesh too. I was pursued into the convent by a dozen howling women calling for pay, barring the door against them, to the astonishment of the worthy papa who kept it; and at Miriam's Well the women were joined by a man, with a large stick, who backed their petition. But him we could afford to laugh at, for we were two, and had sticks likewise.

In the village of Siloam I would not recommend the artist to loiter. A colony of ruffians inhabit the dismal place, who have guns as well as sticks at need. Their dogs howl after the strangers as they pass through; and over the parapets of their walls you are saluted by the scowls of a villainous set of countenances, that it is not good to see with one pair of eyes. They shot a man at mid-day at a few hundred yards from the gates while we were at Jerusalem, and no notice was taken of the murder. Hordes of Arab robbers infest the neighbourhood of the city, with the Sheikhs of whom travellers make terms when minded to pursue their journey. I never could understand why the walls stopped these warriors if they had a mind to plunder the city, for there are but a hundred and fifty men in the garrison to man the long lonely lines of defence.

I have seen only in Titian's pictures those magnificent purple shadows, in which the hills round about lay, as the dawn rose faintly behind them; and we looked at Olivet for the last time, from our terrace, where we were awaiting the arrival of the horses that were to carry us to Jaffa. A yellow moon was still blazing in the midst of countless brilliant stars overhead; the nakedness and misery of the surrounding city were hidden in that beautiful rosy atmosphere of mingling night and dawn. The city never looked so noble; the mosques, domes, and minarets rising up into the calm star-lit sky.

By the gate of Bethlehem there stands one palm-tree, and a house with three domes. Put these and the huge old gothic gate as a background dark against the yellowing eastern sky: the foreground is a deep grey:—as you look into it dark forms of horsemen come out of the twilight: now there came lanterns, more horsemen, a litter with mules, a crowd of Arab horseboys and dealers accompanying their beasts to the gate; all the members of our party come up by twos and threes; and, at last, the great gate opens just before sunrise, and we get into the grey plains.

O! the luxury of an English saddle! An English servant of one of the gentlemen of the mission procured it for me, on the back of a little mare, which (as I am a light weight) did not turn a hair in the course of the day's march—and after we got quit of the ugly, stony, clattering, mountainous Abou Gosh district, into the fair undulating plain, which stretches to Ramleh—carried me into the town at a pleasant hand-gallop. A negro, of preternatural ugliness, in a yellow gown, with a crimson handkerchief streaming over his head, digging his shovel spurs into the lean animal he rode, and driving three others before—swaying backwards and forwards on his horse, now embracing his ears, and now almost under his belly, screaming yallah with the most frightful shrieks, and singing country songs—galloped along ahead of me. I acquired one of his poems pretty well, and could imitate his shriek accurately ; but I shall not have the pleasure of singing it to you in England. I had forgotten the delightful dissonance two days after, both the negro's and that of a real Arab minstrel, a donkey-driver accompanying our baggage, who sang and grinned with the most amusing good-humour.

We halted, in the middle of the day, in a little wood of olive-trees, which forms almost the only shelter between Jaffa and Jerusalem, except that afforded by the orchards in the odious village of Abou Gosh, through which we went at a double quick pace. Under the olives, or up in the branches, some of our friends took a siesta. I have a sketch of four of them so employed. Two of them were dead within a month of the fatal Syrian fever. But we did not know how near fate was to us then. Fires were lighted, and fowls and eggs divided, and tea and coffee served round in tin panikins, and here we lighted pipes and smoked and laughed at our ease. I believe everybody was happy to be out of Jerusalem. The impression I have of it now is of ten days passed in a fever.

We all found quarters in the Greek convent, at Ramleh, where the monks served us a supper on a terrace, in a pleasant sunset ; a beautiful and cheerful landscape, stretching around ; the land in graceful undulations, the towers and mosques rosy in the sunset, with no lack of verdure, especially of graceful palms. Jaffa was nine miles off. As we rode, all the morning we had been accompanied by the smoke of our steamer, twenty miles off at sea.

The convent is a huge caravanserai ; only three or four monks dwell in it, the ghostly hotel-keepers of the place. The horses were tied up and fed in the courtyard, into which we rode ; above were the living-rooms, where there is accommodation, not only for an unlimited number of pilgrims, but for a vast and innumerable host of hopping and crawling things, who usually persist in partaking of the traveller's bed. Let all thin-skinned travellers in the east be warned on no account to travel without the admirable invention described in Mr. Fellowes' book ; nay possibly invented by that enterprising and learned traveller. You make a sack, of calico or linen, big enough for the body, appended to which is a closed chimney of muslin, stretched out by cane hoops, and fastened up to a beam, or against the wall. You keep a sharp eye to look out that no flea or bug is on the look-out, and when assured of this, you pop into the bag, tightly closing the orifice after you. This admirable bug-disappointer I tried at Ramleh, and had the only undisturbed night's rest I enjoyed in the East. To be sure it was a short night, for our party were stirring at one o'clock, and those who got up insisted on talking and keeping awake those who inclined to sleep. But I shall never forget the terror inspired in my mind, being shut up in the bug-disappointer, when a facetious lay-brother of the convent fell upon me and began *tickling* me. I never had the courage again to try the anti-flea contrivance, preferring the friskiness of those animals to the sports of such a greasy grinning wag as my friend at Ramleh.

In the morning, and long before sunrise, our little caravan was in marching order again. We went out with lanterns, and shouts of yallah through the narrow streets, and issued into the plain, where, though there was no moon, there were blazing stars shining steadily overhead. They become friends to a man who travels, especially under the clear eastern sky ; whence they look down as if protecting you, solemn, yellow, and refulgent. They seem *nearer* to you than in Europe ; larger and more awful. So we rode on till the dawn rose, and Jaffa came in view. The friendly ship was lying out in waiting for us ; the horses were given up to their owners ; and in the midst of a crowd of naked beggars, and a perfect storm of curses and yells for backsheesh, our party got into their boats, and to the ship, where we were welcomed by the very best Captain that ever sailed upon this maritime globe, namely, Captain Samuel Lewis, of the Peninsular and Oriental Company's Service.

CHAPTER XIV

FROM JAFFA TO ALEXANDRIA

[From the Provider's Log-Book.]

BILL OF FARE, OCTOBER 12TH.

> Mulligatawny Soup.
> Salt Fish and Egg Sauce.
> Roast Haunch of Mutton.
> Boiled Shoulder and Onion Sauce.
> Boiled Beef.
> Roast Fowls.
> Pillow ditto.
> Ham.
> Haricot Mutton.
> Curry and Rice.
>
> Cabbage.
> French Beans.
> Boiled Potatoes.
> Baked ditto.
>
> Damson Tart.
> Currant ditto.
> Rice Puddings.
> Currant Fritters.

WE were just at the port's mouth—and could see the towers and buildings of Alexandria rising purple against the sunset, when the report of a gun came booming over the calm golden water; and we heard, with much mortification, that we had no chance of getting pratique that night. Already the ungrateful passengers had begun to tire of the ship,—though in our absence in Syria it had been carefully cleansed and purified; though it was cleared of the swarming Jews, who had infected the decks all the way from Constantinople; and though we had been feasting and carousing in the manner described above.

But very early next morning we bore into the harbour, busy with a great quantity of craft. We passed huge black hulks of mouldering men-of-war, from the sterns of which trailed the dirty red flag, with the star and crescent; boats, manned with red-capped seamen, and captains and steersmen in beards and tarbooshes, passed continually among these old hulks, the rowers bending to their oars, so that, at each stroke, they disappeared bodily in the boat. Besides these, there was a large fleet of country ships, and stars, and stripes, and tricolors, and union jacks; and many active steamers, of the French and English companies, shooting in and out of the harbour, or moored in the briny waters. The ship of *our* company, the *Oriental*, lay there —a palace upon the brine, and some of the Pasha's steam-vessels likewise, looking very like Christian boats; but it was queer to look at some unintelligible Turkish flourish painted on the stern, and the long-tailed Arabian hieroglyphics gilt on the paddle-boxes. Our dear friend and comrade of Beyrout (if we may be permitted to call her so), H.M.S. *Trump*, was in the harbour; and the captain of that gallant ship, coming to greet us, drove some of us on shore in his gig.

I had been preparing myself overnight, by the help of a cigar and a moonlight contemplation on deck, for sensations on landing in Egypt. I was ready to yield myself up with solemnity to the mystic grandeur of the scene of initiation. Pompey's Pillar must stand like a mountain, in a yellow plain, surrounded by a grove of obelisks, as tall as palm-trees. Placid sphinxes, brooding o'er the Nile—mighty Memnonian countenances calm—had revealed Egypt to me in a sonnet of Tennyson's, and I was ready to gaze on it with pyramidal wonder and hieroglyphic awe.

The landing quay at Alexandria is like the dockyard quay at Portsmouth: with a few score of brown faces scattered among the population. There are slop-sellers, dealers in marine-stores, bottled-porter shops, seamen lolling about; flies and cabs are plying for hire: and a yelling chorus of donkey-boys, shrieking, 'Ride, sir! —donkey, sir!—I say, sir!' in excellent English, dispel all romantic notions. The placid sphinxes, brooding o'er the Nile, disappeared with that shriek of the donkey-boys. You might be as well impressed with Wapping, as with your first step on Egyptian soil.

The riding of a donkey is, after all, not a dignified occupation. A man resists the offer first, somehow as an indignity. How is that poor little, red-saddled, long-eared creature to carry you? Is there to be one for you and another for your legs? Natives and Europeans, of all sizes, passed by, it is true, mounted upon the same contrivance. I waited until I got into a very private spot, where nobody could see me, and then ascended—why not say descended, at once—on the poor little animal. Instead of being crushed at once, as perhaps the rider expected, it darted forward, quite briskly and cheerfully, at six or seven miles an hour; requiring no spur or admonitive to haste, except the shrieking of the little Egyptian Jamin, who ran along by asinus's side.

The character of the houses, by which you pass, is scarcely Eastern at all. The streets are busy with a motley population of Jews and Armenians, slave-driving-looking Europeans, large-breeched Greeks, and well-shaven buxom merchants, looking as trim and fat as those on the Bourse or on 'Change; only, among the natives, the stranger can't fail to remark (as the Caliph did of the Calendars, in the *Arabian Nights*), that so many of them *have only one eye*. It is the horrid ophthalmia which has played such frightful ravages with them. You see children sitting in the doorways, their eyes completely closed up with the green sickening sore, and the flies feeding on them. Five or six minutes of the donkey-ride brings you to the Frank quarter, and the handsome broad street (like a street of Marseilles), where the principal hotels and merchants' houses are to be found, and where the consuls have their houses, and hoist their flags. The palace of the French Consul-General makes the grandest show in the street, and presents a great contrast to the humble abode of the English representative, who protects his fellow-countrymen from a second floor.

But that Alexandrian two-pair-front of a Consulate, was more welcome and cheering than a palace to most of us. For there lay certain letters, with post-marks of *Home* upon them; and kindly tidings, the first heard for two months:—though we had seen so many men and cities since, that Cornhill seemed to be a year off, at least, with certain persons dwelling (more or less) in that vicinity. I saw a young Oxford man seize his dispatches, and slink off with several letters, written in a tight, neat hand, and sedulously crossed; which any man could see, without looking farther, were the handiwork of Mary Ann, to whom he is attached. The lawyer received a bundle from his chambers, in which his clerk eased his soul regarding the state of Snooks *v.* Rodgers, Smith *ats* Tomkins, etc. The statesman had a packet of thick envelopes, decorated with that profusion of sealing-wax, in which official recklessness lavishes the resources of the country: and your humble servant got just one little, modest letter, containing another, written in pencil characters, varying in size between one and two inches; but how much pleasanter to read than my lord's dispatch, or the clerk's account of Smith *ats* Tomkins,—yes, even than the Mary Ann correspondence! . . . Yes, my dear madam, you will understand me, when I say, that it was from little Polly at home, with some confidential news about a cat, and the last report of her new doll.

It is worth while to have made the journey for this pleasure: to have walked the deck on long nights, and have thought of home. You have no leisure to do so in the city. You don't see the

heavens shine above you so purely there, or the stars so clearly.—
How, after the perusal of the above documents, we enjoyed a file
of the admirable *Galignani;* and what O'Connell was doing; and
the twelve last new victories of the French in Algeria; and, above
all, six or seven numbers of *Punch!* There might have been an
avenue of Pompey's Pillars within reach, and a live sphinx sporting on the banks of the Mahmoodieh canal, and we would not
have stirred to see them, until *Punch* had had his interview, and
Galignani was dismissed.

The curiosities of Alexandria are few, and easily seen.   We
went into the bazaars, which have a much more Eastern look than
the European quarter, with its Anglo-Gallic-Italian inhabitants,
and Babel-like civilisation.   Here and there a large hotel, clumsy
and whitewashed, with Oriental trellised windows, and a couple of
slouching sentinels at the doors, in the ugliest composite uniform
that ever was seen, was pointed out as the residence of some great
officer of the Pasha's court, or of one of the numerous children of
the Egyptian Solomon.   His Highness was in his own palace,
and was consequently not visible.   He was in deep grief, and
strict retirement.   It was at this time that the European newspapers announced that he was about to resign his empire; but the
quidnuncs of Alexandria hinted that a love-affair, in which the old
potentate had engaged with senile extravagance, and the effects
of a potion of hachich, or some deleterious drug, with which he
was in the habit of intoxicating himself, had brought on that
languor and desperate weariness of life and governing, into which
the venerable Prince was plunged.   Before three days were over,
however, the fit had left him, and he determined to live and reign
a little longer.   A very few days afterwards several of our party
were presented to him at Cairo, and found the great Egyptian
ruler perfectly convalescent.

This, and the Opera, and the quarrels of the two *prime donne*,
and the beauty of one of them, formed the chief subject of conversation; and I had these important news in the shop of a
certain barber in the town, who conveyed it in a language composed of French, Spanish, and Italian, and with a volubility quite
worthy of a barber of *Gil Blas*.

Then we went to see the famous obelisk presented by Mehemet
Ali to the British Government, who have not shown a particular
alacrity to accept this ponderous present.   The huge shaft lies on
the ground prostrate, and desecrated by all sorts of abominations.
Children were sprawling about, attracted by the dirt there.
Arabs, negroes, and donkey-boys, were passing, quite indifferent, by
the fallen monster of a stone,—as indifferent as the British Govern-

ment, who don't care for recording the glorious termination of
their Egyptian campaign of 1801. If our country takes the compliment so coolly, surely it would be disloyal upon our parts to be
more enthusiastic. I wish they would offer the Trafalgar Square
Pillar to the Egyptians ; and that both of the huge, ugly monsters,
were lying in the dirt there, side by side.

Pompey's Pillar is by no means so big as the Charing Cross
trophy. This venerable column has not escaped ill-treatment
either. Numberless ship's companies, travelling cockneys, etc.,
have affixed their rude marks upon it. Some daring ruffian even
painted the name of 'Warren's blacking' upon it, effacing other
inscriptions,—one, Wilkinson says, of 'the second Psammetichus.'
I regret deeply, my dear friend, that I cannot give you this document respecting a lamented monarch, in whose history I know you
take such an interest.

The best sight I saw in Alexandria, was a negro holiday ; which
was celebrated outside of the town by a sort of negro village of

huts, swarming with old, lean, fat, ugly, infantine, happy faces, that Nature has smeared with a preparation even more black and durable than that with which Psammetichus's base has been polished. Every one of these jolly faces was on the broad grin, from the dusky mother to the India-rubber child sprawling upon her back, and the venerable jetty senior, whose wool was as white as that of a sheep in Florian's pastorals.

To these dancers a couple of fellows were playing on a drum and a little banjo. They were singing a chorus, which was not only singular, and perfectly marked in the rhythm, but exceedingly sweet in the tune. They danced in a circle ; and performers came trooping from all quarters, who fell into the round, and began waggling their heads, and waving their left hands, and tossing up and down the little thin rods which they each carried, and all singing to the very best of their power.

I saw the chief eunuch of the Grand Turk at Constantinople pass by—(here is an accurate likeness of his beautiful features)—

but with what a different expression ! Though he is one of the greatest of the great in the Turkish Empire (ranking with a Cabinet minister or Lord Chamberlain here), his fine countenance was clouded with care, and savage with ennui.

Here his black brethren were ragged, starving, and happy ; and I need not tell such a fine moralist as you are, how it is the case, in the white as well as the black world, that happiness (republican leveller, who does not care a fig for the fashion) often disdains the turrets of kings, to pay a visit to the 'tabernas pauperum.'

We went the round of the coffee-houses in the evening, both the polite European places of resort, where you get ices and the French papers, and those in the town, where Greeks, Turks, and general company resort, to sit upon uncomfortable chairs, and drink wretched muddy coffee, and to listen to two or three miserable musicians, who keep up a variation of howling for hours together. But the pretty song of the niggers had spoiled me for that abominable music.

CHAPTER XV

TO CAIRO

WE had no need of hiring the country boats which ply on the Mahmoodieh canal to Atfeh, where it joins the Nile, but were accommodated in one of the Peninsular and Oriental Company's fly-boats; pretty similar to those narrow Irish canal-boats, in which the enterprising traveller has been carried from Dublin to

Ballinasloe. The present boat was, to be sure, tugged by a little steamer, so that the Egyptian canal is ahead of the Irish in so far: in natural scenery, the one prospect is fully equal to the other; it must be confessed that there is nothing to see. In truth, there was nothing but this : you saw a muddy bank on each side of you, and a blue sky overhead. A few round mud-huts and palm-trees were planted along the line here and there. Sometimes we would see, on the water-side, a woman in a blue robe, with her son by her, in that tight brown costume with which Nature had supplied him.   Now, it was a hat dropped by one of the party into the water ; a brown Arab plunged and disappeared incontinently after the hat, reissued from the muddy water, prize in hand, and ran naked after the little steamer (which was by this time far ahead of him), his brawny limbs shining in the sun : then, we had half-cold fowls and bitter ale : then, we had dinner,—bitter ale and cold fowls ; with which incidents the day on the canal passed away, as harmlessly as if we had been in a Dutch trackschuyt.

Towards evening we arrived at the town of Atfeh—half land, half houses, half palm-trees, with swarms of half-naked people crowding the rustic shady bazaars, and bartering their produce of fruit or many-coloured grain.   Here the canal came to a check, ending abruptly with a large lock.   Some little fleet of masts and country ships were beyond the lock, and it led into The Nile.

After all, it is something to have seen these red waters.   It is only low green banks, mud-huts, and palm-clumps, with the sun setting red behind them, and the great, dull, sinuous river, flashing here and there in the light.   But it is the Nile, the old Saturn of a stream—a divinity yet, though younger river-gods have deposed him.   Hail ! O venerable father of crocodiles !   We were all lost in sentiments of the profoundest awe and respect ; which we proved, by tumbling down into the cabin of the Nile steamer that was waiting to receive us, and fighting and cheating for sleeping-berths.

At dawn in the morning we were on deck ; the character had not altered of the scenery about the river.   Vast flat stretches of land were on either side, recovering from the subsiding inunda-tions : near the mud villages, a country ship or two was roosting under the date-trees ; the landscape everywhere stretching away level and lonely.   In the sky in the east was a long streak of greenish light, which widened and rose until it grew to be of an opal colour, then orange ; then, behold, the round red disk of the sun rose flaming up above the horizon.   All the water blushed as he got up ; the deck was all red ; the steersman gave his helm to another, and prostrated himself on the deck, and bowed his head eastward, and praised the Maker of the sun : it shone on his white turban as he was kneeling, and gilt up his bronzed face, and sent his blue shadow over the glowing deck.   The distances, which had been grey, were now clothed in purple ; and the broad stream was illuminated.   As the sun rose higher, the morning blush faded away ; the sky was cloudless and pale, and the river and the surrounding landscape were dazzlingly clear.

Looking ahead in an hour or two, we saw the Pyramids.

Fancy my sensations, dear M——— ;—two big ones and a little one :

There they lay, rosy and solemn in the distance,—those old, majestical, mystical, familiar edifices.   Several of us tried to be impressed ; but breakfast supervening, a rush was made at the coffee and cold pies, and the sentiment of awe was lost in the scramble for victuals.

Are we so blasés of the world that the greatest marvels in it do not succeed in moving us ?   Have society, Pall Mall clubs, and a habit of sneering, so withered up our organs of veneration that we can admire no more ?   My sensation with regard to the Pyramids was, that I had seen them before : then came a feeling of shame that the view of them should awaken no respect.   Then I wanted (naturally) to see whether my neighbours were any more enthusiastic than myself—Trinity College, Oxford, was busy with the cold ham : Downing Street was particularly attentive to a bunch of grapes : Fig-tree Court behaved with decent propriety ; he is in good practice, and of a conservative turn of mind, which leads him to respect from principle *les faits accomplis ;* perhaps he remembered that one of them was as big as Lincoln's Inn Fields. But, the truth is, nobody was seriously moved. . . . And why should they, because of an exaggeration of bricks ever so enormous ? I confess, for my part, that the Pyramids are very big.

After a voyage, of about thirty hours, the steamer brought up at the quay of Boulak, amidst a small fleet of dirty comfortless Cangias, in which cottons and merchandise were loading and un-loading, and a huge noise and bustle on the shore.   Numerous villas, parks, and country houses, had begun to decorate the Cairo bank of the stream ere this : residences of the Pasha's nobles, who have had orders to take their pleasure here and beautify the precincts of the capital ; tall factory chimneys also rise here ; there are foundries and steam-engine manufactories.   These, and the pleasure-houses, stand as trim as soldiers on parade ; contrast-ing with the swarming, slovenly, close, tumble-down, eastern old town, that forms the outport of Cairo, and was built before the importation of European taste and discipline.

Here we alighted upon donkeys, to the full as brisk as those of Alexandria, invaluable to timid riders, and equal to any weight. We had a Jerusalem pony race into Cairo ; my animal beating all the rest by many lengths. The entrance to the capital, from Boulak, is very pleasant and picturesque—over a fair road, and the wide planted plain of the Ezbekieh; where are gardens, canals, fields, and avenues of trees, and where the great ones of the town come and take their pleasure. We saw many barouches driving about with fat Pashas, lolling on the cushions; stately-looking colonels and doctors taking their ride, followed by their orderlies or footmen; lines of people taking pipes and sherbet in the coffee-houses; and one of the pleasantest sights of all,—a fine new white building with HOTEL D'ORIENT written up in huge French characters, and which, indeed, is an establishment as large and comfortable as most of the best Inns of the South of France. As a hundred Christian people, or more, come from England and from India every fortnight, this Inn has been built to accommodate a large proportion of them; and twice a month, at least, its sixty rooms are full.

The gardens from the windows give a very pleasant and animated view: the hotel gate is besieged by crews of donkey-drivers; the noble stately Arab women, with tawny skins (of which a simple robe of floating blue cotton enables you liberally to see the colour) and large black eyes, come to the well hard by for water: camels are perpetually arriving and setting down their loads: the court is full of bustling dragomans, ayahs, and children from India; and poor old venerable he-nurses, with grey beards and crimson turbans, tending little white-faced babies that have seen the light at Dumdum or Futtyghur: a copper-coloured barber, seated on his hams, is shaving a camel-driver at the great Inn gate. The bells are ringing prodigiously: and Lieutenant Waghorn is bouncing in and out of the courtyard full of business. He only left Bombay yesterday morning, was seen in the Red Sea on Tuesday, is engaged to dinner this afternoon in the Regent's Park, and (as it is about two minutes since I saw him in the courtyard) I make no doubt he is by this time at Alexandria or at Malta, say, perhaps, at both. *Il en est capable*. If any man can be at two places at once (which I don't believe or deny) Waghorn is he.

Six o'clock bell rings. Sixty people sit down to a quasi-French banquet: thirty Indian officers in mustachoes and jackets; ten civilians in ditto and spectacles; ten pale-faced ladies with ringlets, to whom all pay prodigious attention. All the pale ladies drink pale ale, which, perhaps, accounts for it; in fact the Bombay and Suez passengers have just arrived, and hence this crowding and bustling, and display of military jackets and mustachoes, and ringlets and beauty. The windows are open, and a rush of mosquitoes from the Ezbekieh waters, attracted by the wax candles, adds greatly to the excitement of the scene. There was a little tough old Major, who persisted in flinging open the windows, to admit these volatile creatures, with a noble disregard to their sting—and the pale ringlets did not seem to heed them either, though the delicate shoulders of some of them were bare.

All the meat, ragouts, fricandeaux, and roasts, which are served round at dinner, seem to me to be of the same meat : a black uncertain sort of viand do these 'fleshpots of Egypt' contain. But what the meat is no one knew : is it the donkey ? The animal is more plentiful than any other in Cairo.

After dinner, the ladies retiring, some of us take a mixture of hot water, sugar, and pale French brandy, which is said to be deleterious, but is by no means unpalatable. One of the Indians offer a bundle of Bengal cheroots ; and we make acquaintance with those honest bearded white-jacketed Majors and military Commanders, finding England here in a French hotel kept by an Italian, at the city of Grand Cairo, in Africa.

On retiring to bed you take a towel with you into the sacred interior, behind the mosquito curtains. Then your duty is, having tucked the curtains closely around, to flap and bang violently with this towel, right and left, and backwards and forwards, until every mosquito shall have been massacred that may have taken refuge within your muslin canopy.

Do what you will, however, one of them always escapes the murder : and as soon as the candle is out the miscreant begins his infernal droning and trumpeting ; descends playfully upon your nose and face, and so lightly that you don't know that he touches you. But that for a week afterwards you bear about marks of his ferocity, you might take the invisible little being to be a creature of fancy—a mere singing in your ears.

This, as an account of Cairo, dear M——, you will probably be disposed to consider as incomplete : the fact is, I have seen nothing else as yet. I have peered into no harems. The magicians, proved to be humbugs, have been bastinadoed out of town. The dancing-girls, those lovely Alme, of whom I had hoped to be able to give a glowing and elegant, though strictly moral, description, have been whipped into Upper Egypt, and as you are saying in your mind—— Well it *isn't* a good description of Cairo ; you are perfectly right. It is England in Egypt. I like to see her there with her pluck, enterprise, manliness, bitter ale and Harvey sauce. Wherever they come they stay and prosper. From the summit of yonder Pyramids forty centuries may look down on them if they are minded ; and I say, those venerable daughters of time ought to be better pleased by the examination, than by regarding the French bayonets and General Bonaparte, Member of the Institute, fifty years ago, running about with sabre and pigtail. Wonders he did to be sure, and then ran away, leaving Kleber, to be murdered, in the lurch—a few hundred yards from the spot where these disquisitions are written. But what are his wonders compared to Waghorn? Nap. massacred the Mamelukes at the Pyramids : Wag. has conquered the Pyramids themselves ; dragged the unwieldy structures a month nearer England than they were, and brought the country along with them. All the trophies and captives, that ever were brought to Roman triumph, were not so enormous and wonderful as this. All the heads that Napoleon ever caused to be struck off (as George Cruikshank says) would not elevate him a monument as big. Be ours the trophies of peace ! O my country ! O Waghorn ! *Hæ tibi erunt artes.* When I go to the Pyramids I will sacrifice in your name, and pour out libations of bitter ale and Harvey sauce in your honour.

One of the noblest views in the world is to be seen from the citadel, which we ascended to-day. You see the city stretching beneath it, with a thousand minarets and mosques,—the great river curling through the green plains, studded with innumerable villages. The Pyramids are beyond brilliantly distinct ; and the lines and fortifications of the height, with the arsenal lying below. Gazing down, the guide does not fail to point out the famous Mameluke leap, by which one of the corps escaped death, at the time that his Highness the Pasha arranged the general massacre of the body.

The venerable Patriarch's harem is close by, where he received, with much distinction, some of the members of our party. We were allowed to pass very close to the sacred precincts, and saw a comfortable white European building, approached by flights of steps, and flanked by pretty gardens. Police and law-courts were here also, as I understood ; but it was not the time of the Egyptian assizes. It would have been pleasant, otherwise, to see the chief Cadi in his hall of justice ; and painful though instructive, to behold the immediate application of the bastinado.

The great lion of the place is a new mosque which Mehemet Ali is constructing very leisurely. It is built of alabaster of a fair white, with a delicate blushing tinge ; but the ornaments are European—the noble, fantastic, beautiful Oriental art is forgotten. The old mosques of the city, of which I entered two, and looked at many, are a thousand times more beautiful. Their variety of ornament is astonishing,—the difference in the shapes of the domes, the beautiful fancies and caprices in the forms of the minarets, which violate the rules of proportion with the most happy, daring grace, must have struck every architect who has seen them. As you go through the streets, these architectural beauties keep the eye continually charmed : now, it is a marble fountain, with its arabesque and carved overhanging roof, which you can look at with as much pleasure as an antique gem, so neat and brilliant is the execution of it ; then, you come to the arched entrance to a mosque, which shoots up like—like what ?—like the most beautiful pirouette by Taglioni, let us say. This architecture is not sublimely beautiful, perfect loveliness and calm, like that which was revealed to us at the Parthenon (and in comparison of which the Pantheon and Colosseum are vulgar and coarse, mere broad-shouldered Titans before ambrosial Jove) ; but these fantastic spires, and cupolas, and galleries, excite, amuse, *tickle* the imagination so to speak, and perpetually fascinate the eye. There were very few believers in the famous mosque of Sultan Hassan when we visited it, except the Moslemitish beadle, who was on the look-out for backsheesh, just like his brother officer in an English cathedral ; and who, making us put on straw slippers, so as not to pollute the sacred pavement of the place, conducted us through it.

It is stupendously light and airy ; the best specimens of Norman art that I have seen (and surely the Crusaders must have carried home the models of these heathenish temples in their eyes) do not exceed its noble grace and simplicity. The mystics make discoveries at home, that the Gothic architecture is Catholicism carved in stone (in which case, and if architectural beauty is a criterion or expression of religion, what a dismal barbarous creed must that, expressed by the Bethesda meeting-house and Independent chapels, be ?) ; if, as they would gravely hint, because Gothic architecture is beautiful, Catholicism is therefore lovely and right,—why, Mahommedanism must have been right and lovely too once. Never did a creed possess temples more elegant ; as elegant as the Cathedral at Rouen, or the Baptistery at Pisa.

But it is changed now. There was nobody at prayers ; only the official beadles, and the supernumerary guides, who came for backsheesh. Faith has degenerated. Accordingly they can't build these mosques, or invent these perfect forms, any more. Witness the tawdry incompleteness and vulgarity of the Pasha's new temple, and the woful failures among the very late edifices in Constantinople !

However, they still make pilgrimages to Mecca in great force. The mosque of Hassan is hard by the green plain on which the *Hag* encamps before it sets forth annually on its pious peregrination. It was not yet its time, but I saw in the bazaars that redoubted Dervish, who is the Master of the Hag—the leader of every procession, accompanying the sacred camel ; and a personage almost as much respected as Mr. O'Connell in Ireland.

This fellow lives by alms (I mean the head of the Hag). Winter and summer he wears no clothes but a thin and scanty white shirt. He wields a staff, and stalks along scowling and barefoot. His immense shock of black hair streams behind him, and his brown, brawny body is curled over with black hair, like a salvage man. This saint has the largest harem in the town ; is said to be enormously rich by the contributions he has levied ; and is so adored for his holiness by the infatuated folk, that when he returns from the Hag (which he does on horseback, the chief Mollahs going out to meet him and escort him home in state along the Ezbekieh road), the people fling themselves down under the horse's feet, eager to be trampled upon and killed, and confident of heaven if the great Hadji's horse will but kick them into it. Was it my fault if I thought of Hadji Daniel, and the believers in him ?

There was no Dervish of repute on the plain when I passed ; only one poor, wild fellow, who was dancing, with glaring eyes and grizzled beard, rather to the contempt of the bystanders, as I thought, who by no means put coppers into his extended bowl. On this poor devil's head there was a poorer devil still—a live cock, entirely plucked, but ornamented with some bits of ragged tape and scarlet and tinsel, the most horribly grotesque and miserable object I ever saw.

A little way from him, there was a sort of play going on—a clown and a knowing one, like Widdicombe and the clown with us,—the buffoon answering with blundering responses, which made all the audience shout with laughter ; but the only joke which was translated to me would make you do anything but laugh, and shall therefore never be revealed by these lips. All their humour, my dragoman tells me, is of this questionable sort ; and a young Egyptian gentleman, son of a Pasha, whom I subsequently met at Malta, confirmed the statement, and gave a detail of the practices of private life, which were anything but edifying. The great aim of the women, he said, in the much-maligned Orient, is to administer to the brutality of her lord ; her merit is in knowing how to vary the beast's pleasures. He could give us no idea, he said, of the *wit* of the Egyptian women, and their skill in *double entendre ;* nor, I presume, did we lose much by our ignorance. What I would urge, humbly, however, is this— Do not let us be led away by German writers and æsthetics,

Semilassoisms, Hahnhahnisms, and the like. The life of the East is a life of brutes. The much-maligned Orient, I am confident, has not been maligned near enough ; for the good reason that none of us can tell the amount of horrible sensuality practised there.

Beyond the jack-pudding rascal and his audience, there was on the green a spot, on which was pointed out to me, a mark, as of blood. That morning the blood had spouted from the neck of an Arnaoot soldier, who had been executed for murder. These Arnaoots are the curse and terror of the citizens. Their camps are without the city ; but they are always brawling, or drunken, or murdering within, in spite of the rigid law which is applied to them, and which brings one or more of the scoundrels to death almost every week.

Some of our party had seen this fellow borne by the hotel the day before, in the midst of a crowd of soldiers who had apprehended him. The man was still formidable to his score of captors ; his clothes had been torn off ; his limbs were bound with cords ; but he was struggling frantically to get free ; and my informant described the figure and appearance of the naked, bound, writhing savage, as quite a model of beauty.

Walking in the street, this fellow had just before been struck by the looks of a woman who was passing, and laid hands on her. She ran away, and he pursued her. She ran into the police-barrack, which was luckily hard by ; but the Arnaoot was nothing daunted, and followed into the midst of the police. One of them tried to stop him. The Arnaoot pulled out a pistol, and shot the policeman dead. He cut down three or four more before he was secured. He knew his inevitable end must be death : that he could not seize upon the woman : that he could not hope to resist half a regiment of armed soldiers : yet his instinct of lust and murder was too strong ; and so he had his head taken off quite calmly this morning, many of his comrades attending their brother's last moments. He cared not the least about dying ; and knelt down and had his head off as coolly as if he were looking on at the same ceremony performed on another.

When the head was off, and the blood was spouting on the ground, a married woman, who had no children, came forward very eagerly out of the crowd, to smear herself with it,—the application of criminals' blood being considered a very favourable medicine for women afflicted with barrenness,—so she indulged in this remedy.

But one of the Arnaoots, standing near, said, ' What, you like blood, do you ? (or words to that effect)—Let's see how yours mixes with my comrade's;' and thereupon, taking out a pistol, he shot the woman in the midst of the crowd and the guards who were attending the execution; was seized of course by the latter; and no doubt to-morrow morning will have *his* head off too. It would be a good chapter to write—the Death of the Arnaoot—but I shan't go. Seeing one man hanged is quite enough in the course of a life. *J'y ai été*, as the Frenchman said of hunting.

These Arnaoots are the terror of the town. They seized hold of an Englishman the other day, and were very nearly pistolling him. Last week one of them murdered a shopkeeper at Boulak, who refused to sell him a water-melon at a price which he, the soldier, fixed upon it. So, for the matter of three-halfpence, he killed the shopkeeper; and had his own rascally head chopped off, universally regretted by his friends. Why, I wonder, does not his Highness the Pasha invite the Arnaoots to a *déjeuner* at the Citadel, as he did the Mamelukes, and serve them up the same sort of breakfast? The walls are considerably heightened since Emin Bey and his horse leapt them, and it is probable that not one of them would escape.

This sort of pistol practice is common enough here it would appear; and not among the Arnaoots merely, but the higher orders. Thus, a short time since, one of his Highness's grandsons, whom I shall call Bluebeard Pasha (lest a revelation of the name of the said Pasha might interrupt our good relations with his country)—one of the young Pashas being backward rather in his education, and anxious to learn mathematics, and the elegant deportment of civilised life—sent to England for a tutor. I have heard he was a Cambridge man, and had learned both algebra and politeness under the Reverend Doctor Whizzle, of —— College.

One day when Mr. MacWhirter, B.A., was walking in Shoubra gardens, with his Highness the young Bluebeard Pasha, inducting him into the usages of polished society, and favouring him with reminiscences of Trumpington, there came up a poor fellah, who flung himself at the feet of young Bluebeard, and calling for justice in a loud and pathetic voice, and holding out a petition, besought his Highness to cast a gracious eye upon the same, and see that his slave had justice done him.

Bluebeard Pasha was so deeply engaged and interested by his respected tutor's conversation, that he told the poor fellah to go to the deuce, and resumed the discourse which his ill-timed outcry for justice had interrupted. But the unlucky wight of a fellah was pushed by his evil destiny, and thought he would make yet another application. So he took a short cut down one of the garden lanes, and as the Prince and the Reverend Mr. MacWhirter, his tutor, came along once more engaged in pleasant disquisition, behold the fellah was once more in their way, kneeling at the august Bluebeard's feet, yelling out for justice as before, and thrusting his petition into the royal face.

When the Prince's conversation was thus interrupted a second time, his royal patience and clemency were at an end : ' Man,' said he, ' once before I bade thee not to pester me with thy clamour, and lo ! you have disobeyed me,—Take the consequences of disobedience to a Prince, and thy blood be upon thine own head.' So saying, he drew out a pistol, and blew out the brains of that fellah, so that he never bawled out for justice any more.

The Reverend Mr. MacWhirter was astonished at this sudden mode of proceeding : ' Gracious Prince,' said he, ' we do not shoot an undergraduate at Cambridge even for walking over a college grass-plot.—Let me suggest to your Royal Highness that this method of ridding yourself of a poor devil's importunities, is such as we should consider abrupt and almost cruel in Europe. Let me beg you to moderate your royal impetuosity for the future ; and, as your Highness' tutor, entreat you to be a little less prodigal of your powder and shot.'

' O Mollah !' said his Highness, here interrupting his governor's affectionate appeal,—' You are good to talk about Trumpington and the Pons Asinorum, but if you interfere with the course of justice in any way, or prevent me from shooting any dog of an Arab who snarls at my heels, I have another pistol; and, by the beard of the Prophet ! a bullet for you too.' So saying, he pulled out the weapon, with such a terrific and significant glance at the Reverend Mr. MacWhirter, that that gentleman wished himself back in his Combination Room again ; and is by this time, let us hope, safely housed there.

Another facetious anecdote, the last of those I had from a well-informed gentleman residing at Cairo, whose name (as many copies of this book that is to be, will be in the circulating libraries there) I cannot, for obvious reasons, mention. The revenues of the country come into the august treasury through the means of farmers, to whom the districts are let out, and who are personally answerable for their quota of the taxation. This practice involves an intolerable deal of tyranny and extortion on the part of those engaged to levy the taxes, and creates a corresponding duplicity among the fellahs, who are not only wretchedly poor among themselves, but whose object is to appear still more poor, and guard their money from their rapacious overseers. Thus the Orient is much maligned : but everybody cheats there : that is a melancholy fact. The Pasha robs and cheats the merchants ; knows that the overseer robs him, and bides his time, until he makes him disgorge by the application of the tremendous bastinado ; the overseer robs and squeezes the labourer ; and the poverty-stricken devil cheats and robs in return : and so the government moves in a happy cycle of roguery.

Deputations from the fellahs and peasants come perpetually before the august presence, to complain of the cruelty and ex-actions of the chiefs set over them : but, as it is known that the Arab never will pay without the bastinado, their complaints, for the most part, meet with but little attention. His High-ness's treasury must be filled, and his officers supported in their authority.

However, there was one village, of which the complaints were so pathetic, and the inhabitants so supremely wretched, that the royal indignation was moved at their story, and the chief of the village, Skinflint Beg, was called to give an account of himself at Cairo.

When he came before the presence, Mehemet Ali reproached him with his horrible cruelty and exactions ; asked him how he dared to treat his faithful and beloved subjects in this way, and threatened him with disgrace, and the utter confiscation of his property, for thus having reduced a district to ruin.

'Your Highness says I have reduced these fellahs to ruin,' said Skinflint Beg ; 'what is the best way to confound my enemies, and to show you the falsehood of their accusations that I have ruined them ?—To bring more money from them. If I bring you five hundred purses from my village, will you acknow-ledge that my people are not ruined yet ?'

The heart of the Pasha was touched : 'I will have no more bastinadoing, O Skinflint Beg ; you have tortured these poor people so much, and have got so little from them, that my royal heart relents for the present, and I will have them suffer no farther.'

'Give me free leave—give me your Highness's gracious pardon, and I will bring the five hundred purses as surely as my name is Skinflint Beg. I demand only the time to go home, the time to return, and a few days to stay, and I will come back as honestly as Regulus Pasha did to the Carthaginians,—I will come back and make my face white before your Highness.'

Skinflint Beg's prayer for a reprieve was granted, and he returned to his village, where he forthwith called the elders together : 'O friends,' he said, 'complaints of our poverty and misery have reached the royal throne, and the benevolent heart of the sovereign has been melted by the words that have been poured into his ears. "My heart yearns towards my people of El Muddee," he says; "I have thought how to relieve their miseries. Near them lies the fruitful land of El Guanee. It is rich in maize, and cotton, in sesame, and barley : it is worth a thousand purses ; but I will let it to my children for seven hundred, and I will give over the rest of the profit to them, as an alleviation for their affliction." '

The elders of El Muddee knew the great value and fertility of the lands of Guanee, but they doubted the sincerity of their governor, who, however, dispelled their fears, and adroitly quickened their eagerness to close with the proffered bargain : 'I will myself advance two hundred and fifty purses,' he said ; 'do you take counsel among yourselves, and subscribe the other five hundred ; and when the sum is ready, a deputation of you shall carry it to Cairo, and I will come with my share ; and we will lay the whole at the feet of his Highness.' So the grey-bearded ones of the village advised with one another ; and those who had been inaccessible to bastinadoes, somehow found money at the calling of interest ; and the sheikh, and they, and the five hundred purses, set off on the road to the capital.

When they arrived, Skinflint Beg and the elders of El Muddee sought admission to the royal throne, and there laid down their purses. 'Here is your humble servant's contribution,' said Skinflint, producing his share ; 'and here is the offering of your loyal village of El Muddee. Did I not before say that enemies and deceivers had maligned me before the august presence, pretending that not a piastre was left in my village, and that my extortion had entirely denuded the peasantry ? See ! here is proof that there is plenty of money still in El Muddee : in twelve hours the elders have subscribed five hundred purses, and lay them at the feet of their lord.'

Instead of the bastinado, Skinflint Beg was instantly rewarded with the royal favour, and the former mark of attention was bestowed upon the fellahs who had maligned him : Skinflint Beg was promoted to the rank of Skinflint Bey ; and his manner of extracting money from his people may be studied with admiration in a part of the United Kingdom.[1]

At the time of the Syrian quarrel, and when, apprehending some general rupture with England, the Pasha wished to raise the spirit of the fellahs, and *relever la morale nationale*, he actually made one of the astonished Arabs a colonel. He degraded

[1] At Derrynane Beg, for instance.

him three days after peace was concluded. The young Egyptian colonel, who told me this, laughed and enjoyed the joke with the utmost gusto. 'Is it not a shame,' he said, 'to make me a colonel at three-and-twenty ; I, who have no particular merit, and have never seen any service ?' Death has since stopped the modest and good-natured young fellow's further promotion. The death of ―――― Bey was announced in the French papers, a few weeks back.

My above kind-hearted and agreeable young informant used to discourse, in our evenings in the Lazaretto at Malta, very eloquently about the beauty of his wife, whom he had left behind him at Cairo—her brown hair, her brilliant complexion, and her blue eyes. It is this Circassian blood, I suppose, to which the Turkish aristocracy that governs Egypt, must be indebted for the fairness of their skin. Ibrahim Pasha, riding by in his barouche, looked like a bluff, jolly-faced English dragoon officer, with a grey mustache and red cheeks, such as you might see on a field-day at Maidstone. All the numerous officials riding through the town were quite as fair as Europeans. We made acquaintance with one dignitary, a very jovial and fat pasha, the proprietor of the inn, I believe, who was continually lounging about the Ezbekieh garden, and who, but for a slight Jewish cast of countenance, might have passed any day for a Frenchman. The ladies whom we saw were equally fair ; that is, the very slight particles of the persons of ladies which our lucky eyes were permitted to gaze on. These lovely creatures go through the town by parties of three or four, mounted on donkeys, and attended by slaves holding on at the crupper, to receive the lovely riders lest they should fall, and shouting out shrill cries of Schmaalek, Ameenek (or however else these words may be pronounced), and flogging off the people right and left with the buffalo-thong. But the dear creatures are even more closely disguised than at Constantinople : their bodies are enveloped with a large black silk hood, like a cab-head ; the fashion seemed to be to spread their arms out, and give this covering all the amplitude of which it was capable, as they leered and ogled you from under their black masks with their big rolling eyes.

Everybody has big rolling eyes here (unless to be sure they lose one of ophthalmia). The Arab women are some of the noblest figures I have ever seen. The habit of carrying jars on the head always gives the figure grace and motion ; and the dress the women wear certainly displays it to full advantage. I have brought a complete one home with me, at the service of any lady for a masqued ball. It consists of a coarse blue dress of calico, open in front, and fastened with a horn button. Three yards of blue stuff for a veil ; on the top of the veil a jar to be balanced on the head ; and a little black strip of silk to fall over the nose, and leave the beautiful eyes full liberty to roll and roam. But such a costume, not aided by any stays or any other article of dress whatever, can be worn only by a very good figure. I suspect it won't be borrowed for many balls next season.

The men, a tall handsome noble race, are treated like dogs. I shall never forget riding through the crowded bazaars, my interpreter, or *laquais-de-place*, ahead of me to clear the way—when he took his whip, and struck it over the shoulders of a man who could not or would not make way !

The man turned round—an old, venerable, handsome face, with awfully sad eyes, and a beard long and quite grey. He did not make the least complaint, but slunk out of the way, piteously shaking his shoulder. The sight of that indignity gave me a sickening feeling of disgust. I shouted out to the cursed lackey to hold his hand, and forbade him ever in my presence to strike old or young more ; but everybody is doing it. The whip is in everybody's hands : the pasha's running footman, as he goes bustling through the bazaar ; the doctor's attendant, as he soberly threads the crowd on his mare ; the negro slave, who is riding by himself, the most insolent of all, strikes and slashes about without mercy, and you never hear a single complaint.

How to describe the beauty of the streets to you !—the fantastic splendour ; the variety of the houses, and archways, and hanging roofs, and balconies, and porches ; the delightful accidents of light and shade which chequer them ; the noise, the bustle, the brilliancy of the crowd ; the interminable vast bazaars with their barbaric splendour ! There is a fortune to be made for painters in Cairo, and materials for a whole Academy of them. I never saw such a variety of architecture, of life, of picturesqueness, of brilliant colour, and light and shade. There is a picture in every street, and at every bazaar stall. Some of these, our celebrated water-colour painter, Mr. Lewis, has produced with admirable truth and exceeding minuteness and beauty ; but there is room for a hundred to follow him ; and should any artist (by some rare occurrence) read this, who has leisure, and wants to break new ground, let him take heart, and try a winter in Cairo, where there is the finest climate and the best subjects for his pencil.

A series of studies of negroes alone would form a picture-book delightfully grotesque. Mounting my donkey to-day, I took a ride to the desolate, noble old buildings outside the city, known as the

Tombs of the Caliphs. Every one of these edifices, with their domes, and courts, and minarets, is strange and beautiful. In one of them there was an encampment of negro slaves newly arrived : some scores of them were huddled against the sunny wall ; two or three of their masters lounged about the court, or lay smoking upon carpets. There was one of these fellows, a straight-nosed ebony-faced Abyssinian, with an expression of such sinister good-humour in his handsome face, as would form a perfect type of villany. He sat leering at me, over his carpet, as I endeavoured to get a sketch of that incarnate rascality. ' Give me some money,' said the fellow. ' I know what you are about. You will sell my picture for money when you get back to Europe ; let me have some of it now ?' But the very rude and humble designer was quite unequal to depict such a consummation and perfection of roguery ; so flung him a cigar, which he began to smoke, grinning at the giver. I requested the interpreter to inform him, by way of assurance of my disinterestedness, that his face was a great deal too ugly to be popular in Europe, and that was the particular reason why I had selected it.

Then one of his companions got up and showed us his black cattle. The male slaves were chiefly lads, and the women young, well formed, and abominably hideous ; the dealer pulled her blanket off one of them and bade her stand up, which she did with a great deal of shuddering modesty. She was coal-black, her lips were the size of sausages, her eyes large and good-humoured ; the hair or wool on this young person's head was curled and greased into a thousand filthy little ringlets. She was evidently the beauty of the flock.

They are not unhappy ; they look to being bought, as many a spinster looks to an establishment in England ; once in a family they are kindly treated and well clothed, and fatten, and are the merriest people of the whole community. These were of a much more savage sort than the slaves I had seen in the horrible market at Constantinople where I recollect the following young creature —(indeed it is a very fair likeness of her) whilst I was looking at her and forming pathetic conjectures regarding her fate—smiling very good-humouredly, and bidding the interpreter ask me to buy her for twenty pounds.

From these Tombs of the Caliphs the Desert is before you. It comes up to the walls of the city, and stops at some gardens which spring up all of a sudden at its edge. You can see the first Station-house on the Suez Road ; and so from distance point, to point, could ride thither alone without a guide.

Asinus trotted gallantly into this desert for the space of a quarter of an hour. There we were (taking care to keep our backs to the city walls) in the real actual desert : mounds upon mounds of sand stretching away as far as the eye can see, until the dreary prospect fades away in the yellow horizon ! I had formed a finer idea of it out of *Eothen*. Perhaps in a simoom it may look more awful. The only adventure that befel in this romantic place was, that asinus's legs went deep into a hole : whereupon his rider went over his head, and bit the sand, and measured his length there ; and upon this hint rose up, and rode home again. No doubt one should have gone out for a couple of days' march—as it was, the desert did not seem to me sublime, only *uncomfortable*.

Very soon after this perilous adventure the sun likewise dipped into the sand (but not to rise therefrom so quickly as I had done) ;

and I saw this daily phenomenon of sunset with pleasure, for I was engaged at that hour to dine with our old friend J——, who has established himself here in the most complete Oriental fashion.

You remember J——, and what a dandy he was, the faultlessness of his boots and cravats, the brilliancy of his waistcoats and kid gloves ; we have seen his splendour in Regent Street, in the Tuilleries, or on the Toledo. My first object on arriving here was to find out his house, which he has taken far away from the haunts of European civilisation, in the Arab quarter. It is situated in a cool, shady, narrow alley ; so narrow, that it was with great difficulty—his Highness Ibrahim Pasha happening to pass at the same moment—that my little procession of two donkeys mounted by self and *valet-de-place*, with the two donkey-boys, our attendants, could range ourselves along the wall, and leave room for the august cavalcade. His Highness having rushed on (with an affable and good-humoured salute to our imposing party), we made J.'s quarters ; and, in the first place, entered a broad covered court or porch, where a swarthy tawny attendant, dressed in blue, with white turban, keeps a perpetual watch. Servants in the east lie about all the doors, it appears ; and you clap your hands, as they do in the dear old *Arabian Nights*, to summon them.

This servant disappeared through a narrow wicket, which he closed after him ; and went into the inner chambers to ask if his lord would receive us. He came back presently, and rising up from my donkey, I confided him to his attendant (lads more sharp, arch, and wicked, than these donkey-boys don't walk the *pavé* of Paris or London), and passed the mysterious outer door.

First we came into a broad open court, with a covered gallery running along one side of it. A camel was reclining on the grass there ; near him was a gazelle to glad J. with his dark blue eye ; and a numerous brood of hens and chickens, who furnish his liberal table. On the opposite side of the covered gallery rose up

the walls of his long, queer, many-windowed, many-galleried house. There were wooden lattices to those arched windows, through the diamonds of one of which I saw two of the most beautiful, enormous, ogling, black eyes in the world, looking down upon the interesting stranger. Pigeons were flapping, and hopping, and fluttering, and cooing about. Happy pigeons you are, no doubt, fed with crumbs from the henna-tipped fingers of Zuleikah ! All this court, cheerful in the sunshine, cheerful with the astonishing brilliancy of the eyes peering out from the lattice-bars, was as mouldy, ancient, and ruinous,

as any gentleman's house in Ireland, let us say. The paint was peeling off the rickety, old, carved galleries ; the arabesques over the windows were chipped and worn ;—the ancientness of the place rendered it doubly picturesque. I have detained you a long time in the outer court. Why the deuce was Zuleikah there, with the beautiful black eyes !

Hence we passed into a large apartment, where there was a fountain ; and another domestic made his appearance, taking me in charge, and relieving the tawny porter of the gate. This fellow was clad in blue too, with a red sash and a grey beard. He conducted

me into a great hall, where there was a great, large Saracenic oriel
window.   He seated me on a divan ; and stalking off, for a moment,
returned with a long pipe and a brass chafing-dish : he blew the
coal for the pipe, which he motioned me to smoke, and left me
there with a respectful bow.   This delay, this mystery of servants,
that outer court with the camels, gazelles, and other beautiful-eyed
things, affected me prodigiously all the time he was staying away ;
and while I was examining the strange apartment and its contents,
my respect and awe for the owner increased vastly.

As you will be glad to know how an Oriental nobleman (such
as J. undoubtedly is) is lodged and garnished, let me describe
the contents of this hall of audience.   It is about forty feet long,
and eighteen or twenty high.   All the ceiling is carved, gilt,
painted and embroidered with arabesques, and choice sentences of
Eastern writing.   Some Mameluke Aga, or Bey, whom Mehemet
Ali invited to breakfast and massacred, was the proprietor of this
mansion once ; it has grown dingier, but, perhaps, handsomer,
since his time.   Opposite the divan is a great bay-window, with a
divan likewise round the niche.   It looks out upon a garden about
the size of Fountain Court, Temple ; surrounded by the tall houses
of the quarter.   The garden is full of green.   A great palm-tree
springs up in the midst, with plentiful shrubberies, and a talking
fountain.   The room besides the divan is furnished with one deal
table, value, five shillings ; four wooden chairs, value, six shillings ;
and a couple of mats and carpets.   The tables and chairs are
luxuries imported from Europe.   The regular Oriental dinner is
put upon copper trays, which are laid upon low stools.   Hence
J—— Effendi's house may be said to be much more sumptuously
furnished than those of the Beys and Agas his neighbours.

When these things had been examined at leisure, J—— appeared.
Could it be the exquisite of the ' Europa ' and the ' Trois Frères ' ? A
man—in a long yellow gown, with a long beard, somewhat tinged with
grey, with his head shaved, and wearing on it first a white wadded
cotton nightcap, second, a red tarboosh—made his appearance
and welcomed me cordially.   It was some time, as the Americans
say, before I could 'realise' the *semillant* J. of old times.

He shuffled off his outer slippers before he curled up on the
divan beside me.   He clapped his hands, and languidly called
'Mustapha.'   Mustapha came with more lights, pipes, and coffee ;
and then we fell to talking about London, and I gave him the last
news of the comrades in that dear city.   As we talked, his Oriental
coolness and languor gave way to British cordiality ; he was the
most amusing companion of the ——club once more.

He has adopted himself outwardly, however, to the Oriental

life.   When he goes abroad he rides a grey horse with red housings, and has two servants to walk beside him.   He wears a very handsome grave costume of dark blue, consisting of an embroidered jacket and gaiters, and a pair of trowsers which would make a set of dresses for an English family.   His beard curls nobly over his chest, his Damascus scimitar on his thigh.   His red cap gives him a venerable and Bey-like appearance.   There is no gewgaw or parade about him, as in some of your dandified young Agas.   I should say that he is a Major-General of Engineers, or a grave officer of State.   We and the Turkified European, who found us at dinner, sat smoking in solemn divan.

His dinners were excellent ; they were cooked by a regular Egyptian female cook.   We had delicate cucumbers stuffed with forced-meats ; yellow smoking pilaffs, the pride of the Oriental cuisine ; kid and fowls à l'Aboukir and à la Pyramide ; a number of little savoury plates of legumes of the vegetable-marrow sort ; kibobs with an excellent sauce of plums and piquant herbs.   We ended the repast with ruby pomegranates, pulled to pieces, deliciously cool and pleasant.   For the meats, we certainly ate them with the Infidel knife and fork ; but for the fruit, we put our hands into the dish and flicked them into our mouths in what cannot but be the true Oriental manner.   I asked for lamb and pistachio-nuts, and cream-tarts *au poivre ;* but J.'s cook did not furnish us with either of those historic dishes.   And for drink, we had water freshened in the porous little pots of grey clay, at whose spout every traveller in the East has sucked delighted. Also it must be confessed, we drank certain sherbets, prepared by the two great rivals, Hadji Hodson and Bass Bey—the bitterest and most delicious of draughts! O divine Hodson! a camel's load of thy beer came from Beyrout to Jerusalem while we were there. How shall I ever forget the joy inspired by one of those foaming cool flasks!

We don't know the luxury of thirst in English climes. Sedentary men in cities at least have seldom ascertained it; but when they travel, our countrymen guard against it well. The road between Cairo and Suez is *jonché* with soda-water corks. Tom Thumb and his brothers might track their way across the desert by those landmarks.

Cairo is magnificently picturesque: it is fine to have palm-trees in your gardens, and ride about on a camel; but, after all, I was anxious to know what were the particular excitements of Eastern life, which detained J., who is a town-bred man, from his natural pleasures and occupations in London; where his family don't hear from him, where his room is still kept ready at home, and his name is on the list of his Club; and where his neglected sisters tremble to think that their Frederick is going about with a great beard and a crooked sword, dressed up like an odious Turk. In a 'lark' such a costume may be very well; but home, London, a razor, your sister to make tea, a pair of moderate Christian breeches in lieu of those enormous Turkish shulwars, are vastly more convenient in the long-run. What was it that kept him away from these decent and accustomed delights?

It couldn't be the black eyes in the balcony—upon his honour she was only the black cook, who has done the pilaff, and stuffed the cucumbers. No, it was an indulgence of laziness such as Europeans, Englishmen at least, don't know how to enjoy. Here he lives like a languid Lotus-eater—a dreamy, hazy, lazy, tobaccofied life. He was away from evening parties, he said; he needn't wear white kid gloves, or starched neckcloths, or read a newspaper. And even this life at Cairo was too civilised for him; Englishmen passed through; old acquaintances would call: the great pleasure of pleasures was life in the desert,—under the tents, with still *more* nothing to do than in Cairo; now smoking, now cantering on Arabs, and no crowd to jostle you; solemn contemplations of the stars at night, as the camels were picketed, and the fires and the pipes were lighted.

The night-scene in the city is very striking for its vastness and loneliness. Everybody has gone to rest long before ten o'clock. There are no lights in the enormous buildings; only the stars blazing above, with their astonishing brilliancy, in the blue, peaceful sky. Your guides carry a couple of little lanterns, which re-double the darkness in the solitary, echoing street. Mysterious people are curled up and sleeping in the porches. A patrol of soldiers passes, and hails you. There is a light yet in one mosque, where some devotees are at prayers all night; and you hear the queerest nasal music proceeding from those pious believers. As you pass the madhouse, there is one poor fellow still talking to the moon—no sleep for him. He howls and sings there all the night —quite cheerfully, however. He has not lost his vanity with his reason; he is a Prince in spite of the bars and the straw.

What to say about those famous edifices, which has not been better said elsewhere?—but you will not believe that we visited them, unless I bring some token from them. Here is one:—

That white-capped lad skipped up the stones with a jug of water in his hand, to refresh weary climbers; and, squatting him-self down on the summit, was designed as you see. The vast, flat landscape stretches behind him; the great winding river; the purple city, with forts, and domes, and spires; the green fields, and palm-groves, and speckled villages; the plains still covered with shining inundations—the landscape stretches far, far away, until it is lost and mingled in the golden horizon. It is poor work this landscape-painting in print. Shelley's two sonnets are the best views that I know of the Pyramids—better than the reality;

for a man may lay down the book, and in quiet fancy conjure up a picture out of these magnificent words, which shan't be disturbed by any pettinesses or mean realities,—such as the swarms of howling beggars, who jostle you about the actual place, and scream in your ears incessantly, and hang on your skirts, and bawl for money.

The ride to the Pyramids is one of the pleasantest possible. In the fall of the year, though the sky is almost cloudless above you, the sun is not too hot to bear ; and the landscape, refreshed by the subsiding inundations, delightfully green and cheerful. We made up a party of some half-dozen from the hotel, a lady (the kind soda-water provider, for whose hospitality the most grateful compliments are hereby offered) being of the company, bent like the rest upon going to the summit of Cheops. Those who were cautious and wise, took a brace of donkeys. At least five times during the route did my animals fall with me, causing me to repeat the Desert experiment over again, but with more success. The space between a moderate pair of legs and the ground, is not many inches. By eschewing stirrups, the donkey could fall, and the rider alight on the ground, with the greatest ease and grace. Almost everybody was down and up again in the course of the day.

We passed through the Ezbekieh and by the suburbs of the town, where the garden-houses of the Egyptian noblesse are situated, to old Cairo, where a ferry-boat took the whole party across the Nile, with that noise and bawling volubility in which the Arab people seem to be so unlike the grave and silent Turks ; and so took our course for some eight or ten miles over the devious tract which the still outlying waters obliged us to pursue. The Pyramids were in sight the whole way. One or two thin, silvery clouds were hovering over them, and casting delicate, rosy shadows, upon the grand, simple, old piles. Along the track, we saw a score of pleasant pictures of Eastern life :—The Pasha's horses and slaves stood caparisoned at his door ; at the gate of one country house, I am sorry to say, the Bey's *gig* was in waiting,—a most unromantic chariot : the husbandmen were coming into the city, with their strings of donkeys, and their loads ; as they arrived, they stopped and sucked at the fountain : a column of red-capped troops passed to drill, with slouched gait, white uniforms, and glittering bayonets. Then we had the pictures at the quay : the ferry-boat, and the red-sailed river-boat, getting under weigh, and bound up the stream. There was the grain market, and the huts on the opposite side ; and that beautiful woman, with silver armlets, and a face the colour of gold, which (the nose-bag having been luckily removed) beamed solemnly on us Europeans, like a great, yellow harvest moon. The bunches of purpling dates were

pending from the branches ; grey cranes or herons were flying over
the cool, shining lakes, that the river's overflow had left behind ;
water was gurgling through the courses by the rude locks and
barriers formed there, and overflowing this patch of ground ; whilst
the neighbouring field was fast budding into the more brilliant
fresh green.   Single dromedaries were stepping along, their riders
lolling on their hunches ; low sail boats were lying in the canals :
now, we crossed an old marble bridge ; now, we went, one by one,
over a ridge of slippery earth ; now, we floundered through a small
lake of mud.   At last, at about half a mile off the Pyramid, we
came to a piece of water some two-score yards broad, where a
regiment of half-naked Arabs, seizing upon each individual of the
party, bore us off on their shoulders, to the laughter of all, and
the great perplexity of several, who every moment expected to be
pitched into one of the many holes with which the treacherous
lake abounded.

It was nothing but joking and laughter, bullying of guides,
shouting for interpreters, quarrelling about sixpences.   We were
acting a farce, with the Pyramids for the scene.   There they rose
up enormous under our eyes, and the most absurd, trivial things
were going on under their shadow.   The sublime had disappeared,
vast as they were.   Do you remember how Gulliver lost his awe
of the tremendous Brobdingnag ladies ?   Every traveller must go
through all sorts of chaffering, and bargaining, and paltry experi-
ences, at this spot.   You look up the tremendous steps, with a
score of savage ruffians bellowing round you ; you hear faint cheers
and cries high up, and catch sight of little reptiles crawling
upwards : or, having achieved the summit, they come hopping and
bouncing down again from degree to degree,—the cheers and cries
swell louder and more disagreeable ; presently the little jumping
thing, no bigger than an insect a moment ago, bounces down upon
you expanded into a panting major of Bengal cavalry.   He drives
off the Arabs with an oath,—wipes his red, shining face, with his
yellow handkerchief, drops puffing on the sand in a shady corner,
where cold fowl and hard eggs are awaiting him, and the next
minute you see his nose plunged in a foaming beaker of brandy
and soda-water.   He can say now and for ever, he has been up
the Pyramid.   There is nothing sublime in it.   You cast your
eye once more up that staggering perspective of a zigzag line,
which ends at the summit, and wish you were up there—and
down again.   Forwards !—Up with you !   It must be done.
Six Arabs are behind you, who won't let you escape if you would.

The importunity of these ruffians is a ludicrous annoyance to
which a traveller must submit.   For two miles before you reach

the Pyramids, they seize on you, and never cease howling. Five or six of them pounce upon one victim, and never leave him until they have carried him up and down. Sometimes they conspire to run a man up the huge stair, and bring him, half-killed and fainting, to the top. Always a couple of brutes insist upon impelling you sternwards; from whom the only means to release yourself is to kick out vigorously and unmercifully, when the Arabs will possibly retreat. The ascent is not the least romantic, or difficult, or sublime: you walk up a great broken staircase, of which some of the steps are four feet high. It's not hard, only a little high. You see no better view from the top than you beheld from the bottom; only a little more river, and sand, and rice-field. You jump down the big steps at your leisure; but your meditations you must keep for after-times,—the cursed shrieking of the Arabs prevents all thought or leisure.

——And this is all you have to tell about the Pyramids? O! for shame! Not a compliment to their age and size? Not a big phrase,—not a rapture? Do you mean to say that you had no feeling of respect and awe? Try, man, and build up a monument of words as lofty as they are—they, whom 'imber edax,' and 'aquilo impotens,' and the flight of ages, have not been able to destroy!

—No: be that work for great geniuses, great painters, great poets! This quill was never made to take such flights; it comes of the wing of an humble domestic bird, who walks a common; who talks a great deal (and hisses sometimes); who can't fly far or high, and drops always very quickly; and whose unromantic end is, to be laid on a Michaelmas or Christmas table, and there to be discussed for half-an-hour—let us hope, with some relish.

———————

Another week saw us in the Quarantine Harbour at Malta, where seventeen days of prison and quiet were almost agreeable, after the incessant sight-seeing of the last two months. In the interval, between the 23rd of July and the 27th of October, we may boast of having seen more men and cities than most travellers have seen in such a time:—Lisbon, Cadiz, Gibraltar, Malta, Athens, Smyrna, Constantinople, Jerusalem, Cairo. I shall have the carpet-bag, which has visited these places in company with its owner, embroidered with their names; as military flags are emblazoned, and laid up in ordinary, to be looked at in old age. With what a number of sights and pictures,—of novel sensations, and lasting and delightful remembrances, does a man furnish his mind after such a tour! You forget all the annoyances of travel; but the pleasure remains with you, after that kind provision of nature by which a man forgets being ill, but thinks with joy of getting well, and can remember all the minute circumstances of his convalescence. I forget what sea-sickness is now; though it occupies a woeful portion of my Journal. There was a time on board, when the bitter ale was decidedly muddy; and the cook of the ship deserting at Constantinople, it must be confessed his successor was for some time before he got his hand in. These sorrows have passed away with the soothing influence of time: the pleasures of the voyage remain, let us hope, as long as life will endure. It was but for a couple of days that those shining columns of the Parthenon glowed under the blue sky there; but the experience of a life could scarcely impress them more vividly. We saw Cadiz only for an hour; but the white buildings, and the glorious blue sea, how clear they are to the memory!—with the tang of that gipsy's guitar dancing in the market-place, in the midst of the fruit, and the beggars, and the sunshine. Who can forget the Bosphorus, the brightest and fairest scene in all the world; or the towering lines of Gibraltar; or the great piles of Mafra, as we rode into the Tagus? As I write this, and think, back comes Rhodes, with its old towers and artillery, and that wonderful atmosphere, and that astonishing blue sea which environs the island. The Arab riders go pacing over the plains of Sharon, in the rosy twilight, just before sunrise; and I can see the ghastly Moab mountains, with the Dead Sea gleaming before them; from the mosque, on the way towards Bethany. The black, gnarled trees of Gethsemane lie at the foot of Olivet, and the yellow ramparts of the city rise up on the stony hills beyond.

But the happiest and best of all the recollections, perhaps, are those of the hours passed at night on the deck, when the stars were shining overhead, and the hours were tolled at their time, and your thoughts were fixed upon home far away. As the sun rose I once heard the priest, from the minaret of Constantinople, crying out 'Come to prayer,' with his shrill voice ringing through the clear air; and saw, at the same hour, the Arab prostrate himself and pray, and the Jew Rabbi, bending over his book, and worshipping the Maker of Turk and Jew. Sitting at home in London, and writing this last line of farewell, those figures come back the clearest of all to the memory, with the picture, too, of our ship sailing over the peaceful Sabbath sea, and our own prayers and services celebrated there. So each, in his fashion, and after his kind, is bowing down, and adoring the Father, who is equally above all. Cavil not, you brother or sister, if your neighbour's voice is not like yours; only hope, that his words are honest (as far as they may be), and his heart humble and thankful.

JUVENILIA

THE SNOB

1829

OUR 'SNOB'S' BIRTH, PARENTAGE, AND EDUCATION

'NEVER shall I forget,' said an old crone to me the other day, who, as far as we know, is cotemporary with the alley in which we live—'Never shall I forget the night in which you, Mr. Tudge, made your first appearance among us. Your father had, in his usual jocular manner, turned every one from the fireside, and putting a foot on each hob, with a pot in one hand and a pipe in the other, sat blowing a cloud.' 'Ay, Mrs. Siggins,' said I, 'νεφεληγετα Ζευς, I suppose, as the blind bard has it.' 'Keep your Latin for the collegers,' said she ; 'I know nothing on't. Well, lo and behold, as I was saying, we were all sitting quiet as mice, when just as I had turned over the last page of the Skeleton Chief, or Bloody Bandit, a sound, like I don't know what, came from overhead. Now, no one was upstairs, so, as you may well suppose, the noise brought my heart into my mouth, nay more, it brought your dad to his legs, and you into the world. For your mother was taken ill directly, and we helped her off to bed.' '*Parturiunt montes nas —*' said I, stopping short in confusion. Thank Heaven, the old woman knew not the end of the proverb, but went on with her story. '"Go, Bill," says your father, "see what noise was that." Off went Bill, pale as a sheet, while I attended to your mother. Bill soon came laughing down. '·The boot-jack fell off the peg," says he. "It's a boy," screams I. "How odd!" says your dad. "What's odd?" says I. "The child, and the jack—it's ominous," says he. "As how?" says I. "Call the child Jack," says he.' And so they did, and that's the way, do you see, my name was Jack Clypei Septemplicis Ajax.

Early in life I was sent to a small school in the next street, where I soon learnt to play at marbles, blow my nose in my pinafore, and bow to the mistress. Having thus exhausted her whole stock of knowledge, I migrated to Miss G——'s, in Trumpington Street, and under the tuition of the sisters, became intimately acquainted, before I was nine years of age, with the proper distribution of letters in most three-syllable words of the British tongue, *i.e.*, I became an expert speller.

(*To be continued.*)

EXTRACT FROM A LETTER, FROM ONE IN CAMBRIDGE, TO ONE IN TOWN

OF the Musical Clubs, I shall not say a word,
Since to none but the Members they pleasure afford.
The —— still play as they usually did,
While the good-natured visitors praise what they're bid.
This law 'mid these sons of Apollo will tell,
' To play very loud is to play very well ; '—
A concert '*piano*' they deem quite absurd—
In music like that ev'ry blunder is heard ;
The best singer that Cambridge e'er saw they agree,
Was a friend of my own that could reach double B ;
In fine, I imagine, they think it a crime,
To spare any sound, or to lose any time,
So the laurels of course are by him always won,
Who makes the most noise, and who soonest cries, ' Done.'
Well, enough of the —— ; the —— comes next,
' *Vox et præterea nil* ' is its text ;
For though on its list it still must be confest
That of all Cambridge singers it numbers the best ;
Yet, while, thro' good nature, it falsely permits,
While the rest sing '*piano*'—one screaming in fits,
It cannot expect unconditional praise,
Or more than politeness to amateurs pays.
A word of the ——, and I've done—
They have but one fault, and a laughable one,
When seated at supper, they seem to forget
The purpose for which they pretend to have met ;
I was taken there once, and I found that good eating,
Was the greatest, if not the sole, cause of their meeting.

T. T.

TIMBUCTOO

To the Editor of 'The Snob'

SIR,—Though your name be 'Snob,' I trust you will not refuse this tiny 'Poem of a Gownsman,' which was unluckily not finished on the day appointed for delivery of the several copies of verses on Timbuctoo. I thought, Sir, it would be a pity that such a poem should be lost to the world ; and conceiving *The Snob* to be the most widely circulated periodical in Europe, I have taken the liberty of submitting it for insertion or approbation.— I am, Sir, yours, etc. etc. etc.   T.

TIMBUCTOO

The situation.	In Africa (a quarter of the world)
	Men's skins are black, their hair is crisp and curl'd ;
	And somewhere there, unknown to public view,
	A mighty city lies, called Timbuctoo.
The natural history.	There stalks the tiger,—there the lion roars 5
	Who sometimes eats the luckless blackamoors ;
	All that he leaves of them the monster throws
	To jackals, vultures, dogs, cats, kites, and crows.
	His hunger thus the forest monarch gluts,
	And then lies down 'neath trees called cocoa-nuts. 10
The lion hunt.	Quick issue out, with musket, torch, and brand,
	The sturdy blackamoors, a dusky band !
	The beast is found,—pop goes the musketoons,—
	The lion falls, covered with horrid wounds.
Their lives at home.	At home their lives in pleasure always flow, 15
	But many have a different lot to know !
Abroad.	They're often caught, and sold as slaves, alas !
Reflections on the foregoing.	Thus men from highest joy to sorrow pass.
	Yet though thy monarchs and thy nobles boil
	Rack and molasses in Jamaica's isle ! 20
	Desolate Afric ! thou art lovely yet ! !
	One heart yet beats which ne'er shall thee forget.
	What though thy maidens are a blackish brown,
	Does virtue dwell in whiter breasts alone ?
	Oh no, oh no, oh no, oh no, oh no ! 25
	It shall not, must not, cannot, e'er be so.
	The day shall come when Albion's self shall feel

Stern Afric's wrath, and writhe 'neath Afric's steel.
I see her tribes the hill of glory mount,
And sell their sugars on their own account ;   30
While round her throne the prostrate nations come,
Sue for her rice, and barter for her rum.   32

Line 1 and 2.   See Guthrie's Geography.

The site of Timbuctoo is doubtful ; the Author has neatly expressed this in the Poem, at the same time giving us some slight hints relative to its situation.

Line 5.   So Horace.—leonum arida nutrix.

Line 8.   Thus Apollo   ἐλώρια τεῦχε κύνεσσιν
                        Οἰωνοῖσί τε πᾶσι.

Line 5–10.   How skilfully introduced are the animal and vegetable productions of Africa !   It is worthy to remark the various garments in which the Poet hath clothed the Lion.   He is called 1st, the Lion ; 2nd, the Monster (for he is very large) ; and 3rd, the Forest Monarch, which he undoubtedly is.

Line 11–14.   The Author confesses himself under peculiar obligations to Denham's and Clapperton's Travels, as they suggested to him the spirited description contained in these lines.

Line 13.   'Pop goes the musketoons.'   A learned friend suggested 'Bang,' as a stronger expression ; but, as African gunpowder is notoriously bad, the Author thought ' Pop' the better word.

Line 15–18.   A concise but affecting description is here given of the domestic habits of the people,—the infamous manner in which they are entrapped and sold as slaves is described,—and the whole ends with an appropriate moral sentiment.   The Poem might here finish, but the spirit of the bard penetrates the veil of futurity, and from it cuts off a bright piece for the hitherto unfortunate Africans, as the following beautiful lines amply exemplify.

It may perhaps be remarked that the Author has here 'changed his hand' ; he answers that it was his intention so to do.   Before it was his endeavour to be elegant and concise, it is now his wish to be enthusiastic and magnificent.   He trusts the Reader will perceive the aptness with which he hath changed his style : when he narrated facts he was calm, when he enters on prophecy he is fervid.

The enthusiasm which he feels is beautifully expressed in lines 25, 26.   He thinks he has very successfully imitated in the last six lines the best manner of Mr. Pope, and in lines 19–26 the pathetic elegance of the Author of Australasia and Athens.

The Author cannot conclude without declaring that his aim in writing this Poem will be fully accomplished, if he can infuse in the breasts of Englishmen a sense of the danger in which they lie.   Yes—Africa ! If he can awaken one particle of sympathy for thy sorrows, of love for thy land, of admiration for thy virtue, he shall sink into the grave with the proud consciousness that he has raised esteem, where before there was contempt, and has kindled the flame of hope, on the smouldering ashes of Despair !

TO GENEVIEVE

A Disinterested Epistle

Say do I seek, my Genevieve !
  Thy charms alone to win ?
Oh no ! for thou art fifty-five,
  And uglier than sin !

Or do I love the flowing verse
  Upon thy syren tongue ?
Oh no ! those strains of thine are worse
  Than ever screech-owl sung.

Since then I thus refuse my love
  For songs or charms to give,
What could my tardy passion move ?
  Thy money, Genevieve !

A Literary Snob.

MRS. RAMSBOTTOM IN CAMBRIDGE

RADISH GROUND BUILDINGS.

DEAR SIR,

I was surprised to see my name in Mr. Bull's paper, for I give you my word I have not written a syllabub to him since I came to reside here, that I might enjoy the satiety of the literary and learned world.

I have the honour of knowing many extinguished persons. I am on terms of the greatest contumacy with the Court of Aldermen, who first recommended your weakly dromedary to my notice, knowing that I myself was a great literati. When I am at home, and in the family way, I make Lavy read it to me, as I consider you the censure of the anniversary, and a great upholder of moral destruction.

When I came here, I began reading Mechanics (written by that gentleman whose name you whistle). I thought it would be something like the Mechanic's Magazine, which my poor dear Ram used to make me read to him, but I found them very foolish. What do I want to know about weights and measures and bull's-eyes, when I have left off trading? I have therefore begun a course of ugly-physics, which are very odd, and written by the Marquis of Spinningtoes.

I think the Library of Trinity College is one of the most admiral objects here. I saw the busks of several gentlemen whose statutes I had seen at Room, and who all received there edification at that College. There was Aristocracy who wrote farces for the Olympic Theatre, and Democracy, who was a laughing philosopher.

I forgot to mention, that my son George Frederick is entered at St. John's, because I heard that they take most care of their morals at that College. I called on the tutor, who received myself and son very politely, and said he had no doubt my son would be a tripod, and he hoped perspired higher than polly, which I did not like. I am going to give a tea at my house, when I shall be delighted to see yourself and children.

Believe me, dear Sir,

Your most obedient and affectionate

DOROTHEA JULIA RAMSBOTTOM.

A STATEMENT OF FAX RELATIVE TO THE LATE MURDER

By D. J. RAMSBOTTOM

'Come I to speak in Cæsar's funeral.'—MILTON, JULIUS CÆSAR, *Act iii.*

ON Wednesday the 3rd of June as I was sitting in my back parlour taking tea, young Frederick Tudge entered the room; I reserved from his dislevelled hair and vegetated appearance that something was praying on his vittles. When I heard from him the cause of his vegetation, I was putrified! I stood transfigured! His Father, the Editor of 'The Snob,' had been macerated in the most sanguine manner. The drops of compassion refused my eyes, for I thought of him, whom I had lately seen high in health and happiness; that ingenuous indivisable, who often and often when seated alone with me, has 'made the table roar,' as the poet has it, and whose constant aim in his weakly dromedary was to delight as well as to reprove. His son Frederick, too young to be acquainted with the art of literal imposition, has commissioned me to excommunicate the circumstances of his death, and call down the anger of the Proctors and Court of Aldermen on the phlogitious perforators of the deed.

It appears that as he was taking his customary rendezvous by the side of Trumpington Ditch, he was stopped by some men in under-gravy dresses, who put a pitch-plaister on him, which completely developed his nose and eyes, or, as Shakespeare says, 'his visible ray.' He was then dragged into a field, and the horrid deed was replete! Such are the circumstances of his death; but Mr. Tudge died like Wriggle-us, game to the last; or like Cæsar, in that beautiful faction of the poet, with which I have headed my remarks, I mean him who wanted to be Poop of Room, but was killed by two Brutes, and the fascinating hands of a perspiring Senate.

With the most sanguinary hopes that the Anniversary and Town will persecute an inquiry into this dreadful action, I will conclude my repeal to the pathetic reader; and if by such a misrepresentation of fax I have been enabled to awaken an apathy for the children of the late Mr. Tudge, who are left in the most desultory state, I shall feel the satisfaction of having exorcised my pen in the cause of Malevolence, and soothed the inflictions of indignant Misery.

D. J. RAMSBOTTOM.

P.S.—The publisher requests me to state that the present No is published from the MS. found in Mr. Tudge's pocket, and one more number will be soon forthcoming containing his inhuman papers.

TO THE FREE AND INDEPENDENT SNOBS
OF CAMBRIDGE!

FRIENDS! ALDERMEN! AND SNOBS!

I am a woman of feminine propensities, and it may seem odd that I should come forward in a public rapacity; but having heard that Cambridge is about to send a preventative to Parliament, I cannot, on so momentary an occasion, refrain from offering a few reservations of my own on the subject.

I beg leave to offer MR. FREDERICK TUDGE as a bandit for so legible a position.

I pledge myself that my young friend shall become a radical deformity in the state; certain I am that his principals are libertine, that his talents will lead him to excess, and finely, that he will tread in the shoes of that execrated saint, his murdered father!

No one can deny that his claims on the free electors of Cambridge are great, *very* great! For it is well known his father ever resisted with his pen the efforts of the Mayor and Cooperation. Must it not then be the height of infanticide if they do not with heart and hand, following the example of their eternal slave,

D. J. RAMSBOTTOM,

EXCLAIM:

TUDGE AND 'LIBERTY?' ! ! !

THE END OF ALL THINGS

GOOD heavens! Do we live in a savage land? Shall crime heaped upon crime go unnoticed? Shall the perpetrators of deeds of the blackest dye, escape their merited punishment? Alas!

alas! it seems so. My honoured father rests in a bloody grave, his bones have become dust, and his flesh has fattened a thousand worms, and yet his murderers live secure in the rank a cap and gown has obtained for them. But this is not all, listen again, my dear friends, to a tale of startling horror.

Mrs. Ramsbottom during the summer months has been accustomed every evening to walk in Grandchester Fields till rather a late hour, deeming the halo of her own innocence a sufficient protection. But on Sunday evening last a man enveloped in a long cloak (seemingly a military gentleman) followed her home, and as she entered her house, rushed in behind her and closed the door. He then pulled out a brace of pistols, and, threatening her with death unless she complied, made her swear to forbear canvassing the aldermen for myself, Mr. Tudge, junior. Horrible deed! it stirs up my manly blood even to mention it.

Well, the next morning three gentlemen called upon me, and offered to enter me at one of the small colleges, if I would withdraw from the poll. That I accepted their offer is evident from the date of this account, and now that I have received from them a sum sufficient to defray all my college expenses, I think it no longer incumbent upon me to keep my promise, and so, most worthy burgesses, I still solicit—YOUR VOTE AND INTEREST.

But to my general readers I have to address a few more words. I had hoped by hard study so to improve my mind as to be able during the next term to carry on this journal, with the assistance of Mrs. R. But all my hopes have vanished : Mrs. R. has gone mad, through the fright she sustained on Sunday night, and has been sent home to her friends, and I, having now become a gownsman, cannot carry on a work adverse to University principles. Therefore, my dear friends, thanking you for your great and invariable kindness, and hoping though unseen that I may still be an object of affection and respect, I beg leave to bid you all, though with tears in my eyes, an eternal farewell.

F. TUDGE.

St. John's College.

THE GOWNSMAN

1829–1830

(formerly called) 'The Snob,' a Literary and Scientific Journal,
now conducted by Members of the University.

DEDICATION.

TO ALL PROCTORS,

BOTH PAST, PRESENT, AND FUTURE

THE DISTINGUISHED PATRONS OF ALL THAT ACADEMICAL
TALENT AND MORALITY,
WITH WHICH THEY THEMSELVES ARE SO EMINENTLY GIFTED,
WHOSE TASTE IT IS OUR PRIVILEGE TO FOLLOW,
WHOSE VIRTUES IT IS OUR DUTY TO IMITATE,
AND WHOSE PRESENCE IT IS OUR INTEREST TO AVOID ;
THIS HUMBLE VOLUME,
WHOSE ONLY AIM HAS BEEN THE REAL WELFARE
OF ALL TRUE KNOWLEDGE AND GOODNESS,
BY DETECTING THE ASS IN THE SKIN OF THE LION, THE WOLF
IN THE CLOTHING OF THE LAMB ;
IS
WITH ALL THE RESPECT USUALLY PAID TO THE SAME,
MOST AFFECTIONATELY DEDICATED,
BY THEIR FAITHFUL SERVANT,

THE GOWNSMAN.

LETTER FROM MRS. RAMSBOTTOM

Dear Mr. Editor,—

I wish people would not go propagating candles about me; I saw in The Snob (and I assure you I feel quite indigent at it) that I was dead! I am still in Radish-ground Buildings, and I am alive as you see by my telegraph.

D. J. Ramsbottom.

I send you my opinion on several things, which have happened in Cambridge, and which I thought called for my critical debilities. They are contained in a letter to a friend, which I wrote on Saturday. I have not kept back a sillabus of it, this I assure you is a complete fac-totum.

I told you, my dear friend, that I am residing in Cambridge, the seat of a renowned University, which is two Proctors and a number of young men, who are said to be in stature capillairy, but why, I cannot make out.

I daresay that you know that our gracious Sovereign (they were guineas before his time) was almost blown up by a wretch named Fox, one fifth of November. So ever since the young men on that day, have asalted the Snobs, which is the townspeople. They fit a good deal on the fifth, but the Snobs beat them, being as numerous as the sands in the otion. On the six instinct, as the papers say, the Universary men went out with the odd revolution of scouring the streets, which, to be sure, are very dirty, but I suppose they did it to see whether the Snobs would prevent them.

I cannot describe the battle which took place on that occasion, it would require the pen of Homo. There was two great arrows on the Snob side, which was a butcher and a miller, they made a great slatter in the ranks of the Gownsmen.

The Gownsmen were very brave, every one of them says he knocked down at least five in the malay; though I think they had been better employed in squaring at the circle than squaring at the townsmen——

*   *   *   *   *

I must bid you a jew, my dear Jemima, ever your confectioner,
Dorothea Julia R——.

Proscrip.—Let me advise you to buy the Gownsman, a

Cambridge paper; there was a beautiful Epithet in the last number, and I daresay I shall send some of my poetic diffusions, which I think are fit for desertion.

———————

The part in hysterics is not of a nature for the 'world's kin,' it is only a piece of private infirmity.

MODERN SONGS.—No. 5

Air—' I'd be a Butterfly.'

I'D be a tadpole, born in a puddle,
    Where dead cats, and drains, and water-rats meet;
Then under a stone I so snugly would cuddle,
    With some other tad that was pretty and sweet.
I'd never seek my poor brains for to muddle,
    With thinking why I had no toes to my feet;
But under a stone I so snugly would cuddle,
    With some other tad as was pretty and sweet.

If I could borrow the wand of a fairy,
    I'd be a fish and have beautiful fins—
But yet in this puddle I'm cleanly and airy,
    I'm washed by the waters, and cool'd by the winds!
Fish in a pond must be watchful and wary,
    Or boys will catch them with worms and hooked pins.
I'd be a tadpole, cleanly and airy,
    Washed by the waters, and wiped by the winds.

What though you tell me each black little rover
    Dies in the sun when the puddle is dry,—
Do you not think that when it's all over
    With my best friends I'll be happy to die?
Some may turn toads with great speckled bellies,
    Swim in the gutter, or spit on the road,
I'll stay a tadpole, and not like them fellers,
    Be one day a tad, and the other a toad!

FROM ANACREON

Prepare thy silver, god of fire,
  And light thy forges up ;
No soldier I to ask of thee
Bright arms and glittering panoply ;
To these let warrior chiefs aspire—
  I ask a mighty cup ?

A mighty cup ! but draw not on it
  Orion grim with clubs advancing,
Or heavenly wains, or rampant bears,
What cares Anacreon for the stars ?
Draw Love and my Bathyllus on it,
  'Mid clustering vines with Bacchus dancing.

THE NATIONAL STANDARD OF LITERATURE, SCIENCE, MUSIC, THEATRICALS, AND THE FINE ARTS

1833–1834.

LOUIS PHILIPPE

HERE is Louis Philippe, the great Roi des Français,
(Roi de France is no longer the phrase of the day ;)

His air just as noble, his mien as complete,
His face as majestic, his breeches as neat ;
His hat just so furnished with badge tricolor,
Sometimes worn on the side, sometimes sported before,
But wherever 'tis placed, much in shape and in size,
Like an overgrown pancake 'saluting men's eyes.'
From hat down to boots, from his pouch to umbrella,
He here stands before you, a right royal fellow.

Like 'the king in the parlour' he's fumbling his money,
Like 'the queen in the kitchen,' his speech is all honey.
Except when he talks it, like Emperor Nap,
Of his wonderful feats at Fleurus and Jemappe ;
But, alas ! all his zeal for the multitude's gone,
And of no numbers thinking, except number one !
No huzzas greet his coming, no patriot-club licks
The hand of 'the best of created republics.'
He stands in Paris as you see him before ye,
Little more than a snob—There's an end of the story.

ADDRESS

UNDER the 'heading' of this NATIONAL STANDARD of ours there
originally appeared the following :
'Edited by F. W. N. Bayley, Esq., the late Editor and
Originator of "The National Omnibus," the first of the cheap
Publications ; assisted by the most eminent Literary Men of the
Day.'
Now we have *changé tout cela* ; no, not exactly *tout* cela ; for
we still retain the assistance of a host of literary talent, but
Frederick William Naylor Bayley has gone. We have got free
of the Old Bailey, and changed the Governor. Let it not be
imagined for a moment that we talk in the slightest disparagement
of our predecessor in office ; on the contrary, we shall always continue to think him a clever fellow, and wish him all kinds of
success in the war he is carrying on against Baron Dimsdale.
He apparently has exchanged the pen for the sword.
Having the fear of the Fate of Sir John Cam Hobhouse before
our eyes, we give no pledges, expressed or understood, as to the
career which it is our intention to run. We intend to be as free
as the air. The world of books is all before us where to choose

our course.   Others boast that they are perfectly independent of all considerations extraneous to the sheet in which they write, but none that we know of reduce that boast to practice : we therefore boast not at all.   We promise nothing, and, if our readers expect nothing more, they will assuredly not be disappointed.

They must be a little patient, however, for a while.   We cannot run a race with our elder rivals, who, in consequence of their age, strange as it may seem to pedestrians, must beat their juniors in swiftness.   To drop metaphor, we are not yet sufficiently in favour with those magnates of literature, the publishers, to get what in the trade is called 'the early copies'; and therefore we have it not in our power to review a book before it is published. Whether those who trust to such criticisms are likely to form a just judgment of the books so reviewed, is another question, which we should be inclined to answer in the negative.   To speak plainly, the critics are as much the property of the booksellers as the books themselves, and the oracles speak by the inspiration of those who own them.   We shall, however, mend even in that particular in due course of time ; and when our arrangements are duly matured (which we hope will be next week), we trust that we shall present our readers with 'a superior article,' at what we are sure may safely be called 'an encouraging price.'

In the mean time, we shall tell a story.   One of the results of the manner in which our poor-laws are administered, is a system of forced marriages.   A parish, anxious to get rid of a young woman who is pressing on its resources, often advances her a portion, if she can find a husband.   The sum given is not very magnificent, seldom amounting to more than five pounds.   A very pretty girl in a parish, of which we, like Cervantes, in the beginning of *Don Quixote*, do not choose to recollect the name, obtained one of their splendid dowries, and was married accordingly.   A lady, who patronised the bride, shortly after the marriage saw the bridegroom, who by no means equalled Adonis in beauty.   'Good Heavens!' said she to the girl, 'how could you marry such a fright as that?'   'Why, ma'am,' was the reply, 'he certainly is not very handsome ; but what sort of a husband can one expect for five pounds?'

We leave the moral to the reader, as well as its application to us.   But we shall prove to them, nevertheless, that the sort of Paper we shall give them for twopence is not to be despised.

MR. BRAHAM

SONNET. By W. WORDSWORTH

SAY not that Judah's harp hath lost its tone,
Or that no bard hath found it where it hung,

MR. BRAHAM.

Broken and lonely, voiceless and unstrung,
Beside the sluggish streams of Babylon;

Sloman ![1] repeats the strain his fathers sung,
And Judah's burning lyre is Braham's own !
Behold him here.   Here view the wondrous man,
Majestical and lovely, as when first
In music on a wondering world he burst,
And charmed the ravished ears of Sov'reign Anne ![2]

Mark well the form, O ! reader, nor deride
The sacred symbol—Jew's harp glorified—
Which circled with a blooming wreath is seen
Of verdant bays ; and thus are typified
The pleasant music and the baize of green
Whence issues out at eve, Braham with front serene !

N. M. ROTHSCHILD, ESQ.

HERE's the pillar of 'Change ! Nathan Rothschild himself,
    With whose fame every bourse in the universe rings ;
The first [3] Baron Juif ; by the grace of his pelf,
Not 'the king of the Jews,' but 'the Jew of the kings.'

The great incarnation of cents and consols,
    The eighths, halves, and quarters, scrip, options, and shares ;
Who plays with new kings as young Misses with dolls ;
    The monarch undoubted of bulls and of bears !

O, Plutus ! your graces are queerly bestowed !
    Else sure we should think you behaved *infra dig.*,
When with favours surpassing, it joys you to load
    A greasy-faced compound of donkey and pig.

[1] It is needless to speak of this eminent vocalist and improvisatore.   He nightly delights a numerous and respectable audience at the Cider-cellar ; and while on this subject, I cannot refrain from mentioning the kindness of Mr. Evans, the worthy proprietor of that establishment.   N.B.—A *table d'hôte* every Friday.— *W. Wordsworth.*

[2] Mr. Braham made his first appearance in England in the reign of Queen Anne.—W. W.

[3] Some years ago, shortly after the elevation (by the Emperor of Austria) of one of the Rothschilds to the rank of Baron, he was present at a soirée in Paris, which he entered about the same time as the Duc de Montmorenci. 'Ah !' said Talleyrand, 'Voici le premier baron Chrétien, et le premier baron Juif.' The Montmorencies boast, and we believe justly, that they are the first Christian barons. We all know that the Rothschilds may make the same claim of precedence among the Jews.

Here, just as he stands with his head pointed thus,
  At full-length, gentle reader, we lay him before ye ;

N. M. ROTHSCHILD, ESQ.

And we then leave the Jew (what we wish he'd leave us,
  But we fear to no purpose), *a lone* in his glory.

LONDON CHARACTERS : No. 1

WE cannot afford rhymes to the hero whom we have here
depicted ; he is decidedly a subject for the pedestrian Muse of
prose.   He is No. 1 of our London Characters : as Shakespeare,
or somebody else, advises us to catch the ideas as they fly, we fix
the idea-bearer as he runs.

It was impossible to refrain from taking him (graphically, we mean, for we do not belong to the police, 'whether it be new or old'), as we saw him scudding along with the rapidity of a hare, at the Coldbath-fields meeting of last week, which of course we attended. 'Britons, be firm,' spoke the valorous placard *on* the breast. 'Let this particular and individual Briton run for his life!' spoke the more direct monitor *within* the breast. There was no delay in making the decision—the motion was carried, and

a very rapid motion it was. The poor National Convention was run away with in a van; the new constitution, and the members of it, were equally knocked on the head; and why should our friend the bill-sticker have pasted himself against the wall merely to be torn down by the police? If his placard was stationary, it was no reason that *he* should be so.

On the whole, the world of politics might take a useful lesson from the bill-stickers. They are beyond question the most active agents in disseminating among the public the political or literary opinions of all sides, and yet they never quarrel. It was truly refreshing, during the angry contest between Sir John Cam Hobhouse, Colonel Evans, and Mr. Bickham Escott, to see their ambulatory agents mixing at street-corners and other places where placardmen do congregate, with the most harmonious cordiality. They did their duty, but they never suffered it to interfere with their private friendships. It is highly probable that few of them read Ariosto, at least with critical eye, but their conduct much reminded us of the panegyrics in Orlando Furioso on the mutual courtesy of the ancient knights towards each other. We murmured to ourselves,

O gran bontà de' cavalièri antichi,

and so forth ; and rejoiced to find that glorious characteristic of the chivalry of the Round Table revived under our own eyes by the corporation of placard-bearers. All around in Covent-Garden everything was indignation ; the very cabbages and turnip-tops were moved ; orators spoke on the hustings and off the hustings in all the fervour of excited zeal ; the eyes of the market, the town, the county, the kingdom, the continent, the world, turned with anxious glare on the result of the contest ; and there, meanwhile, 'in the hot-press and tumult of the hour,' the very men whose hats and bosoms, and sides and bellies, were stuck with the most impassioned cries and watchwords of their respective parties, whose hands uplifted the banners which waved above the conflict as the guide-stars of the current of war, walked about with all the coolness of the peripatetic school, to which they unquestionably belong. It was something truly cheering to those who wish for the banishment of the angry passions from the human breast, to witness the philosophical air of abstraction which these sages exhibited ; they were *in* politics, but not *of* them ; like the *Public Ledger*, they were open to all parties, but influenced by none ; and evidently being of opinion, with Swift, that party is the madness of the many for the gain of the few, suffered not their minds to be disheartened by any such insanity, meditated upon their own gains, and thought only on their *shilling a day and their board*.

Interesting race ! We here consign one of the fraternity to wood. What to him was Lee ? no more than Governor Le of Canton ; and, as for the eminent chairman, Mr. Mee, our running friend would willingly have quoted Virgil, had he happened to have known him ; and exclaiming to the police, 'MEE, MEE—in MEE convertite telum,' left the National Convention to its fate, with the sole regret that he did not insist on his shillings *before* operations commenced.

A. BUNN

1.

WHAT gallant cavalier is seen
So dainty set before the queen,
 Between a pair of candles?

A. BUNN.

Who looks as smiling and as bright,
As oily, and as full of light,
 As is the wax he handles?

2.

Dressed out as gorgeous as a lord,
Stuck to his side a shining sword,
　　A-murmuring loyal speeches,
The gentleman who's coming on,
Is Mr. Manager A. Bunn
　　All in his velvet breeches.

3.

He moves, our gracious queen to greet,
And guide her to her proper seat,
　　(A bag-wigged cicerone).
O Adelaide ! you will not see,
'Mong all the German com-pa-ny
A figure half so droll as he,
　　Or half so worth your money.

LOVE IN FETTERS,

A Tottenham-Court-Road Ditty,

Showing how dangerous it is for a Gentleman to fall in love with an ' Officer's Daughter.'

AN OWER TRUE TALE

1.

I FELL in love, three days ago,
With a fair maid as bright as snow,
　　Whose cheeks would beat the rose ;
The raven tresses of her hair
In blackness could with night compare,
　　Like Venus's her nose :
Her eyes, of lustre passing rare,
　　Bright as the diamond glowed,
If you would know, you may go see,
If you won't go, pray credit me ;
　　　　'Twas at the back
　　　　Of the Tabernac,
In Tottenham Court Road.

2.

The street in which my beauty shone
Is named in compliment to John ;
   Her house is nigh to where
A massy hand all gilt with gold,
A thundering hammer doth uphold,
   High lifted in the air ;
What home it is you shall be told
   Before I end my ode ;

LOVE IN FETTERS.

If you would know, go there and see,
If you won't go, then credit me ;
     'Twas at the back
      Of the Tabernac
In Tottenham Court Road

3.

Smitten with love at once I wrote
A neat triangular, tender note,
   All full of darts and flame ;
Said I, ' Sweet star,' —but you may guess
How lovingly I did express
   My passion for the dame ;

I signed my name and true address,
　But she served me like a toad.
If you would know, pray come and see,
If you won't come, then credit me ;
　　　'Twas at the back
　　　Of the Tabernac
In Tottenham Court Road.

4.

Next morn, 'tis true, an answer came,
I started when I heard my name,
　　As I in bed did lie ;
Says a soft voice, ' Are you the cove
Wot wrote a letter full of love ?
　　' Yes, yes,' I cried, ' 'tis I ;'
' An answer's sent,' said he— O Jove !
　　What a sad note he showed.
If you would know, pray come and see,
If you will not, then credit me ;
　　　'Twas at the back
　　　Of the Tabernac,
In Tottenham Court Road.

5.

By a parchment slip I could discern
That by me stood a bailiff stern,
　　My Rosamunda's sire !
I served the daughter with verse and wit,
And the father served me with a writ,
　　An exchange I don't admire :
So here in iron bars I sit
　　In quod securely stowed,
Being captivated by a she,
Whose papa captivated me ;
　　　All at the back
　　　Of the Tabernac,
In Tottenham Court Road.

Woman: the Angel of Life. A Poem. By Robert Montgomery, Author of the ' Omnipresence of the Deity,' ' The Messiah,' etc. 12mo, pp. 198. London, 1833. Turrill.

THERE is one decidedly pleasant line in this book. It is, ' Frederick Schoberl, jun., 4, Leicester Street, Leicester Square.'

It sounds like softest music in attending ears, after having gone through 183 pages of Montgomery's rhyme, flanked by some fifteen pages of Montgomery's prose. We never had any notion that the name of Schoberl would have sounded so harmoniously in our ears, until we found it to be the term and conclusion of the work called 'Woman,' set up as the last milestone to show that our wearisome pilgrimage was at an end. And yet we are unjust in calling it wearisome, for the poem is of the most soothing kind. 'Not poppy nor mandragora, nor all the drowsy syrups of this world,' can compare with the gentle narcotic here afforded us by Turrill. Many have been the trades of that eminent person. He was a knife-grinder and a haberdasher, a stationer and fancy penman, a Windsor soap vendor, and a commissioner for the sale of Hunt's roasted corn and Godbold's vegetable balsam. He then went into the publishing line, and he now appears as a vendor of opiates. In the most desperate case of want of sleep, an application of Woman—we mean Turrill and Montgomery's Woman—is a never failing specific. Well may they sing, with *Macheath*—

> When the heart of a man is oppressed with cares,
> The mist is dispelled when Bob's Woman appears
> Like the syrup of poppies she gently, gently
> Closes the eyelids and seals the ears.
> > Page after page will induce a doze,
> > Drawing soft melody from the nose.

He who, as Dr. Johnson says, would not snore over Montgomery's 'Woman,' must be more or less than human.—*Rambler*, vol. i., p. 186. Ed. 1763.

Therefore do we speak of it with respect, and recommend it to the favourable notice of the Apothecaries' Company, for insertion in their next Pharmacopœia. Montgomery's former works were absurd. You could not help being jolly with 'Satan'; he created a laugh beneath the ribs of 'Death.' 'Oxford' was droll to a *degree*, and so forth ; but here, in 'Woman,' everything is dead. Page after page there is the same sound, somnolent, sonorous snore. It is not enough to say that the book is *dull*—it is dullness ; the embodied appearance of 'the mighty Mother' herself. On the honour of critics, we shall open the book at random. Here, then, we pounce on page 80, and it is a description of Dante. Dante and Bob Montgomery ?

> 'Powers
> Eternal ! Such names blended !'

Read it, dear reader, if you can.

> ' With paleness on his awful brow
> Who riseth like a spectre now
> From darkness, where his fancy dared
> To wander with an eye unscared,
> And gaze on visions, such as roll
> Around that blighted angel's soul
> Who baffles in his dread domain
> An immortality of pain ?
> 'Tis Dante, whose terrific flight
> Through caverns of Cimmerian night
> Imagination vainly tries
> To track the unappalled eyes !
> Severe, august, and sternly great,
> The gloom of his remorseless fate.
> Around him hung that dismal air
> That broodeth o'er intense despair ;
> Till frenzy half began to raise
> A wildness in his fearful gaze,
> As roaming over crag and wood,
> He battled with bleak solitude ;
> But sooner might the maniac roar
> Of ocean cease to awe the shore,
> When starlight comes with fairy gleam,
> Than pity lull his tortured dream.
> Oh ! 'tis not in the poet's art
> To paint the earthquake of his heart.
> The storm of feeling's ghastly strife,
> When she, who formed his life of life,
> Had vanished like a twilight ray,
> Too delicate on earth to stay :—
> For love had heated blood and brain,
> A fire in each electric vein ;
> A passion, whose exceeding power,
> Was heaven or hell to each wild hour.'

It is well for Montgomery that Dante is dead, else he would have doomed him to Caina for this. It is, however, about the best passage in the poem.

But we must quote something about woman ; and our partiality for our native charmers induces us to take the following : —

> ' But where is woman most arrayed,
> With all that mind would see displayed ?
> Oh, England ! round thy chainless isle
> How fondly doth the godhead smile,

And crowd within thy little spot
A universe of glorious lot !
But never till the wind-rocked sea
Have borne us far from home and thee,
The patriotic fervours rise
To hallow thy forsaken skies !
Though nature with sublimer stress,
Hath stamped her seal of loveliness
On climes of more colossal mould,
How much that travelled eyes behold
Would sated wonder throw away
To take one look where England lay ;
To wander down some hawthorn lane,
And drink the lark's delightful strain ?
Or floating from a pastured dell
To hear the sheep's romantic bell ?
While valeward as the hills retire
Peeps greyly forth the hamlet spire,
And all around it breathes a sense
Of weal, and worth, and competence ;
But far beyond all other dowers
Thy daughters seem, earth's human flowers !
The charm of young Castilian eyes
When lovingly their lashes rise,
And blended into one rich glance,
The lightnings of the soul advance,
Wild hearts may into wonder melt,
And make expression's magic felt ;
Or girded by the dream of old,
In Sappho's Lesbian Isle behold
A shadow of primeval grace
Yet floating o'er some classic face ;
But where, in what imperial land,
Hath nature with more faultless hand
Embodied all that beauty shows—
Than round us daily lives and glows ?
Here mingled with the outward night
Of charms that coolest gaze invite,
Th' enamel of the mind appears
Undimm'd by woe, unsoil'd by years !
To wedded hearts, devoid of strife,
Here home becomes the heaven of life ;
And household virtues spring to birth
Beside the love-frequented hearth ;
While feelings soft as angels know
Around them freshly twine and grow.'

And so and so, and so and so,
Does Bob Montgomery onward go,
In snuffling, snoring, slumbery verse,
Smooth as the motion of a hearse ;
A swell of sound, inducing sleep,
But not a thought in all the heap.
A spinning Jenny would compose
A hundred thousand lines like those,
From rising until setting sun,
And after all no business done.

The conclusion of the whole poem, we admit, is pretty ; and therefore we extract it :—

' Angel of life ! that home is thine
Till human hearts become divine ;
To feelings in their fond repose,
And Love his godhead can disclose
Where nature most reveals its worth ;
And if there be a home on earth
To charm the clouds of time away.
Born of her magic, blend their sway.
Domestic hours Elysium call,
The glory and the might of all ;
And self from out the selfish take,
The hopes that keep the heart awake ;
Of what our softer moods bestow
The grace, the lustre, and the glow.'

These are nice verses.   On examination, we find that the compositor, by some queer blunder, has printed them backwards ; but, as it does not seem to spoil the sense, we shall not give him the trouble of setting them up again.   They are just as good one way as the other ; and, indeed, the same might be said of the whole book.

DRAMA—COVENT GARDEN

[*By a Friend*]

ONE night last week we stretched ourselves along three empty benches in Covent Garden theatre, to hear the horrid parody—the disgusting burlesque, which goes under the name of ' Zauberflöte.' We must do justice to Messrs. Dobler and Hertz, as well as to

Madame Schroeder, by saying that they sustained their parts most ably ; but for the rest—for the company of the hideous screech-owls which Bunn, or some other gentleman of equally good taste, has collected at Covent Garden—the quaverings of a cracked ballad-singer, the screams of Miss Pearson herself, are melody to the howls of these high-Dutch monsters.

After an overture, tolerably ill-played, the curtain rose, and Herr Haitzinger, wrapped in a red table-cloth, came rushing over the stage, flying from a serpent or dragon, or some such thing, which wriggled and writhed on a most manifest rope, with felonious intent to frighten and devour Prince Tamino, enacted by Haitzinger aforesaid. Prince Haitzinger, fatigued by his running, squeaked out a melancholy recitative, and sank on a grassy plank, prepared to receive him. Scarcely was he silent, when three women—monsters in black bombazeen, each holding a tin spear, and representing the maiden attendants of the Queen of Night, entered and gave vent to a series of strains, such as—— but comparison is out of the question ; we never heard such before, and devoutly hope we never may again. The opening chorus of the ' Zauberflötte ' the most divine music of the divine Mozart, was mangled—burked—murdered, in such a manner by these German impostors, that the three men who, with ourselves, were in the pit, very nearly fainted ; however, as we were on duty, we made a point of not indulging our feelings, and resolutely listened on. Speaking with all deference to Bunn's elegant and well-known taste, and with the most tender and compassionate feeling for the fair sex, we had no idea that mothers could have conceived three such beings as these German Graces ; the first, with a licentious giggle—with a chin, moreover, as long as her mouth, and a mouth as long as the three-foot spear which she waved, made herself conspicuous by the freedom of her manners, the undeviating suavity of her smile, and the enormous thickness of her Allemannian ankles. The music was murder ; the spirit of Mozart was desecrated ; the audience was made to eat dirt, as Hajji Baba says : only, luckily, there were not many sufferers.

After these ladies had concluded their manœuvres, Madame Stoll Böhm appeared : she went through a variety of musical evolutions impossible to describe : (reader, be thankful you did not hear them !) among other feats, she executed a shake of a quarter of an hour's length, at which the solitary man in the gallery gave a faint and hollow clap, which sadly reverberated through the almost empty house.

For the drama, it is utterly indescribable. The *new* scenery has appeared in half-a-dozen Easter pieces. The *new* dresses have figured in the *Israelites in Egypt*. The whole opera was mangled, garbled, and distorted, agreeing in this with the music.

Papageno omitted his songs, (for which we were sorry, for he sang and acted very well) : would to heaven Papagen*a* had done the same ! Madame Meissinger is a nuisance so intolerable, that positively she ought to be indicted. She is not, however, paid above fifty pounds a week, so that we have not much reason to complain. The three boys, who advise and instruct, and lead Tamino in his wanderings, and who, whenever he is in doubt or fear, inspire him by their presence, and console him with their

COVENT GARDEN.

sweet minstrelsy, were enacted by a round-faced old woman and two Jewesses—Behold their likenesses.

They stuttered under their songs, and staggered under the weight of their enormous palm-branches, vying in discord with the 'attendants of the Queen of Night.' For the rest the house was nearly empty ; and if, as was the fact, the discord was horrible, there were very few to be affected by it.

GAMMA.

The above criticism has been sent us by a gentleman whose opinion we asked with regard to the opera. Having attended ourselves at Covent Garden, we are compelled to say that we fully agree with our correspondent, though we should not have spoken quite so freely regarding the personal defects of the ladies of the chorus. Bunn 'Maximus' must resort to some other method of filling his benches and his treasury.

PETRUS LAUREUS

WHO sits in London's civic chair,
With owlish look and buzzard air,
The wise and worshipful Lord Mayor?
Sir Peter!

Who, spectacle astride on nose,
Pours forth a flood of bright bon-mots,
As brilliant and as old as Joe's?
Sir Peter!

Who, sworn to let thieves thrive no longer,
Shows to the rogues that law is stronger,
And proves himself a *costermonger?*
Sir Peter!

Who, fairly *saddled* in his seat,
Affords the Queen a *bit* to eat,
And *bridles* up before the great?
       Sir Peter!

O happy be your glorious *rein*,
And may its *traces* long remain,
To *check* and *curb* the rogues in grain!
       Sir Peter!

And when to *leatherary* ease
Returned, you give up London's keys,
May luck thy patent axles grease.
       Sir Peter!

FOREIGN CORRESPONDENCE

PARIS: *Saturday, June* 22.

THIS is a most unfavourable moment for commencing a Parisian correspondence. All the world is gone into the country, with the exception of the deputies, who are occupied in voting supplies; an occupation necessary, but not romantic, and uninteresting to the half-million of Englishmen who peruse the 'National Standard.' However, in all this dearth of political and literary news, the people of France are always rich enough in absurdities to occupy and amuse an English looker-on. I had intended, after crossing the Channel to Boulogne, to have stayed there for a while, and to have made some profound remarks on the natives of that town: but of these, I believe, few exist; they have been driven out by the English settlers, one of whom I had the good fortune to see. He did not speak much, but swore loudly; he was dressed in a jacket and a pair of maritime inexpressibles, which showed off his lower man to much advantage. This animal, on being questioned, informed me that the town was d—— pretty, the society d—— pleasant, balls delightful, and cookery excellent. On this hint, having become famished during a long and stormy journey, I requested the waiter of the hotel to procure some of the delicacies mentioned by the settler. In an hour he returned with breakfast; the coffee was thin, the butter bad, the bread sour, the delicacies mutton-chops. This was too much for human patience. I bade adieu to the settler, and set off for Paris forthwith.

I was surprised and delighted with the great progress made by the Parisians since last year. Talk of the 'march of mind' in England, La jeune France completely distances us : all creeds, political, literary, and religious, have undergone equal revolutions, and met with equal contempt. Churches, theatres, painters, booksellers, kings, and poets, have all bowed before this awful spirit of improvement, this tremendous 'zeitgeist.' In poetry and works of fiction, this change is most remarkable. I have collected one or two specimens, which I assure you are taken from works universally read and admired. I have, however, been obliged to confine ourselves to the terrific ; the tender parts are much too tender for English readers. In England it was scarcely permitted in former days to speak of such a book as the memoirs of the celebrated M. de Faublas ; in France it was only 'a book of the boudoir'—taken in private by ladies, like their cherry-brandy ; now the book is public property. It is read by the children, and acted at the theatres ; and for Faublas himself, he is an absolute Joseph compared to the Satanico-Byronico heroes of the present school of romance. As for murders, etc., mere Newgate-Calendar crimes, they are absolute drugs in the literary market. Young France requires something infinitely more piquant than an ordinary hanging matter, or a commonplace *crim. con.* To succeed, to gain a reputation, and to satisfy La jeune France, you must accurately represent all the anatomical peculiarities attending the murder, or crime in question ; you must dilate on the clotted blood, rejoice over the scattered brains, particularise the sores and bruises, the quivering muscles and the gaping wounds ; the more faithful, the more natural ; the more natural, the more creditable to the author, and the more agreeable to La jeune France.

I have before me a pleasing work with the following delectable title — ' Champavert : Immoral Tales. By Petrus Borel, the Lycanthrope ! ' After having perused this pretty little book, I give the following summary of it, for the benefit of English readers : —

Tale 1, ' M. de l'Argentière,' contains a rape, a murder, an execution.

Tale 2, ' Jacques Barraon,' concludes thus :

' Immediately he seized him by the throat—the blood gushed out, and Juan screamed aloud, falling on one knee and seizing Barraon by the thigh ; who, in turn, fastened on his hair, and struck him on the loins, while, with a back stroke, *il lui étripe le ventre.* (The manœuvre is extraordinary, and the language utterly untranslateable.) They rolled on the ground; now Juan is uppermost, now Jacques—they roar and writhe!

'Juan lifted his arm, and broke his dagger against the wall. Jacques nailed his in Juan's throat! Covered with wounds and blood, uttering horrid screams, they seemed a mere mass of blood flowing and curdling! Thousands of obscene flies and beetles might be seen hovering round their mouths and nostrils, and buzzing round the sores of their wounds.

'Towards night a man stumbled over the corpses. "They are only negroes," said he, and went his way.'

It is, as the reader will see, quite impossible to translate properly this elegant passage; it conveys a force, originality, and good taste, which can never be transferred to our language.

Tale 3, 'Andrea Vesalius.' Three adulteries, four murders. The victims are a wife and her three lovers, murdered first, and dissected afterwards, by Andrea Vesalius.

Tale 4, 'Three-fingered Jack.' Contains only one suicide, and the death of Jack in fair fight.

Tale 5, 'Dina.' One rape, one murder, one suicide.

Tale 6, 'Passereau.' Two murders, and some intrigues—very prettily described.

Tale 7, 'Champavert.' This is the history of the Lycanthrope himself. He was an extraordinary and melancholy young man, remarkable for a strong poetical genius, and a long beard, both of which he had manifested from the age of seventeen. This history contains a couple of seductions, a child murder, and two suicides. Whether Champavert were a fictitious or real personage, I know not; there is, however, a long, circumstantial account of his suicide here given; and I trust for the honour of France that the Lycanthrope actually lived and died in the manner described in the book.

My dear young ladies, who are partial to Lord Byron, and read Don Juan slily in the evening; who admire French fashions, and dishes, and romances, —it is for your profit and amusement that this summary has been made. You will see by it how far this great nation excels us in genius and imagination, even though Bulwer and Disraeli still live and write.

The costume of Jeune France is as extraordinary as its literature. I have sent a specimen, which I discovered the other day in the Tuileries. It had just been reading the *Tribune*, and was leaning poetically against a tree; it had on a red neck-cloth, and a black flowing mane; a stick or club, intended for ornament as well as use, and a pair of large though innocent spurs, which had never injured anything except the pantaloons of the individual who wore them. Near it was sitting an old gentleman, who is generally to be seen of a sunny day in the Tuileries, reading his Crebillon or his prayer-book : a living illustration of times past, a strange contrast with times present.

THE COSTUME OF 'JEUNE FRANCE' (JUNE 1833)

French Costume : Old and New School.

FOREIGN CORRESPONDENCE

PARIS : *Saturday, June* 29.

THERE is no doubt that the 'National Standard,' though the best conducted journal in the world, has a most senseless, impotent, and unmeaning title. National Standard : what does it signify ? It may be a newspaper, or a measure for brandy ; a banner for

King William, or a flag for King Cobbett : you should take advice by the papers of this country, and fix on a name more striking. These observations have been inspired by the title of a journal which is about to appear here, ' Le Necrologe : Journal des Morts ' ; a pretty, romantic, and melancholy title printed on a sentimental paper, handsomely edged with black, and bearing an urn for a frontispiece. O death ! O life ! O *jeune France !* what a triumph of art and taste is here ! Fancy *The Mourning Adver- tiser ; The Sexton's Miscellany ; The Raw Head and Bloody Bones ; the Undertaker's Manual ; The Pick-axe, or the Grave- digger's Vade Vecum,* published every morning for breakfast, and treating of all the most fashionable deaths, murders, suicides, and executions in Europe. What a pleasing study for melancholy young men and tender young ladies ! Then one has the advantage of swallowing sentiment and history at the same time, and, (as *Figaro* says,) while living, one is a subscriber to it ; when dead, an article. The November suicides in England used to be a staple article of French satire ; they used to think that London Bridge was built for the mere convenience of throwing one's self from it into the Thames, and that our lamp-posts were only cast-iron sub- stitutes for gibbets ; in regard to lamp-posts, however, we borrowed our learning from them ; and, as to suicides, the advantage is now decidedly on the French side. Half-a-dozen fellows ' asphyxient ' themselves every morning, and servant-maids with low spirits and wages generally adopt this means of retirement, as one easy, expeditious, and certain. I heard just now of a young gentleman, who had arrived at the mature age of sixteen, and of another more venerable by a couple of years, who some time ago brought their lives to a conclusion in charcoal. They had, together, written a drama, which was represented at the *Porte St. Martin,* and succeeded ; it procured for them, no doubt, a few dozen francs, and an eternity of half-a-dozen nights, which seemed entirely to answer their hopes and satisfy their ambition. Their enjoyment was complete, their cup of fame was full ; and they determined, like young sages as they were, to retire from the world before their happiness should fade, or their glory tarnish ; thinking no doubt that their death, their last and noblest action, would establish beyond all question their immortality.

So they purchased the means of their death (it is very cheap, twopenny - worth will kill half a thousand young poets), they retired to their *sixième,* they shut out the world, and closed up the windows ; and when, some hours after, the door of their apartment was forced open, their spirits and the charcoal-smoke flew out together, leaving only the two corpses to be admired by the public, and buried by the same. In France, they dropped tears on their bodies; they would have employed stakes, instead of tears, in our less romantic country. However, peace be to their ashes! they are now, no doubt, comfortably situated in the heaven where they will find Cato and Addison, and Eustace Budgell, and all the suicidal philosophers; and some day or other, Liston, Talma, and all the great tragedians.

I asked my informer the names of these young unfortunates, and the title of their tragedy. He had forgotten both! So much for their reputation.

The theatres are in a flourishing condition: they have all at this moment some piece of peculiar attraction. At the *Ambigu Comique* is an edifying representation of 'Belshazzar's Feast.' The second act discovers a number of melancholy Israelites sitting round the walls of Babylon, with their harps on the willows! A Babylonian says to the leader of the chorus, 'Sing us one of the songs of Zion'; the chorus answers, 'How can we sing in a strange land?' and so on; the whole piece is a scandalous parody of the Scripture, made up of French sentiment and French decency. A large family of children were behind me, looking with much interest and edification at the Queen rising from her bath! This piece concludes with a superb imitation of Martin's picture of Belshazzar. Another piece at the *Porte St. Martin*, called 'Bergami,' vivifies Hayter's picture of the House of Lords, at Queen Caroline's trial. There was a report this morning that a courier had arrived from England, for the express purpose of forbidding this piece; and supposing, from that circumstance, that it must contain something very terrible, I called at the *Porte St. Martin* to see it; but I was sadly disappointed, for there was nothing in it but a little Platonic dialogue between Bergami, who is an angel, and the Queen, who is an injured woman. Bergami appears first in the character of a post-boy, and makes such delightful remarks on the weather, the scenery and Italian politics, that the warm-hearted queen is subdued at once, and makes him forthwith her equerry. The first act ends, and the Queen gets into a carriage. In the second she gets into a packet (that unlucky packet!); in the third she gets into a balcony; in the fourth she gets into a passion, as well as she may, for Bergami is assassinated by Lord Ashley (on which fact we beg to congratulate his lordship); and, accordingly, she goes to the House of Lords, to make her complaint against him for this act of unpoliteness; here the scene is very animated (it is taken from the picture). *Sir* Brougham makes a speech, about injured women, patriotism, and so forth, Lord Eldon replies, the Ministerial bench cheers, the

Opposition jeers, and the Queen comes in majestically, bowing right and left, and uttering the noblest sentiments.

Presently a row is heard in the streets ; the mob is in arms for the Queen ! Lord Eldon motions the Minister for War ; he rushes out to quell the disturbance, the Queen follows him, but the

LIGIER, THE FRENCH ACTOR, AS 'RICHARD' IN *BERGAMI*.

attempts of both are ineffectual ; windows are broken, stones are flung, Lord Eldon disappears, *Sir* Brougham bolts, and Lord Liverpool (a stout man in a white waistcoat, with a large tin star), falls to the earth, struck violently in the stomach with a leather brick-bat, and the curtain, of course, drops with the Prime Minister. The French nation was exalted by this exhibition to a pitch of immoderate enthusiasm, and called stoutly for the *Marseillaise.* I did not see the fifth act, in which the Queen is poisoned (Lord Ashley again!), but returned home to give an account of this strange tragedy. There is a third play, of much more importance than the two former, of which I had wished to give some account, 'Les Enfans d'Edouard,' by M. Casimir Delavigne, one of the best acted tragedies I had ever the good fortune to see; but I have made this letter so long, that I must reserve this for some future day. I could not, however, refrain from sending a little sketch of Ligier, who performs the part of *Richard*, in this play, in a manner, I think, which Kean never equalled. Beside Ligier, there is the admirable Mademoiselle Mars, and that most charming, gay, graceful, *naïve* actress, Madame Anais Aubert. It would be worth an English actor's while to come to Paris, and study the excellent manner of the French comedians; even Cooper might profit by it, and Diddear go away from the study a wiser and better man. Here is too much about theatres, you will say; but, after all, is not this subject as serious as any other?

THE CHARRUAS.

FOREIGN CORRESPONDENCE.

The Charruas

PARIS, *July* 6.

THE wondering reader may fancy that the scene here given was designed in the wilds of America rather than in this gay city of

Paris, but he will see, if he takes the trouble of reading the following article (from the pen of M. Jules Janin), how the figures above represent three unfortunate Charruas, who have quitted South America to shiver under the cold Parisian sun.

'Allons! Let us go and see the savages; they are lodged in the Champs Elysées, in one of those half-built houses, those ruins of yesterday, the view of which is sad without being solemn. Here are the heroes of our drama, not taller than the brave Agamemnons and Alexanders of the Théatre Français, but well-built and active, bold cavaliers, and gallant horse-tamers. They are perfidious, idle, revengeful, cruel cannibals; some of them, perfect dramatic characters, in fact. In truth, they possess all the qualities requisite for the modern drama; they can ride, fight, betray, revenge, assassinate, and eat raw flesh; it is true that they don't know a word of French—but what of that? it is all the better for a theatre nowadays.

'When I saw them huddled together in their court, I declare I thought that I was looking at some modern tragedy; these brave savages wore costumes hideous and fanciful; they were all three seated in different solemn attitudes. First, the cacique, with hair uncombed, and fierce and heavy looks; he would have made a capital tyrant for a melodrama; the next, a lean, livid, animal, with a sidelong look, and an indefinable smile, reminded me of Cooper's *Magna*; the third was gay, careless, and merry enough; and then came the timid and gentle Guynuya. She sat alone in the corner of the court, with her head on her bosom, bending under the weight of her captivity, like a princess of Ilium of old. This woman is truly sublime: it is true she is fickle and faithless, that she loves pleasure and change, that she has not our ideas of conjugal fidelity; but she has more passion and love than all the heroines of our tragedy; and, above all, she has the passion of grief. I was much touched by this woman and her sorrows; her arms are all scarred over with wounds, and each of these wounds is the history of a sorrow. They were inflicted by herself: there is a scar for each friend she has lost; for every child of which she has been deprived there is a finger gone; she has lost two fingers, and there are nearly eighty scars on her arm; and this woman is not yet eighteen years old!

'Have you, in all the range of your drama, such an heroine as this? Have you, in all your poetry, so profound a grief as hers? And, for heroes, here is one whose shoulder has been laid open by a hatchet; and who, for the last miserable white Frenchwoman, who blunders through your ballets and your choruses, would go gladly to the Bois de Boulogne and defy a dozen gentlemen at once! You call your heroes cruel, and your heroines tender! Here is a hero who poisons his own arrows, and a woman who gashes her arms with a wicked knife with as much ease as you would flourish a fan! See how utterly you are beaten off your own ground by the first arrival from the plains of Paraguay. Thus, in fact, it is; as soon as one quits the poetical drama for that of the heart, and literary truth for common truth, one must expect to be vanquished by the first matter-of-fact competitor, whether savage or not; by all which I mean to say, as Lord Byron has said before, that truth is stranger than fiction.

'Now these heroes of the Champs Elysées are as poetic as the heroes of Homer. Vaimaca Peru is a great chief, a veritable cacique, a specimen, in fact, of vagabond royalty, no more called upon to uncover his head than are other vagabond royalties. Senaqué is the devoted friend of his chief, a subject faithful and sorrowful, more sorrowful, indeed, than his destitute master; and this is a common case about ruined thrones. The next, the young man, is careless and brave; and, although conquered, happy still, because he is young and looks to the future. The woman Guynuya is truly the epic heroine, resigned to her fate; her very smile is full of tears, her sufferings are consoled by her weaknesses. Do you know that these savages have come from the extremity of Southern America? that they were made prisoners after long and bloody battles? that they have come hither to Paris as a last asylum? and that this is the St. Helena of the vanquished cacique? For a long time they fought under Ribera; a year ago their tribe was destroyed, and they fled into the desert, bearing with them, not their harps, like the Hebrews, but the skulls of their enemies, the ornaments of their cabins. And now, vanquished prisoners, fugitives, they have come so far to find an asylum, and to receive the visit of that amateur of monsters, M. Geoffroy St. Hilaire.

'How times are changed! Formerly, when the grand kingdom of France was a Christian kingdom, the arrival of these savages would have caused a sensation amidst the catholicism of Paris. There would have been a tender solicitude evinced for the welfare of their immortal souls. They would have found, most likely, the king's mistress for a godmother, and the king's brother for a godfather; they would have been the objects of infinite dissertations, philosophical and religious: Jansenists and Jesuits would have disputed over these four souls with a ferocity altogether ecclesiastical. Our savages, meanwhile, would have been baptized, fêted, and amused, and sent back to their country loaded with presents and honours. At present, what is their fate, poor monarchs of the deserts ? They have been received by the Academy of Sciences, and next, they will go to St. Cloud, and see the king, that is, if the master of the ceremonies permits it. The director of the opera will give them a box some night when all the boxes are empty ; then they will go to the *Porte St. Martin*, then to Franconi's, and then to some cabaret of the lowest order, where the grisette, come out for her Sunday, will scarcely deign to look at them, seeing that she prefers her quadrille to all the savages in the world. Poor fellows ! they will be lucky enough if they do not, like their brethren of the North,[1] die in the hospital, with a sister of charity on each side of them.

'I did not forget to caress the ostrich, which gallops about in the court ; he is a careless and gentle ostrich, who much pleased me ; having nothing to give him, I offered him a piece of money, which he did me the honour of accepting, and which he swallowed and pocketed with the grace of a civilised individual.

'JULES JANIN.'

I have curtailed this article of M. Janin, which is, I think, a tolerable specimen of the French style of periodical writing. It concludes with a long paragraph expressing the writer's joy at escaping from the savages into the Champs Elysées, and some remarks on the civilised world in general. The paragraph proves that M. Janin was in a fright, and no wonder ; three cannibals with knives and poisoned arrows are no pleasant companions, even for a brave Frenchman. In the sketch given above, the stout man is the chief; the lady Guynuya has her back turned, a piece of unpoliteness in which she persisted during the whole of my visit. They play cards all day, laugh, eat raw beef, and drink all they can get.

[1] The Osages, who were exhibited at Paris some years ago, and died there.

FOREIGN CORRESPONDENCE

Paris: July 13.

THE figure above is a copy of the statue which shortly is to decorate
the column on the Place Vendôme.   It is, as everybody knows, to
be elevated about the 29th of the month ; but his majesty the king
of the French, being averse to *émeutes de dépenses* of all kinds, has
determined that it shall be erected privily in the night season, and
shall have no needless extravagance or unnecessary publicity to
accompany its elevation.

The statue has been cast of bronze, or brass made of Austrian cannon (the victories of Napoleon are, luckily, not all used up), and represents, as the reader beholds, the little corporal in his habit of war.   The column, up to 1814, was surmounted with a representation of the Emperor Napoleon, with robes and sceptre imperial ; it bore on its base the following sonorous inscription :—

NEAPOLIO. IMP. AUG.
MONUMENTUM BELLI GERMANICI
ANNO MDCCCV.
TRIMESTRE SPATIO PROFLIGATI
EX ÆRE CAPTO
GLORIÆ EXERCITUS MAXIMI DICAVIT.

In 1814 the inscription was removed, the statue torn down, and a dirty white flag replaced it.   It seemed a lame and impotent conclusion to the series of victories which are carved on the column itself, and wind from the base to the summit, as if these battles had been fought and won for the sole purpose of re-establishing the white flag aforesaid.

Next week, however, Napoleon will make his second appearance on the column.   He certainly ought to make a short speech on the occasion, which, we think, would run something in this manner.

The Emperor, after having raised his bronzed spy-glass to his brazen eye, and regarded the multitude who are waiting to hear his oration, begins :

'Ladies and gentlemen !   (Tremendous applause.)

'Unaccustomed as I am to public speaking, and overpowered by feelings of the deepest and tenderest nature, you may readily fancy my inability to address you with the eloquence demanded by your presence, and by this occasion.

'Ladies and gentlemen : this is the proudest moment of my life !   (Bravo, and cheers.)

'I thank you for having placed me in a situation so safe, so commanding, and so salubrious.   From this elevation I can look on most parts of your city.   I see the churches empty, the prisons crowded, the gambling-houses overflowing : who, with such sights before him as these, gentlemen, and *you*, would not be proud of the name of Frenchmen.   (Great cheers.)

'The tricolor waves over the Tuileries as it used in my time. It must be satisfactory to Frenchmen to have re-established their glorious standard, and to have banished for ever the old white flag ; and though I confess myself that I cannot perceive any other benefit you have wrought by your resistance to a late family, you of course can. (Applause, mingled with some unseemly groans from the police.)

'I apprehend that the fat man [1] with the umbrella, whom I see walking in the gardens of the Tuileries, is the present proprietor. May I ask what he has done to deserve such a reward from you? Does he found his claim on his own merits, or on those of his father?' (A tremendous row in the crowd: the police proceed to *empoigner* several hundred individuals.) 'Go your ways' (said the statue, who was what is vulgarly called a dab at an impromptu); 'go your ways, happy Frenchmen! You have fought, you have struggled, you have conquered; for whom? for the fat man with the umbrella!

'I need not explain what were my intentions and prospects, if I had had the good fortune to remain amongst you. You were yourselves pleased to receive them with some favour. The rest of Europe, however, did not look on them in the same light, and expressed its opinion so strongly that we, out of mere politeness, were obliged to give up our own.

'I confess myself that I was somewhat arbitrary and tyrannical: but what is our fat friend below? Is it not better to be awed by a hero than to be subdued by a money-lender? to be conquered by a sword than to be knocked down by an umbrella?' (Here there was an immense cry of 'A bas les Parapluies!' Some further arrests took place.)

'Perhaps, if it be not a bore (Go on), you will allow me to say a word concerning those persons who so strongly voted my own removal and the re-establishment of the white cloth, now folded up for ever.

'The Russians are occupied in strangling, murdering, and banishing; I could not possibly have chosen for them a better occupation.

'The English, with their £800,000,000 of debt, have destroyed their old institutions, and have as yet fixed on no new ones.' (Here a further crowd were marched of by the police.) 'I congratulate you. Gentlemen, *they*, too, have policemen.[2]

'The Portuguese are fighting about two brothers, both of whom they detest. Heaven preserve the right, whichever he may be.

'From Italy there are delightful accounts of revolts, and deaths thereon consequent.

---

[1] Napoleon here makes an irreverent and personal allusion to King Louis Philippe. His stoutness and his umbrella were depicted some two months ago, in our Paper.

[2] This struck us as rather a vulgar allusion on the part of the statue.

'The Germans are arresting students for want of a better employment. The Spaniards are amusing themselves with sham fights ; what a pity they cannot be indulged with real ones !

'And the family : for whom about five hundred thousand lives were sacrificed,—where are they ? The king is doting, and the dauphin is mad in a château in Germany ; and the duchess must divide her attentions between her son and her daughter !

'And yourselves, gentlemen, you have freedom of the press,— but your papers are seized every morning, as in my time. You have a republic, but beware how you speak of the King ! as in my time also. You are free ; but you have seventeen forts to keep you in order. I don't recollect anything of the sort in my time.

'Altogether, there is a very satisfactory quantity of bullying, banishing, murdering, taxing, and hanging, throughout Europe. I perceive by your silence——' Here the emperor stopped : the fact was, there was not a single person left in the Place Vendôme ; they had all been carried off by the police !

FOREIGN LITERATURE

To the Editor of the National Standard

SIR,—

I was much pleased with the following pretty pastoral in the Breton dialect, which I found lately in some numbers of the French Literary Journal. I have added a version of my own which perhaps may be acceptable to the readers of your paper. It has, at least, the merit of being literal. W.

> CHOESES me boue er plach yoang,
>   Hi e garau perpet,
> Mas helas ! me halon paûr
>   Hi des me zileset.
>
> Pi greden en em hare,
>   Contant oue me halon,
> Bourmen he don didrompet
>   Ia gole glaharet on.
>
> Na me chahuet m'en, doucic,
>   Ne zelet quit do'heign ;
> Zel er haranté tromp lus
>   Ne de quet ehiu teign.

Ma me guelet m'en, doucic,
　　Ha pe veign me hunon ;
Dàhlet hon comzan gwen oh
　　Drouc e rand dem halon.

Ha pe glehuan en druhumel
　　Da geneign ar er bar ;
Me lar gahus e li halon,
　　Neh quet pel doh hi far.

Ha re veign marhue, doucic,
　　Hui lareign ar me be,
Che tu be en deu yoang
　　Marhue quet carante !

[Translation]

ONCE my heart was gay and glad,
　　When she loved me, nothing grieved me,
But 'tis weary now and sad,
　　Since that she has thus deceived me.

Look not on me when we meet,
　　But I pray thee pass me by ;
For I dare not, maiden sweet,
　　Meet the glances of thine eye.

When I'm lonely, maiden dear,
　　Pass me by, and speak not to me,
For the honied words I hear
　　From thy faithless lips undo me.

Once the turtle's song I heard
　　Through the greenwood ringing clear,
Happy is thy heart, O bird !
　　For thy true love hovers near !

When perchance to my gravestone,
　　Maiden sweet, your steps are moving,
You will say that there lies one
　　Who has died of too much loving.

ORIGINAL PAPERS—A TALE OF WONDER

ONCE upon a time there was an old woman who lived in a village not very far off, and who went to market to buy a sack of beans. Now, she had to walk back ten miles over a dreary common ; a long step at most times, but a terrible pull when one has a sack of beans on one's back. It was night before she got half-way ; and the moon was hid, and the snow was falling, and the old woman was ready to drop : she was tired and hungry ; so she was right glad when she came to a house, which, though an ugly-looking place at the best, she thought quite good enough for her to rest in.

She took out a penny and asked for a bed, and the woman of the house let her go into a loft, where she slept on her sack of beans.

Now the house belonged to thieves, and this was one of their wives who let in the woman with her sack.

But, though the old woman was so tired, she could not sleep, but lay tossing about on her straw quite uneasy. Presently she saw a light in the room below, and two men, each with a knife and a lantern.

And she felt desperately frightened, as you may fancy, for she thought they might want to murder her, and then eat her, which was often done in those days, when there were a great many ogres and giants.

Well, the two men with the knives went on till they came to a bed where a gentleman was sleeping, who had been overtaken like the old woman, and who had got with him a large portmanteau : there he lay as sound as possible, snoring away in a manner quite pleasant to hear. As soon as the two rogues saw how fast asleep he was, the biggest took hold of his legs, and the little one took out his knife and cut the gentleman's throat, slick ! at one slash !

As soon as they had stuck him, they left him there all bloody, took the portmanteau, and went away again downstairs ; the old woman with the sack became mighty uneasy, thinking that it was to be her turn next, and that it was all over with her for certain ; whereas, Heaven had sent her there on purpose to detect and punish these wicked men. As soon as they got downstairs, the woman must have told them of the poor old creature in the loft, for presently up they came again, knives and lanterns and all.

The poor old lady was terribly frightened, as you may think, especially when the big man took hold of her legs, (as he had done below stairs,) and the little one came up to her head, with his lantern and his long knife!

However, she did not move a muscle, only she snored to make believe she was asleep.

'Let's leave her,' says the big man; 'she's asleep, and can tell no tales.'

'Let's *kill* her,' says the little one; 'she'll do to feed the pigs!'

All this while the old woman lay as still as a stone; and at last, as they did not suspect that she was awake, they let her off, and went downstairs. So she escaped like a brave old woman as she was! She saw them wrap up the dead man below in his sheet, and carry him to the courtyard; presently they called the pigs, and out they came, grunting and snuffling round the trough, which was the coffin that these wicked monsters gave the poor murdered gentleman.

You may suppose that she did not sleep much that night; but the next morning, as soon as it was light, she thanked the woman of the house, took up her sack, and set off home as though nothing had happened; trudging over the common as fast as her poor legs would carry her, though that was not very fast, she trembled so. Now the little man (he that had stuck the gentleman) suspected that all was not right, and he followed her and came up with her before she had got a mile on the road. As soon as she saw him coming, the bold old lady puts down her sack, and sits waiting for him on a stone.

'What's the matter, misses?' says he.

'Why my sack is heavy, and my old legs is rather weak; I wish some honest man would give me his arm, and help me on my road a bit.'

So the little fellow gave her his arm, and there they went across the common, talking about beans and the weather, and what not, as if they had been two angels; he saw her almost home, and you may be sure that when she got there she fell down on her knees and said her prayers; as well she might, after getting off so well.

While she was in the middle of her prayers in comes her husband, and as soon as she'd done, he asked for a bit of bacon and some of the beans, so she cut a large piece, and plenty of beans. While it was boiling, she told her husband of all she had seen the night before. 'I must go to the Justice,' says she, 'and tell him the whole story.' 'Go to the Justice—go to the devil,' says he; 'as for the gentleman, it is all over with him now, and some of these rogues' comrades will kill us if we peach.'

With that he stuck his fork into the saucepan, to catch hold of a bit of the bacon; well, as sure as I'm sitting here, instead of pulling out a bit of pork, what does he find at the end of his fork, but a man's head !

'It's the gentleman's head,' said the wife. 'But what can we do ?' says her husband, who was rather flustered.

'You can revenge me !' says the head. 'Last night I was wickedly murdered, and eaten by pigs, as your wife can swear to ; I shall have no rest till I see those robbers at the gallows ; and what's more, I'll never leave you till then !'

So the farmer told the Justice, and the thieves were hanged ; and all the pigs drowned who had eaten the gentleman's body.

'And the head ?'

'Why it was buried in the field where the farmer sowed the beans, and there was never such crops as came from that field.'

'And the brave old woman ?'

Why, though she was seventy years old, she had a son, and lived happy ever after.

OUR LEADER

1.

A REPORT to our ears most astounding has wandered,
That we are about to be done with our *Standard*.
'Pon our lives, in our lives we were never more slandered :
    Which nobody can deny,
       Deny,
    Which nobody can deny.

2.

At a time when we most are entitled to brag,
Should our *Standard*, d'ye think, be commencing to *flag*,
When we're praised all alike by sage and by wag ?
    Which nobody can deny,
       Deny,
    Which nobody can deny.

3.

When loved and admired in all parts of the town,
Good fame and good fortune both surely our own,
Absurd it would be if our *Standard* went down :
    Which nobody can deny,
       Deny,
    Which nobody can deny.

4.

Such stories, of course, all our readers will vote
As nonsense, all wholly unworthy of note,
And they'll see that our *Standard* right gaily will float :
    Which nobody can deny,
        Deny,
    Which nobody can deny.

To descend, however, to plain prose, for our Pegasus is getting tired of this ambling canter, we have only to say, that we have been most credibly and upon good authority informed, that a report has been most sedulously sent abroad that the *National Standard* was about to be given up : nay, to such an extent was the story carried in some quarters, that it was positively alleged that it was given up : and that we were dead, defunct, extinct. We confess that we do haunt a churchyard, and so far there may be a *primâ facie* case to justify the calumny ; but, except that circumstance, there is nothing else to affect our vitality. We are not only alive, but likely to live ; not merely breathing the breath of life, but halé, active, healthy, full of spirits and pugnacity.

How or why the rumour got abroad concerning us we do not know, and shall take no pains to enquire ; but certain it is, that during the last week we have been as much pestered after our death as ever was *Partridge* the astrologer. We were nearly killed by our exertions in answering the demands made about our life, and shortened our breath considerably in perpetual bawlings to show that it was prolonged. We hope, however, that now, when an incredulous public beholds us appearing as usual at our accustomed hour, they will relax their want of faith, and confess that those who have gulled them by the reports of our total extinction calculated too sanguinely upon that extent of credulity which has for some centuries been a distinctive mark of the inhabitants of this our too-favoured island—to say nothing of its amiable metropolis.

No, good readers, we are not dead : we are, on the contrary, active and energetic in making all sorts of new arrangements for opening the new campaign with redoubled strength and quintupled resources. Those, therefore, who were rejoicing over our demise should put on mourning for our still continuing to walk the earth—in sheets, we admit, and attended by devils—but still in as flesh-and-blood a fashion as ever characterised a being made of paper. But, on reflection, we cannot even conjecture who it could be to whom our extinction would prove a matter of joy. Even those rivals of ours in the periodical world, whom we have no doubt somewhat annoyed by our success—even they, in the handsomest manner, expressed their grief at the prospect of our premature departure ; and we have no doubt that, if we had not made our appearance in due course this morning, the *Literary Gazette* and the *Athenæum* would be in sable attire. As it is, we are confident that their readers have already discovered that the one is dull and the other dismal, which, no doubt, they have attributed to the true cause. As for the public in general, our departure would be a calamity so hard to be borne by that excellent body, and its results so disastrous, that we avert our eyes from the considerations, and shall not stop to examine what is too hideous even for thought.

Enough of this. Most seriously, then,—a report has been spread with the utmost sedulousness, in all quarters where it was supposed it could have had the greatest effect, that the *National Standard* was about to be forthwith given up. That report, as this publication will of itself prove, is untrue. We have no notion of giving up the paper, and we assure our advertising friends in particular that they have been most grossly imposed upon.

ORIGINAL PAPERS

[A correspondent has sent us the following strange and fantastic story, from the German of Hoffmann. The humour is, perhaps, a little strained, and the language too simple ; but if our readers are of the same opinion as ourselves, they will not regret the space it occupies in our columns.]

THE HISTORY OF KRAKATUK

From the German of E. A. HOFFMANN

PERLIPAT'S mother was the wife of a king—that is, a queen ; and, in consequence, Perlipat, the moment she was born, was a princess by birth. The king was beside himself for joy as he saw his beautiful little daughter lying in her cradle ; he danced about, and hopped on one leg, and sang out, ' Was anything ever so beautiful as my Perlipatkin ?' And all the ministers, presidents, generals, and staff-officers, hopped likewise on one leg, and cried out, ' No, never !' However, the real fact is, that it is quite impossible, as long as the world lasts, that a princess should be

born more beautiful than Perlipat. Her little face looked like
a web of the most beautiful lilies and roses, her eyes were the
brightest blue, and her hair was like curling threads of shining
gold. Besides all this, Perlipat came into the world with two rows
of pearly teeth, with which, two hours after her birth, she bit the
lord chancellor's thumb so hard that he cried out, 'O gemini!'
Some say he cried out, 'O dear!' but on this subject people's
opinions are very much divided, even to the present day. In short,
Perlipat bit the lord chancellor on the thumb, and all the kingdom
immediately declared that she was the wittiest, sharpest, cleverest
little girl, as well as the most beautiful. Now, everybody was
delighted except the queen—she was anxious and dispirited, and
nobody knew the reason; everybody was puzzled to know why
she caused Perlipat's cradle to be so strictly guarded. Besides
having guards at the door, two nurses always sat close to the
cradle, and six other nurses sat every night round the room; and
what was most extraordinary, each of these six nurses was obliged
to sit with a great tom-cat in her lap, and keep stroking him all
night, to amuse him, and keep him awake.

Now, my dear little children, it is quite impossible that *you*
should know why Perlipat's mother took all these precautions; but
I know, and will tell you all about it. It happened that, once on
a time, a great many excellent kings and agreeable princesses were
assembled at the court of Perlipat's father, and their arrival was
celebrated by all sorts of tournaments, and plays, and balls. The
king, in order to show how rich he was, determined to treat them
with a feast which should astonish them. So he privately sent for
the upper court-cook-master, and ordered him to order the upper
court-astronomer to fix the time for a general pig-killing, and a
universal sausage-making; then he jumped into his carriage, and
called, himself, on all the kings and queens; but he only asked
them to eat a bit of mutton with him, in order to enjoy their
surprise at the delightful entertainment he had prepared for them.
Then he went to the queen, and said, 'You already know, my love,
the partiality I entertain for sausages.' Now the queen knew
perfectly well what he was going to say, which was that she herself
(as indeed she had often done before) should undertake to superintend the sausage-making. So the first lord of the treasury was
obliged to hand out the golden sausage-pot and the silver saucepans; and a large fire was made of sandal-wood; the queen put
on her damask kitchen-pinafore; and soon after the sausage soup
was steaming and boiling in the kettle. The delicious smell
penetrated as far as the privy-council-chamber; the king was
seized with such extreme delight, that he could not stand it any

longer. 'With your leave,' said he, 'my lords and gentlemen'— jumped over the table, ran down into the kitchen, gave the queen a kiss, stirred about the sausage-brew with his golden sceptre, and then returned back to the privy-council-chamber in an easy and contented state of mind. The queen had now come to the point in the sausage-making, when the bacon was cut into little bits and roasted on little silver spits. The ladies of honour retired from the kitchen, for the queen, with a proper confidence in herself, and consideration for her royal husband, performed *alone* this important operation. But just when the bacon began to roast, a little whispering voice was heard, 'Sister, I am a queen as well as you, give me some roasted bacon, too;' then the queen knew it was Mrs. Mouserinks who was talking. Mrs. Mouserinks had lived a long time in the palace; she declared she was a relation of the king's, and a queen into the bargain, and she had a great number of attendants and courtiers underground. The queen was a mild, good-natured woman; and although she neither acknowledged Mrs. Mouserinks for a queen nor for a relation, yet she could not, on such a holiday as this, grudge her a little bit of bacon. So she said, 'Come out, Mrs. Mouserinks, and eat as much as you please of my bacon.' Out hops Mrs. Mouserinks, as merry as you please, jumped on the table, stretched out her pretty little paw, and ate one piece of bacon after the other, until, at last, the queen got quite tired of her. But then out came all Mrs. Mouserinks' relations, and her seven sons, ugly little fellows, and nibbled all over the bacon; while the poor queen was so frightened that she could not drive them away. Luckily, however, when there still remained a little bacon, the first lady of the bedchamber happened to come in; she drove all the mice away, and sent for the court mathematician, who divided the little that was left as equally as possible among all the sausages. Now sounded the drums and the trumpets; the princes and potentates who were invited rode forth in glittering garments, some under white canopies, others in magnificent coaches, to the sausage feast. The king received them with hearty friendship and elegant politeness; then, as master of the land, with sceptre and crown, sat down at the head of the table. The first course was polonies. Even then it was remarked that the king grew paler and paler; his eyes were raised to heaven, his breast heaved with sighs; in fact, he seemed to be agitated by some deep and inward sorrow. But when the blood-puddings came on, he fell back in his chair, groaning and moaning, sighing and crying. Everybody rose from table; the physicians in ordinary in vain endeavoured to feel the king's pulse: a deep and unknown grief had taken possession of him.

At last—at last, after several attempts had been made, several violent remedies applied, such as burning feathers under his nose, and the like, the king came to himself, and almost inaudibly gasped out the words, 'Too little bacon!' Then the queen threw herself in despair at his feet: 'Oh, my poor unlucky royal husband,' said she, 'what sorrows have you had to endure! but see here the guilty one at your feet; strike—strike—and spare not. Mrs. Mouserinks and her seven sons, and all her relations, ate up the bacon, and—and——' Here the queen tumbled backwards in a fainting-fit! But the king arose in a violent passion, and said he, 'My lady of the bedchamber, explain this matter.' The lady of the bedchamber explained as far as she knew, and the king swore vengeance on Mrs. Mouserinks and her family for having eaten up the bacon which was destined for the sausages.

The lord chancellor was called upon to institute a suit against Mrs. Mouserinks and to confiscate the whole of her property; but as the king thought that this would not prevent her from eating his bacon, the whole affair was entrusted to the court machine and watch maker. This man promised, by a peculiar and extraordinary operation, to expel Mrs. Mouserinks and her family from the palace for ever. He invented curious machines, in which pieces of roasted bacon were hung on little threads, and which he set round about the dwelling of Mrs. Mouserinks. But Mrs. Mouserinks was far too cunning not to see the artifices of the court watch and machine maker; still all her warnings, all her cautions, were vain: her seven sons, and a great number of her relations, deluded by the sweet smell of the bacon, entered the watch-maker's machines, where, as soon as they bit at the bacon, a trap fell on them, and then they were quickly sent to judgment and execution in the kitchen. Mrs. Mouserinks, with the small remnants of her court, left the place of sorrow, doubt, and astonishment. The court was rejoiced; but the queen alone was sorrowful; for she knew well Mrs. Mouserinks' disposition, and that she would never allow the murder of her sons and relations to go unrevenged. It happened as she expected. One day, whilst she was cooking some tripe for the king, a dish to which he was particularly partial, appeared Mrs. Mouserinks and said, 'You have murdered my sons, you have killed my cousins and relations, take good care that the mouse, queen, do not bite your little princess in two. Take care.' After saying this, she disappeared; but the queen was so frightened, that she dropped the tripe into the fire, and thus for the second time Mrs. Mouse-rinks spoiled the dish the king liked best: and of course he was very angry. And now you know why the queen took such extraordinary care of princess Perlipatkin: was not she right to fear that Mrs. Mouserinks would fulfil her threat, come back, and bite the princess to death?

The machines of the machine-maker were not of the slightest use against the clever and cunning Mrs. Mouserinks; but the court astronomer, who was also upper-astrologer and star-gazer, discovered that only the Tom-cat family could keep Mrs. Mouserinks from the princess's cradle; for this reason each of the nurses carried one of the sons of this family on her lap, and, by continually stroking him down the back, managed to render the otherwise unpleasant court service less intolerable.

It was once at midnight, as one of the two chief nurses, who sat close by the cradle, awoke as it were from a deep sleep; everything around lay in profound repose; no purring, but the stillness of death; but how astonished was the chief nurse when she saw close before her a great ugly mouse, who stood upon his hind legs, and already had laid his hideous head on the face of the princess. With a shriek of anguish, she sprung up; everybody awoke; but Mrs. Mouserinks (for she it was who had been in Perlipat's cradle), jumped down, and ran into the corner of the room. The tom-cats went after, but too late; she had escaped through a hole in the floor. Perlipat awoke with the noise, and wept aloud. 'Thank heaven,' said the nurses, 'she lives!' But what was their horror, when, on looking at the before beautiful child, they saw the change which had taken place in her! Instead of the lovely white and red cheeks which she had had before, and the shining golden hair, there was now a great deformed head on a little withered body; the blue eyes had changed into a pair of great green gogglers, and the mouth had stretched from ear to ear. The queen was almost mad with grief and vexation, and the walls of the king's study were obliged to be wadded, because he was always dashing his head against them for sorrow, and crying out, 'O luckless monarch!' He might have seen how that it would have been better to have eaten the sausage without bacon, and to have allowed Mrs. Mouserinks quietly to stay underground. Upon this subject, however, Perlipat's royal father did not think at all, but he laid all the blame on the court watch-maker, Christian Elias Drosselmeier, of Nuremburg. He therefore issued this wise order, that Drosselmeier should before four weeks restore the princess to her former state, or at least find out a certain and infallible means for so doing; or, in failure thereof, should suffer a shameful death under the axe of the executioner.

Drosselmeier was terribly frightened; but, trusting to his

learning and good fortune, he immediately performed the first operation which seemed necessary to him. He carefully took princess Perlipat to pieces, took off her hands and feet, and thus was able to see the inward structure; but there, alas! he found that the princess would grow uglier as she grew older, and he had no remedy for it. He put the princess neatly together again, and sunk down in despair at her cradle; which he never was permitted to leave.

The fourth week had begun,—yes, it was Wednesday! when the king, with eyes flashing with indignation, entered the room of the princess; and, waving his sceptre, he cried out, 'Christian Elias Drosselmeier, cure the princess, or die!' Drosselmeier began to cry bitterly, but little princess Perlipat went on cracking her nuts. Then first was the court watch-maker struck with the princess's extraordinary partiality for nuts, and the circumstance of her having come into the world with teeth. In fact, she had cried incessantly since her metamorphosis, until some one by chance gave her a nut; she immediately cracked it, ate the kernel, and was quiet.

From that time the nurses found nothing so effectual as to bring her nuts. 'O holy instinct of natural, eternal and unchangeable sympathy of all beings! thou shewest me the door to the secret. I will knock, and thou wilt open it.' He then asked permission to speak to the court astronomer, and was led out to him under a strong guard. These two gentlemen embraced with many tears, for they were great friends; they then entered into a secret cabinet, where they looked over a great number of books which treated of instincts, sympathies, and antipathies, and other deep subjects. The night came; the court astronomer looked to the stars, and made the horoscope of the princess, with the assistance of Drosselmeier, who was also very clever in this science. It was a troublesome business, for the lines were always wandering this way and that; at last, however, what was their joy to find that the princess Perlipat, in order to be freed from the enchantment which made her so ugly, and to become beautiful again, had only to eat the sweet kernel of the nut Krakatuk.

Now the nut Krakatuk had such a hard shell that an eight-and-forty-pound cannon could drive over without breaking it. But this nut was only to be cracked by a man who had never shaved, and never worn boots; he was to break it in the princess's presence, and then to present the kernel to her with his eyes shut; nor was he to open his eyes until he had walked seven steps backwards without stumbling.

Drosselmeier and the astronomer worked without stopping three days and three nights; and, as the king was at dinner on Saturday,. Drosselmeier, (who was to have had his head off Sunday morning early,) rushed into the room, and declared he had found the means of restoring the princess Perlipat to her former beauty. The king embraced him with fervent affection, promised him a diamond sword, four orders, and two new coats for Sundays. 'We will go to work immediately after dinner,' said the king in the most friendly manner, 'and thou, dear watch-maker, must see that the young unshaven gentleman in shoes be ready with the nut Krakatuk. Take care, too, that he drink no wine before, that he may not stumble as he walks his seven steps backwards like a crab: afterwards he may get as tipsy as he pleases.' Drosselmeier was very much frightened at this speech of the king's; and it was not without fear and trembling that he stammered out that it was true that the means were known, but that both the nut Krakatuk, and the young man to crack it, were yet to be sought for; so that it was not impossible that nut and cracker would never be found at all. In tremendous fury the king swung his sceptre over his crowned head, and cried, with a lion's voice, 'Then you must be beheaded, as I said before.'

It was a lucky thing for the anxious and unfortunate Drosselmeier that the king had found his dinner very good that day, and so was in a disposition to listen to any reasonable suggestions, which the magnanimous queen, who deplored Drosselmeier's fate, did not fail to bring forward. Drosselmeier took courage to plead that, as he had found out the remedy and the means whereby the princess might be cured, he was entitled to his life. The king said this was all stupid nonsense; but, after he had drunk a glass of cherry-brandy, concluded that both the watch-maker and the astronomer should immediately set off on their journey, and never return, except with the nut Krakatuk in their pocket. The man who was to crack the same was, at the queen's suggestion, to be advertised for in all the newspapers, in the country and out of it.

Drosselmeier and the court astronomer had been fifteen years on their journey without finding any traces of the nut Krakatuk. The countries in which they were, and the wonderful sights they saw, would take me a month at least to tell of. This, however, I shall not do: all I shall say is, that at last the miserable Drosselmeier felt an irresistible longing to see his native town Nuremberg. This longing came upon him most particularly as he and his friend were sitting together smoking a pipe in the middle of a wood in Asia. 'O Nuremberg, delightful city! Who's not seen thee, him I pity! All that beautiful is, in London, Petersburg, or Paris, are nothing when compared to thee! Nuremberg, my own city!'

As Drosselmeier deplored his fate in this melancholy manner, the astronomer, struck with pity for his friend, began to howl so loudly that it was heard all over Asia. But at last he stopped crying, wiped his eyes, and said, 'Why do we sit here and howl, my worthy colleague? Why don't we set off at once for Nuremberg? Is it not perfectly the same where and how we seek this horrid nut Krakatuk?' 'You are right,' said Drosselmeier; so they both got up, emptied their pipes, and walked from the wood in the middle of Asia to Nuremberg at a stretch.

As soon as they had arrived in Nuremberg, Drosselmeier hastened to the house of a cousin of his, called Christopher Zachariah Drosselmeier, who was a carver and gilder, and whom he had not seen for a long, long time. To him the watch-maker related the whole history of Princess Perlipat, of Mrs. Mouserinks, and the nut Krakatuk; so that Christopher Zachariah clapped his hands for wonder, and said, 'O, cousin, cousin, what extraordinary stories are these!' Drosselmeier then told his cousin of the adventures which befell him on his travels : how he had visited the grand duke of Almonds, and the king of Walnuts; how he had inquired of the Horticultural Society of Acornshausen; in short, how he had sought everywhere, but in vain, to find some traces of the nut Krakatuk. During this recital Christopher Zachariah had been snapping his fingers, and opening his eyes, calling out, hum! and ha! and oh! and ah! At last, he threw his cap and wig up to the ceiling, embraced his cousin, and said, 'Cousin, I'm very much mistaken, *very* much mistaken, I say, if I don't myself possess this nut Krakatuk!' He then fetched a little box, out of which he took a gilded nut, of a middling size. 'Now,' said he, as he showed his cousin the nut, 'the history of this nut is this : Several years ago, a man came here on Christmas-Eve with a sackful of nuts, which he offered to sell cheap. He put the sack just before my booth, to guard it against the nut-sellers of the town, who could not bear that a foreigner should sell nuts in their native city. At that moment a heavy waggon passed over his sack, and cracked every nut in it except one, which the man, laughing in an extraordinary way, offered to sell me for a silver half-crown of the year 1720. This seemed odd to me. I found just such a half-crown in my pocket, bought the nut, and gilded it, not knowing myself why I bought it so dear and valued it so much.' Every doubt with respect to its being the nut which they sought was removed by the astronomer, who, after removing the gilding, found written on the shell, in Chinese characters, the word Krakatuk.

The joy of the travellers was excessive, and Drosselmeier's

cousin, the gilder, the happiest man under the sun, on being promised a handsome pension and the gilding of all the gold in the treasury into the bargain. The two gentlemen, the watchmaker and the astronomer, had put on their night-caps and were going to bed, when the latter (that is, the astronomer) said, 'My worthy friend and colleague, you know one piece of luck follows another, and I believe that we have not only found the nut Krakatuk, but also the young man who shall crack it, and present the kernel of beauty to the princess ; this person I conceive to be the son of your cousin!' 'Yes,' continued he, 'I am determined not to sleep until I have cast the youth's horoscope.' With these words he took his night-cap from his head, and instantly commenced his observations. In fact, the gilder's son was a handsome well-grown lad, who had never shaved, and never worn boots.

At Christmas he used to wear an elegant red coat embroidered with gold ; a sword, and a hat under his arm, besides having his hair beautifully powdered and curled. In this way he used to stand before his father's booth, and with a gallantry which was born with him, crack the nuts for the young ladies, who, from this peculiar quality of his, had already called him 'Nutcrackerkin.'

Next morning the astronomer fell delighted on the neck of the watch-maker, and cried, 'We have him,—he is found ! but there are two things, of which, my dear friend and colleague, we must take particular care : first, we must strengthen the under-jaw of your excellent nephew with a tough piece of wood, and then, on returning home, we must carefully conceal having brought with us the young man who is to bite the nut ; for I read by the horoscope that the king, after several people have broken their teeth in vainly attempting to crack the nut, will promise to him who shall crack it, and restore the princess to her former beauty,—will promise, I say, to this man the princess for a wife, and his kingdom after his death.' Of course the carver and gilder was delighted with the idea of his son marrying the Princess Perlipat and becoming a prince and king ; and delivered him over to the two deputies. The wooden jaw which Drosselmeier had fixed in his young and hopeful nephew answered to admiration, so that in cracking the hardest peach-stones he came off with distinguished success.

As soon as Drosselmeier and his comrade had made known the discovery of the nut, the requisite advertisements were immediately issued ; and as the travellers had returned with the means of restoring the princess's beauty, many hundred young men, among whom several princes might be found, trusting to the soundness of their teeth, attempted to remove the enchantment of the princess. The ambassadors were not a little frightened when

2 G

they saw the princess again. The little body with the wee hands and feet could scarcely support the immense deformed head! The hideousness of the countenance was increased by a woolly beard, which spread over mouth and chin. Everything happened as the astronomer had foretold. One dandy in shoes after another broke teeth and jaws upon the nut Krakatuk, without in the slightest degree helping the princess, and as they were carried away half-dead to the dentist (who was always ready), groaned out—that was a hard nut!

When now the king in the anguish of his heart had promised his daughter and kingdom to the man who would break the enchantment, the gentle Drosselmeier made himself known, and begged to be allowed the trial. No one had pleased the princess so much as this young man; she laid her little hand on her heart, and sighed inwardly, Ah! if *he* were the person destined to crack Krakatuk, and be my husband! Young Drosselmeier, approaching the queen, the king, and the princess Perlipat in the most elegant manner, received from the hands of the chief master of ceremonies the nut Krakatuk, which he immediately put into his mouth, and —crack! crack!—broke the shell in a dozen pieces; he neatly removed the bits of shell which yet remained on the kernel, and then with a most profound bow presented it to the princess, shut his eyes, and proceeded to step backwards. The princess swallowed the kernel; and oh! wonderful wonder! her ugliness disappeared, and, instead, was seen a form of angel beauty, with a countenance like lilies and roses mixed, the eyes of glancing azure, and the full locks curling like threads of gold. Drums and trumpets mingled with the rejoicings of the people. The king and the whole court danced upon one leg, as before, at Perlipat's birth, and the queen was obliged to be sprinkled all over with eau de Cologne, since she had fainted with excessive joy. This great tumult did not a little disturb young Drosselmeier, who had yet his seven steps to accomplish: however, he recollected himself, and had just put his right foot back for the seventh step, when Mrs. Mouserinks, squeaking in a most hideous manner, raised herself from the floor, so that Drosselmeier, as he put his foot backwards, trod on her, and stumbled,—nay, almost fell down. What a misfortune! The young man became at that moment just as ugly as ever was the princess Perlipat. The body was squeezed together, and could scarcely support the thick deformed head, with the great goggling eyes and wide gaping mouth. Instead of the wooden roof for his mouth, a little wooden mantel hung out from behind his back. The watch-maker and astronomer were beside themselves with horror and astonishment; but they saw how Mrs.

Mouserinks was creeping along the floor all bloody   Her wicked-ness, however, was not unavenged, for Drosselmeier had struck her so hard on the neck with the sharp heel of his shoe, that she was at the point of death ; but just as she was in her last agonies, she squeaked out in the most piteous manner, 'O Krakatuk, from thee I die ! but Nutcracker dies as well as I ; and thou, my son, with the seven crowns, revenge thy mother's horrid wounds !   Kill the man who did attack her, that naughty, ugly wicked Nut-cracker !'   Quick with this cry died Mrs. Mouserinks, and was carried off by the royal housemaid.   Nobody had taken the least notice of young Drosselmeier.   The princess, however, reminded the king of his promise, and he immediately ordered the young hero to be brought before him.   But when that unhappy young man appeared in his deformed state, the princess put her hands before her and cried out, 'Away with that nasty Nutcracker !'   So the court-marshal took him by his little shoulder and pushed him out of the door.

The king was in a terrible fury that anybody should ever think of making a nut-cracker his son-in-law : he laid all the blame on the watch-maker and astronomer, and banished them both from his court and kingdom.   This had not been seen by the astronomer in casting his horoscope ; however, he found, on reading the stars a second time, that young Drosselmeier would so well behave himself in his new station, that, in spite of his ugliness, he would become prince and king.   In the meantime, but with the fervent hope of soon seeing the end of these things, Drosselmeier remains as ugly as ever ; so much so, that the nutcrackers in Nuremberg have always been made after the exact model of his countenance and figure.

ADDRESS

As this is the last day of our publishing year, it may be considered necessary that we should address our readers in a farewell speech from our throne critical, explaining all that we have done, and promising all that we intend to do.   But we suppose that what we *have* done is already sufficiently appreciated without further comment ; and we have found, even from our own brief experience, to say nothing of our reflections on the proceedings of others, that the making of promises is so easy a matter that all persons of adequate knowledge of the world are inclined to look upon them as nothing better than the sure precursors to non-performance.

We are the youngest brother of the literary brood, and we therefore make our last appeal for the year, most appropriately, upon Innocents' Day. We trust that none of our readers will be of a disposition so Herodian as to vote for our immediate demolition; but we know that it has been often announced that our life was destined to be short. Certain of the *stamina* which we enjoy, we ventured to doubt the correctness of such anticipations; and, like the man in Islington, we have lived on, if for no other purpose than that of showing 'the rogues they lied.' We are now about to commence a new year, and with the change of figure, to make other changes,—we hope for the better.

One, which we think we ought first to announce, is that we are going to rise a step in the pence table. It is with reluctance that we give up our old motto, 'ALL FOR TWOPENCE'; but, yielding, as the poet says, to the advice of friends, we are about to change it to *Threepence*. What the reasons for the advice so tendered to us by our worthy and friendly counsellors may be, we leave to the ingenuity of our readers to determine. We shall still continue to be the cheapest of the literary Journals; and we think there will be no fear that, with our present aids and appliances, and the additional steam which we intend to put on, we shall make way with the best among them.

The additional penny, which we beg, can be of no great importance to the individual subscriber, but is, as he may suppose, very material to us. It will enable us to effect many improvements, which, from the extreme lowness of the price, were hitherto impracticable; and will procure more amusement, more variety, and more profit for the reader, and we need not say for ourselves.

Among those proposed improvements will be: a series of Original Tales, by the most popular English authors, and of Translations from the best French and German stories: the first of these stories will appear next week, and will be entitled 'King Odo's Wedding,' from the German of Count Platen. A series of papers under the title of 'The Traveller,' *with engravings*, illustrative of scenery and costume: the first of the series will be entitled 'The Rhine and its Legends'; this will appear on the 10th of January. Careful notices of the most interesting foreign works in all languages; for a regular supply of which, arrangements have been made with Mr. Schloss, of the Strand.

And now, having explained our intentions for the future, we cannot better conclude than by thanking the kind reader for his favours to us during the past year. Many long hours and weary nights have we laboured through, to cater for his Saturday's feast.

We have, at no great cost to him, and at small profit to ourselves, made him acquainted with *some hundreds* of books, pleasant and dull ; we have praised, with him when we found genius or merit, and laughed, with him, at dulness and pretension.   May these, our weekly meetings, long continue ! and, though we can neither boast of the aid of puffings, or the condescending patronage of publishers, we desire no other praise but what the public may award us, and no other patronage than that which we may merit at their hands.

ORIGINAL PAPERS — KING ODO'S WEDDING

MANY hundred years ago, there lived in the city of Aix-la-Chapelle a young lady of high birth and wonderful beauty, who was courted by all the nobles of Germany, but who was so cold and proud that she would listen to none.

Indeed, so haughty was she that she declared she would wed none but a king, and that, rather than do otherwise, she would retire to a convent and take the veil.   Now Heaven loves not that that should be done from pride which should come from religion and lowliness of spirit, and accordingly it punished this young lady in an awful manner, as you shall hear.   The same imperious temper which had turned away so many of her suitors estranged the heart of her parents, and they said that it should happen to her even as she had said ; and that, as she would not marry a mortal man, she should become the spouse of the Church ; and accordingly she was sent to a convent, where she bitterly bewailed the consequences of her pride, and the loss of the world and its vanities.

A year had passed, and that altar which had received her vows as a novice was now about to accept them as a nun.   The bells rung from the convent tower, the altar was decked with flowers and heaped up with holy relics and vessels of gold and jewels ; the priests were in gorgeous clothing, and all the sisters of the convent sate in state in their stalls down the aisle.

And the beautiful Lady Adelhaid was led forth to the altar, dressed for the last time in her worldly attire, with flowers in her coal-black hair, which hung in shining clusters over a neck that was whiter far than the snow.

She came to the altar, and the holy service began ; the priests sang the mass, the red-robed choristers swung the censers of gold, and the loud organ pealed through column and aisle, joining melodiously with the shrill song of the nuns.

Now Odo, King of Nebelland, held his court at that time at Aix-la-Chapelle ; he was a man who gave himself up to pleasure and lust, and was hated alike of God and man ; and it chanced that he rode by the convent-gate at the moment that the service had begun, and, as he saw the people flocking to the chapel, he asked of one near him what was the cause of the festival? And they told him how the beautiful Lady Adelhaid was about to take the veil. 'I have not been in a church for the last ten years,' said the unbelieving king, 'and have a mind to go now, and see what sport there may be there.' So he leapt from his golden chariot, and, followed by his knights and warriors, entered the holy chapel. It was strange to see the bold looks of those fierce men as they stalked through the aisle, and the terrified countenances of the modest and pious sisters.

They reached the altar, laughing and talking aloud, just at the moment when the abbess had unloosed the beautiful locks of Adelhaid, and was about to sever them from her head. The devoted nun looked pale and sad, and turned towards Odo with a look of such despair and sorrow, that he could not withstand the expression of her dark and tender eyes.

'Stop!' shouted the king in a voice of thunder, as he rushed to the altar, followed by his soldiers. The trembling abbess dropped the fatal scissors, and let fall the long hair, which fell to the ground, covering as with a black veil the wondering and kneeling novice. The priests rushed behind the altar, and the little choristers fled away screaming like a flock of startled birds.

The king had been struck by the rare beauty of the kneeling woman, and thought that he had never in his dreams seen anything so lovely. He lifted her from her knees, and as she clung to him as a condemned felon does to his hope for mercy, or a drowning man to a branch or a rope, he spoke in a fierce voice, and said, as he pressed her in his arms, 'No veil,' said he, 'shall hide this sweet face, no scissors shall cut these long locks, no hair-cloth shirt tear this fair bosom.' And there was none in church who dare say him nay.

'She is the bride of the Church,' said the lady abbess, faintly. 'She is the bride of King Odo,' replied he. 'Yes, yours,— yours only,' whispered Adelhaid, as she clasped her dazzling arm around her new spouse.

The men-at-arms set up a loud shout as they closed round the king and his lady, and marched in triumph from the church, which had thus been made witness to an awful sacrilege instead of a holy ceremony.

A wild and wicked orgy was held that night in the palace of King Odo. He sate at the head of his table, and by his side was Adelhaid—not pale and desperate as in the morning at the altar, but radiant in her beauty, and burning with fierce desires. The revel continued until midnight, equalling in riot and magnificence the last feast of the Babylonian king, when his kingdom passed away from him, and when he himself was weighed and found wanting!

But at midnight the monarch and his bride retired from the feast, and entered the nuptial chamber, the scene of his riot and wickedness, and the spot where his punishment was to commence. Scarcely were they alone ere a fearful tempest arose, which seemed to shake the tall towers of the castle, and to inspire with awe and terror the trembling bride; but the king laughed her fears to scorn, and strove but in vain to console her.

But he soon beheld a terrible confirmation of her fears, and an awful punishment for his own disbelief. The door of the chamber opened, and a long procession of white-robed nuns came mournfully chanting and singing around the marriage-bed.

Odo, who was so bold that he would have outfaced Satan himself, allowed no sign of fear to escape him, but gazed upon the train which poured into the chamber; while, far away as he could see, stair and hall and courtyard were thronged by the ghostly company.

'Whence come you,' said he? 'and what seek you?'

And the leader of the train replied, 'We seek our sister'; and she laid her fleshless hand on the shoulder of Adelhaid, and bid her arise and follow her.

The woman, who seemed under the influence of an irresistible spell, rose from her bed; and instantly the ghostly regiment of nuns closed round her, as the warriors had done in the morning when they bore her from the chapel, singing in a shrill voice:

> Sister, come! thy couch is spread
>   Yonder in the churchyard dreary;
> We will sing around thy bed,
>   Not a joyful nuptial lay,
>   Such as greeted you to-day—
> But a mournful miserere.
>   Sister, rise, thine hour is come,
>   We will lead thee to thy home.
>
> Pillowed on her husband's breast,
>   Though she find no slumber now,
> Sweetly shall our sister rest
>   In her quiet couch below.

Come ! 'tis softer far than this is,—
  There the worm on lip and cheek,
  And on bosom fair and sleek,
Eagerly will rain his kisses.

Come ! the marriage lamp it burns,
  Round the bed the glowworms glister,
And Death, the lusty bridegroom, yearns
  For the coming of our sister.

To this effect was the mournful ditty they sang, as they bore
away their victim to the place whence she had come in the
morning.

The king rose from his couch and followed the ghostly train.
They came to the convent-gate, and it opened before them ; the
bells set up a mournful tolling, and the chapel organ pealed forth
a solemn dirge, though there was no human hand to lift the
bellows or to touch the keys.

As in the morning, the nuns ranged themselves in their stalls
down the aisle ; in the midst was a great open space, with a black
yawning grave below.   The victim was led forth, and the service
for the dead was sung.

And, when they came in the morning, a black stone was found
in the midst of the chapel, and none knew how it came thither,
nor how the gates had been opened to admit King Odo, who lay
dead upon the stone.

FATHER GAHAGAN'S EXHORTATION

'Now there ye are, all of yez, gathered together to hear what
I've got to say, and forward enough ye are all, big and little, in
comin' round me for a mouthful of advice.   But, by my conscience,
it's backward enough ye are in comin' forward when the money
is to be paid to support your clargy.   There is not one of yez
cares a pin's point where I am to get a mouthful, an' ye drinkin'
the whishkey, an' makin' bastes of yourselves—Och ! my shame
on yez !   Now then, listen to what I'm goin' to say to yez, an'
that's this, that the divil a thing myself will have to say or do
wid yez, for yer misdoins.   I wash my hands out of yez altogether ;
only jist mind one thing—you'll all die, every mother's sowl of yez
will die, big and little, an' then ye'll come to the day of judgment,
and I'll be there, an' St. Patrick, an' all the saints will be there,

too ; an' St. Patrick will say to me, " Father Gahagan," sis he, he'll say, " Father Gahagan, I say, what kind of a congregation is this you've brought us here, at-all at-all ? ? "

' An' then he'll say, " Father Gahagan," sis he, he'll say, " was there much drinkin', an' swearin', among 'em ? " " Why, no, sir," sis I, I'll say, " not a grate dale of that neither barrin' of a Sunday or a holy day, or so, when the likes is in a manner allowable," I'll say. " But, Father Gahagan," he'll say, " Father Gahagan, did they pay you your *chapple* dues regularly ? " And, och, bad luck to yez, ye graceless set of thieves, what will I be able to say for yez thin, at-all at-all ? (After a pause.) So that, ye wikid graceless writches, bad as ye are, ye had better not reduce me to this dilemmy anyhow, if it was only to avoid bringin' disgrace upon poor ould Ireland, an' that, too, in the presence of Saint Patrick himself. An' now that ye've all heard what I have got to say, ye know yer rimedy.'

DRAMA—PLAYS AND PLAY-BILLS

> Il eut l'emploi qui certes n'est pas mince
> Et qu'a la cour, ou tout se peint en beau,
> On appelloit être l'ami du prince ;
> Mais qu'a la ville, et surtout en province,
> Les gens grossiers ont nommé maquereau.

WE could not refrain from quoting the above lines after reading the manifestos which Mr. Yates, or the literary gentleman who composes the play-bills for the Adelphi Theatre, has published this week.

Every wall in London bears the following elegant inscriptions :—

IMMENSE SUCCESS !
ADELPHI AMAZONS !
SPLENDID WOMEN !

The other is to this effect :—

ADELPHI.
LURLINE.
WOMEN BATHING AND SPORTING !

Mr. Yates's faithful performance of the French blackguard in *Victorine* established for him and his theatre a reputation on which he appears to have lived for two years past ; for, since the production of that excellent play, we do not recollect to have seen a piece at the Adelphi which would bear a second attendance.

He has therefore acted with much acute discretion in producing a new species of dramatic entertainment, having justly perceived that the ancient order of plays was no longer grateful to the public. Suiting himself philosophically to the spirit of the age, he has treated us, in the first place, with the amorous intrigues of the interesting Faublas, and now with *Lurline* and the 'Splendid Women Bathing and Sporting !' What a keen invention !—what a satire on the age and the drama !—what a delicate inducement to a gentleman to go to the theatre !

We saw *Lurline*, and spoke of it with some praise in our last number : unluckily, we were not aware of the peculiar and decent excitement which 'the piece is supposed to awaken. We might have suggested one or two improvements for the next posting-bills ; thus, for instance, ' *Lurline* :—Splendid Women—for fuller information enquire at, the box-office.' Or, ' Women Bathing and Sporting. The private door is in Malden Lane.' However, all these points must already have been seen by the Management, and will no doubt be remedied before a week is over.

As the Christmas holidays are drawing to an end, we would recommend all parents who have young girls to instruct, or little boys to amuse, to send instantly for boxes, (which are very scarce). *The Rake and his Pupil* will much remove the ignorant innocence of the daughters, and ' The Women Bathing and Sporting' highly interest the ripening and expanding sensibilities of the sons.

ORIGINAL PAPERS — THE MINSTREL'S CURSE

A LONG time ago, there stood in a certain country in Germany a tall and stately castle. From its towers you might behold seas and kingdoms, while pleasant gardens encircled its foot, and a number of sweet crystal streams ran glittering around it.

Now a king, who was famous for his power and his victories, kept state in this palace ; but woe be to him on whom fell the looks of the king ! for there was death in his looks, and terror in his thoughts ; when he spoke, it was murder, and when he wrote, it was blood !

It happened that two minstrels passed, on a certain day, on

the road to the king's palace; one was old and feeble, and the other youthful, with golden locks. The old man, with a harp slung on his back, rode a sorry old horse, but his young and blooming companion tripped merrily by his side. 'Be ready, my son,' said the old harper, 'with the sweetness of your music, and the deepest of your tones; if ever you took heed as to your singing, be cautious now, for stony is the heart which we must melt to-day.'

So they entered the hall, where the king sat under a royal canopy, with his queen by his side. The red sun setting in a storm is not so fierce as were the looks of the king; the moonlight sleeping upon a lake is not milder than were the sweet eyes of the lady; she gladly welcomed the two minstrels, and there was a silence in the hall to listen to their singing.

Then the old man took the harp, and he struck it with such skill and sweetness, that the fierce warriors gathered round, were melted, and hung silent on the sounds; while the notes of the young man pealed clearly in sweet accordance with the old minstrel's deep voice.

First, they sung of love and spring, and of the golden time when worth and freedom, truth and holiness still dwelt upon earth; now they raised the thoughts of their hearers to heaven, and now they melted them to tears. The courtiers, who had been jesting, jeered no longer; the stern warriors knelt down and prayed; and the queen, dissolved in a sweet sorrow, took from her bosom a rose, which she threw towards the minstrels.

Now in the midst of their music only the king had been calm; but his wrath rose when he saw the queen's action. 'You have charmed away my people,' shouted he,—'now would you mislead my wife?' And therewith he drew his great sword from his side, and flung it at the breast of the young minstrel. And now the bosom poured out the red blood only, in place of the glorious songs.

The courtiers cowered frightened together, and the poor boy sunk dead into his master's arms. The old man in the meanwhile said no word and uttered no cry; but he bore him out mournfully, to the castle-gate, and sat him on the steed.

Then he paused for a moment, and he hung up his harp on a pillar by the gate; and with a voice that made all hearers tremble, he said:

'Woe unto you, proud halls! never shall minstrel's music echo again in your walls; neither harp nor singing! There shall be no sound here but the noise of sighs and wailing, until the time that my revenge shall be fulfilled.

'Woe unto you, fair gardens! ye gleam now in the spring sun;

—I turn towards you the face of the dead, so that your flowers may be turned to ashes, and your shining streams to sand.

'And woe to you, murderer and curse of minstrelhood! In spite of your laurels and your power, your kingdom shall pass away, and your name be forgotten.'

Thus spake the minstrel; his cry was heard by heaven, and his words fulfilled. The walls of the palace are now levelled with dust, and the towers have crumbled to ashes; there stands but one solitary pillar, to mark the spot, and proclaim the ruin.

And all around, there are black marshes instead of pleasant gardens; there is no tree or river near the spot to give a freshness or a shade; for the king, no minstrel sings his deeds, no history of heroes makes mention of him, he is sunk and forgotten. Such was the curse of the minstrel.

[Why did not our correspondent give us a poetical translation of Uhland's excellent ballad, in place of a prose version?—ED.]

ORIGINAL PAPERS—*ETUDÉ SUR MIRABEAU* PAR VICTOR HUGO

WE have translated from a French paper the following fragments of an essay by Victor Hugo, on the character and life of Mirabeau.

The Editor of the journal speaks of M. Hugo's performance as one of the finest specimens of French writing; our readers may judge for themselves of the thoughts, at least, if not of the style, of the author of 'Nôtre Dame de Paris.'

'Mirabeau the writer is something far less than Mirabeau, whether he be occupied in demonstrating to the young American Republic the absurdity of its proposed Order of Cincinnatus and the inconsistency of a chivalry of labourers;—whether he torture the philosophic Joseph II., Voltaire's Titus, Madame de Pompadour's Roman and Imperial Model;—whether he ferret out, from the false bottoms of the cabinets of Berlin, that history which caused so much indignation in France, that it was publicly burnt (a foolish blunder, by the way, for of these books, burnt by the hangman's hands, some fiery sparks and particles escape, and as the wind blows, either settle on the gilded roofs of the European aristocracy, or the coverings of royal palaces, or the heads of hot and angry men);—whether he abuse in their passage that cartful of quacks which clattered so loudly on the pavement of the eighteenth century, Necker, Beaumarchais, Lavater, Calonne,

Cagliostro ;—in fact, whatever may be the work he writes, his thoughts are always sufficient for the subject ; but his style is never sufficient for his thoughts. His idea is constantly grand and noble, but, before it can escape from his mind, it seems to bend and diminish under his manner of expression, which seems as if it were a door too narrow for his great thoughts to pass under. Except in his eloquent letters to Madame de Monnier, where he is all himself, where he seems to speak rather than to write, and which are as much harangues of love as his discourses at the Constituent Assembly were harangues of revolution ;— except, we say, in this instance, the style which he found at his writing is, in general, mean, heavy, ill-pointed, low in epithets, poor in images, or only offering, and that very rarely, a few fanciful mosaics of metaphors, possessing no connexion with each other. One feels that the ideas of this man are not, like the ideas of the great men born prose-writers, made of that pliable material which bends itself to all the delicacies of expression—which insinuates itself, burning and liquid, into all the corners of the mould prepared for it by the writer, and then fixes—first lava, afterwards granite. One feels, in reading him, how many things one would fain know are still in the head of the writer ; one knows that one has before one only a "nearly,"—that genius like his is not formed for expressing itself completely in a book,—that a pen is not the best possible conductor for the fluids gathered in that head of thunder !'

Bravo ! Was there ever such a collection of metaphors, such a mixture of sublimity and absurdity, affectation and nature ! Here is a column or more of most ingenious similes ; and all to prove that Mirabeau's writing was not by any means so good as his speaking. When Mr. Moore reads the above, he will go raving mad. What a waste of valuable materials ! Why, on every one of these similes he could have made a poem, and for every one of his poems he would have received a ten-pound note ; it is a clear waste of means, a most riotous and reckless outlay of a hundred pounds at least. In Persia, when the Shah is particularly pleased with a poet, he stuffs his mouth with sugar-candy ; here the poet seems to be performing the same office by the public ; and, to tell the truth, one is almost choked with the sweet food.

But our readers must delay yet a little while, and read the following graphic and fantastic description of Mirabeau the orator :—

'Mirabeau the speaker is Mirabeau. Mirabeau the speaker is the water that flows, or the fire that burns, or the bird which flies ; it is a thing which makes its own proper sound, a nature which accomplishes its law, a sight ever sweet and sublime !

'Mirabeau at the tribune is himself,—himself entire, himself all-powerful! There, there is no desk or table, no solitary cabinet, or silent meditation, but a marble which he may strike, and a stair which he may scale. A tribune is a kind of cage for a wild beast, where he may move at will, where he may pause and breathe, may raise his hand or fold his arms, may point his words with his actions, or illuminate his thoughts by the glance of his eye!

'At the tribune, everything in Mirabeau is powerful; his gesture, fierce and abrupt, was full of empire; his colossal shoulders moved heavily like the back of an elephant, with its tower armed for war; his voice, when he uttered but a word from his seat, was like the roar of a lion in a menagerie; his hair, when he moved his hat, like its mane; his brow, like that of Jupiter,—*cuncta supercilio movens*, seemed to awe everything; his hands seemed sometimes as if they would knead the marble; his head was endowed with a magnificent hideousness, which at moments was electric and terrible. At first, when nothing was decided as to the fate of royalty,—when the monarchical party as yet seemed the stronger of the two, it happened that, having obtained some seeming advantage over the ill-guarded and ill-armed Republicans,—when Royalists were pushing the assault, and crying victory, the monstrous head of Mirabeau appeared at the breach, and petrified the assailants. The genius of the Revolution had forged an ægis with the amalgamated doctrines of Voltaire, Helvetius, Bayle, Diderot, Locke, and Montesquieu, and had placed the Gorgon head of Mirabeau in the middle of the shield!'

Here our readers have him,—a lion, an elephant, a god, and a gorgon! Walk up, ladies and gentlemen; walk up, and see this wonderful animal! Surely such a beast was never before stirred by the poetic pole of so intellectual a showman! Will our readers follow us through Victor Hugo's opinions on France, its present state, and its future prospects? They will laugh, rather, at his political belief, which is altogether French, absurd, and unnatural, but which has a dash of sublimity about it that makes it fully worth the reading. The first proposition is delightful.

'Mirabeaux are no longer necessary, therefore they are no longer possible. God does not create such persons when they are useless; He does not throw corn like this to the wind.'

Of course, we are to take M. Hugo's word for it that Mirabeaux are no longer necessary; besides, the argument is backed by a simile, and nothing therefore can be more satisfactory.

'In fact,' continues the bard, 'what would be the use of a

Mirabeau at present? A Mirabeau is a thunderbolt : who is there to destroy? Where, in the political world, are those eminences which may call and attract the thunder? We are not now as in 1789, when in the social system there were so manifest disproportions.

'At present the soil is levelled ; everything is flat, settled, united.' The whole thing is as clear as the Pons Asinorum : Mirabeau is a thunderbolt ; there is no need of thunder at present, therefore there is no need of Mirabeau ; that is, he is not necessary, therefore he is impossible. Any one who will swallow the premises can have no possible difficulty in bolting the conclusion.

'We do not mean to say that, because we are no longer in need of Mirabeau, we are not in want of great men. For, on the contrary, much still remains to do ; everything is pulled down— nothing is built again.

'There are at present two classes : the men of the revolution, and the men of the progress. The men of the revolution are employed to dig up the old political ground, to form the furrows, and cast the seed ; but the men of the progress must watch the seasons in their slow advance, must guard the crop, and gather it ; the duty and the hope for these men must now begin.

'We shall find them. France has, in the civilisation of the globe, an initiative too important ever to fear a want of special men for special purposes ; she is the majestic mother of all ideas amongst all people. One may say that for two centuries France has nourished the world with the milk of her breast ; she is noble in blood, and fruitful of womb ; her genius is inexhaustible ; her bosom supplies her with all the intelligence of which she hath need ; she has men who are always of a measure with events ; in her occasion, she neither wanted Mirabeau to commence revolutions, or Napoleon to end them ! '

This is a grand piece of oratory, which will apply, however, equally well to Germany, Wapping, or any other country.

'Providence will certainly not refuse to us the great social man, nor the mere political character, whom at present we need.

'In waiting his arrival, however, the men who make the history of the present time are petty indeed. It is true that it is a pity that the great bodies of statesmen at present possess neither general sympathies or enlarged ideas,—that the time which should be devoted to constructing the great constitutional edifice is merely given to trifling,—that men will not remark that general intelligence can be the only cause of general equality,—that the beautiful beginnings of 1789 have only brought with them certain corollaries, such as are the fish's tail to the fair head of the syren, and that the

French Revolution has had but bungling doctors to assist it in its labours. But nothing that has as yet been done is irreparable; no essential principle has been smothered in its birth; all the ideas that were born in 1788 were strong and healthy, and are each day attaining more strength and growth.'

'The present period is open to all kinds of criticism, but it demands at least a benevolent judge.

'We do not doubt that the epoch in which we live is stormy and troublesome. Our statesmen for the most part know not what they do; they labour blindly at night, and in the morning, when they wake, they will be surprised at the fruits of their labour,— perhaps pleased, perhaps frightened,—who knows?

'On no subject have we a definite law; the press, so powerful, and so useful formerly, is nothing now but a series of negations. We have no ascertained formula for civilisation, no calculated progression for improvement; and yet we have firm confidence and firm hope!

'Who does not feel that, in this tumult and tempest,—in this combat of systems and ambitions, which raises so much cloud and dust around us,—behind this curtain which still hides from sight the great, social, uncompleted statue,—under this cloud of passions and theories and chimeras,—in the midst of this Babel of human tongues, which speak all languages by all mouths,—beneath this whirlwind of things, of men, and ideas, which men call the nineteenth century, some mighty work is in progress?

'But God is calm, and finisheth His work!'

We do not know whether we have succeeded in laying before our readers the vein of misty sublimity, and true poetry, which runs through M. Hugo's bombastic claptrap; if not, the fault must be in our crude and careless translation; and we must refer those who are curious about Mirabeau, or incredulous concerning Victor Hugo, to the *Journal des Débats* of last week, from which we have extracted the fragments given above.

NOTE

A Legend of the Rhine was originally serialised in *George Cruikshank's Table Book* during 1845, when it was illustrated by the editor. It was reprinted in *Jeames's Diary, A Legend of the Rhine,* and *Rebecca and Rowena* (Appleton's Popular Library of the Best Authors, New York, 1853), and in *Miscellanies* (vol. 3 ; London, 1856).

Rebecca and Rowena (1850) is a much altered version of *Proposals for a Continuation of Ivanhoe, In a Letter to Monsieur Alexandre Dumas, by Monsieur Michael Angelo Titmarsh,* which appeared in *Fraser's Magazine,* vol. 34, pp. 237-245, 359-367 (August, September, 1848). *The Song of King Canute* was transferred from *Miss Tickletoby's Lectures on English History* in *Punch* to *Rebecca and Rowena.* The burlesque was not illustrated in *Fraser's Magazine,* and the illustrations were drawn by Richard Doyle for the issue in book-form. The original title-page ran : Rebecca | and Rowena. | A | Romance upon Romance. | By Mr. M. A. Titmarsh. | With illustrations by Richard Doyle. | London : | Chapman and Hall, 186 Strand. | 1850.

Punch's Prize Novelists appeared in *Punch* from April to October 1847. *George de Barnwell, Codlingsby, Lords and Liveries, Barbazure,* and *Phil Fogarty* were reprinted in *Punch's Prize Novelists, The Fat Contributor,* and *Travels in London* (Appleton's Popular Library of the Best Authors, New York, 1853) ; and also, under the title of *Novels by Eminent Hands,* in *Miscellanies* (vol. 2 ; London, 1856). *Crinoline* and *Stars and Stripes* were first reprinted in the Library edition of the Collected

Works (vol. 16, 1869). *A Plan for a Prize Novel*, which, strictly speaking, is not one of the *Novels by Eminent Hands*, was also first printed in *Punch*—on February 22, 1851. This was reprinted in a supplementary volume of the Library edition of the Collected Works (vol. 24, 1886).

Notes of a Journey from Cornhill to Grand Cairo was published in 1846, and contained a coloured frontispiece and several illustrations by the Author. The original title-page ran: Notes of a Journey | From | Cornhill to | Grand Cairo, | by way of | Lisbon, Athens, Constantinople, | and Jerusalem : | Performed in the Steamers of the Peninsular and | Oriental Company. | By Mr. M. A. Titmarsh, | Author of 'The Irish Sketch Book,' etc. | London : | Chapman and Hall, 186 Strand. | MDCCCXLVI.

Under the heading of *Juvenilia* are included the writings of Thackeray before he became a professional man of letters. He was not a precocious lad, but he began to write and draw at an early age. While at the Charterhouse he parodied Miss Landon's hyper-sentimental poem 'Violets' in a style which shows clearly that even then he had the sense of humour and the eye for the ridiculous which distinguished his later work.

VIOLETS (L. E. L.).	CABBAGES (W. M. T.).
Violets ! deep blue violets !	Cabbages ! bright green cabbages !
April's loveliest coronets :	April's loveliest gifts, I guess.
There are no flowers grow in the vale,	There is not a plant in the garden laid,
Kissed by the sun, woo'd by the gale,	Raised by the dung, dug by the spade,
None with the dew of the twilight wet,	None by the gardener watered, I ween,
So sweet as the deep blue violet.	So sweet as the cabbage, the cabbage green.
I do remember how sweet a breath	I do remember how sweet a smell
Came with the azure light of a wreath,	Came with the cabbage I loved so well,
That hung round the wild harp's golden chords	Served up with the best that beautiful looked,
That rang to my dark-eyed lover's words.	The beef that dark-eyed Ellen cooked.

I have seen that dear harp rolled
With gems of the East and bands of gold,
But it never was sweeter than when set
With leaves of the dark blue violet.

And when the grave shall open for me—
I care not how soon that time may be—
Never a rose shall bloom on my tomb,
It breathes too much of hope and bloom ;
But let me have there the meek regret
Of the bending and deep blue violet.

I have seen beef served with radish of horse,
I have seen beef served with lettuce of cos,
But it is far nicer, far nicer, I guess,
As bubble and squeak, beef and cabbages.

And when the dinner-bell sounds for me—
I care not how soon that time may be—
Carrots shall never be served on my cloth,
They are far too sweet for a boy of my broth ;
But let me have there a mighty mess
Of smoking hot beef and cabbages.

Probably about this time he also wrote some lines of doggerel which show his tendency to indulge in almost impossible rhymes that was always a distinguishing feature of his humorous poetry. These begin : 'In the romantic little town of Highbury'; and were reprinted by Anthony Trollope in the monograph on Thackeray in the 'English Men of Letters' series. Another early effort was a *Holyday Song*, printed in full in *The Grey-Friar* by Mr. Davies, of which a few verses may be here reproduced.

> Now let us dance and sing,
> While Carthusian bells do ring ;
> Joy twangs the fiddle-string,
>   And Freedom blows the flute.

> Tiddle-dum and Tiddle-di—
> What a joke for you and I—
> Dulce domum, let us cry—
>   Charterhouse adieu.

> Purblind Cupid still drag on
> Some more days ere he can brag on
> Killing game to fill a waggon,
>   And thy shooting-jacket too !

Yet, oh stay ! thou beauteous sister
Who has caused heartburn and blister
To that paragon young mister,
  Joseph Carne !

Queen of Beauty ! Star of Harrow !
Thou has shot thro' heart and marrow
And stricken Makepeace with thy arrow
  In the head-brain.

At Cambridge he contributed to a little weekly paper, called *The Snob : a Literary and Scientific Journal NOT ' Conducted by Members of the University.'* The first number appeared on April 9, 1829 ; and the eleventh and last bears the date of June 18. This was continued after the long vacation under the title of *The Gownsman.* It is believed that he edited the seventeen numbers, which came out between November 5, 1829, and February 25, 1830 ; but only a few of his contributions have been identified. While still up at Trinity College he wrote a parody of a speech of Lalor Sheil upon Penenden Heath, which he was not allowed to deliver, but of which, before he left town, he took the precaution to send copies to the leading journals for insertion. This *jeu d'esprit* was printed in *The Western Luminary,* and is here inserted rather because it was his first appearance in the public prints than because of its merits.

IRISH MELODY

(Air : *The Minstrel Boy*)

Mister Sheil into Kent has gone
  On Penenden Heath you'll find him ;
Nor think you that he came alone,
  There's Doctor Doyle behind him.

' Men of Kent,' said the little man,
  ' If you hate Emancipation,
You're a set of fools.' He then began
  A cut and dry oration.

He strove to speak, but the men of Kent
  Began a grievous shouting,
When out of the waggon the little man went,
  And put a stop to his spouting.

REBECCA AND ROWENA

ROMANCE UPON ROMANCE.

Mr MICHAEL ANGELO TITMARSH

ILLUSTRATED BY RICHARD DOYLE.

LONDON:
CHAPMAN AND HALL, 186, STRAND.
1850.

Price 5s. plain, or 7s. 6d. coloured.

REDUCED FACSIMILE OF THE ORIGINAL COVER

' What though these heretics heard me not ! '
Quoth he to his friend Canonical,
' My speech is safe in the *Times*, I wot,
And eke in the *Morning Chronicle*.'

On January 5, 1833, F. W. N. Bayley brought out *The National Standard and Journal of Literature, Science, Music, Theatricals, and the Fine Arts*. Thackeray soon became a contributor, and with the nineteenth number took over the editorship, which change he announced in the first *Address*, on May 11. Some weeks later he bought the paper. The last number of the year contained a second *Address*, in which the future success of the journal is spoken of as assured. The next issue bore a fresh title : *The National Standard and Literary Representative ;* but, in spite of the editor's confidence, the paper issued its last number on February 1, 1834. It is generally — and, there is reason to believe, correctly — believed that Thackeray related the tale of this venture in the pages of *Lovel the Widower*.

None of the drawings or articles — with the exception of the burlesque poem *Timbuctoo* — printed under the heading of *Juvenilia* have ever before been included in any complete edition of Thackeray's works.

L. M.